A-Level Year 1 & AS
Biology

Revising for Biology exams is stressful, that's for sure — even just getting your notes sorted out can leave you needing a lie down. But help is at hand...

This brilliant CGP book explains **everything you'll need to learn**, all in a straightforward style that's easy to get your head around. We've also included **exam questions** to test how ready you are for the real thing.

There's even a free Online Edition you can read on your computer or tablet!

How to get your free Online Edition

Go to **cgpbooks.co.uk/extras** and enter this code...

2887 6319 6894 2356

This code only works for one person. If somebody else has used
this book before you, they might have already claimed the Online Edition.

A-Level revision? It has to be CGP!

Contents

Published by CGP
From original material by Richard Parsons.

Editors:
Ciara McGlade, Claire Plowman, Hayley Thompson.

Contributors:
Sophie Anderson, Gloria Barnett, James Foster, Paddy Gannon, Barbara Green, Liz Masters, Adrian Schmit.

ISBN: 978 1 78294 285 6
With thanks to Rachael Rogers for the proofreading.
With thanks to Laura Jakubowski for the copyright research.

Clipart from Corel®
Printed by Elanders Ltd, Newcastle upon Tyne.

The Scientific Process

'How Science Works' is all about the scientific process — how we develop and test scientific ideas. It's what scientists do all day, every day (well, except at coffee time — never come between a scientist and their coffee).

Scientists Come Up with **Theories** — Then **Test Them**...

Science tries to explain **how** and **why** things happen — it **answers questions**. It's all about seeking and gaining **knowledge** about the world around us. Scientists do this by **asking** questions and **suggesting** answers and then **testing** them, to see if they're correct — this is the **scientific process**.

1) **Ask** a question — make an **observation** and ask **why or how** it happens.
E.g. why is trypsin (an enzyme) found in the small intestine but not in the stomach?

2) **Suggest** an answer, or part of an answer, by forming a **theory** (a possible **explanation** of the observations) e.g. pH affects the activity of enzymes. (Scientists also sometimes form a **model** too — a **simplified picture** of what's physically going on.)

3) Make a **prediction** or **hypothesis** — a **specific testable statement**, based on the theory, about what will happen in a test situation. E.g. trypsin will be active at pH 8 (the pH of the small intestine) but inactive at pH 2 (the pH of the stomach).

4) Carry out a **test** — to provide **evidence** that will support the prediction (or help to disprove it). E.g. measure the rate of reaction of trypsin at various pH levels.

The evidence supported Quentin's Theory of Flammable Burps.

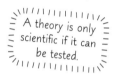

A theory is only scientific if it can be tested.

...Then They **Tell** Everyone About Their **Results**...

The results are **published** — scientists need to let others know about their work. Scientists publish their results in **scientific journals**. These are just like normal magazines, only they contain **scientific reports** (called papers) instead of the latest celebrity gossip.

1) Scientific reports are similar to the **lab write-ups** you do in school. And just as a lab write-up is **reviewed** (marked) by your teacher, reports in scientific journals undergo **peer review** before they're published.

2) The report is sent out to **peers** — other scientists that are experts in the **same area**. They examine the data and results, and if they think that the conclusion is reasonable it's **published**. This makes sure that work published in scientific journals is of a **good standard**.

3) But peer review **can't guarantee** the science is **correct** — other scientists still need to **reproduce** it.

4) Sometimes **mistakes** are made and bad work is published. Peer review **isn't perfect** but it's probably the best way for scientists to self-regulate their work and to publish **quality reports**.

...Then **Other Scientists** Will **Test** the Theory Too

Other scientists read the published theories and results, and try to **test the theory** themselves. This involves:
- Repeating the **exact same experiments**.
- Using the theory to make **new predictions** and then testing them with **new experiments**.

If the **Evidence** Supports a Theory, It's **Accepted** — for Now

1) If all the experiments in all the world provide good evidence to back it up, the theory is thought of as **scientific 'fact'** (for now).

2) But it will never become **totally indisputable** fact. Scientific **breakthroughs or advances** could provide new ways to question and test the theory, which could lead to **new evidence** that **conflicts** with the current evidence. Then the testing starts all over again...

And this, my friend, is the **tentative nature of scientific knowledge** — it's always **changing** and **evolving**.

The Scientific Process

So scientists need evidence to back up their theories. They get it by carrying out experiments, and when that's not possible they carry out studies. But why bother with science at all? We want to know as much as possible so we can use it to try and improve our lives (and because we're nosy).

Evidence Comes from Lab Experiments...

1) Results from **controlled experiments** in **laboratories** are **great**.
2) A lab is the easiest place to **control variables** so that they're all **kept constant** (except for the one you're investigating).
3) This means you can draw meaningful **conclusions**.

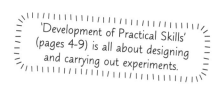
'Development of Practical Skills' (pages 4-9) is all about designing and carrying out experiments.

...and Well-Designed Studies

1) There are things you **can't** investigate in a lab, e.g. whether stress causes heart attacks. You have to do a study instead.
2) You still need to try and make the study as controlled as possible to make it **valid**. But in reality it's **very hard** to control **all the variables** that **might** be having an effect.
3) You can do things to help, e.g. have **matched groups** — **choose two groups** of people (those who have quite stressful jobs and those who don't) who are **as similar as possible** (same mix of ages, same mix of diets etc.). But you can't easily rule out every possibility.

Samantha thought her study was very well designed — especially the fitted bookshelf.

Society Makes Decisions Based on Scientific Evidence

1) Lots of scientific work eventually leads to **important discoveries** or breakthroughs that could **benefit humankind**.
2) These results are **used by society** (that's you, me and everyone else) to **make decisions** — about the way we live, what we eat, what we drive, etc.
3) All sections of society use scientific evidence to make decisions, e.g. politicians use it to devise policies and individuals use science to make decisions about their own lives.

Other factors can **influence** decisions about science or the way science is used:

Economic factors

- Society has to consider the **cost** of implementing changes based on scientific conclusions — e.g. the **NHS** can't afford the most expensive drugs without **sacrificing** something else.
- Scientific research is **expensive** so companies won't always develop new ideas — e.g. developing new drugs is costly, so pharmaceutical companies often only invest in drugs that are likely to make them **money**.

Social factors

- **Decisions** affect **people's lives** — E.g. scientists may suggest **banning smoking** and **alcohol** to prevent health problems, but shouldn't **we** be able to **choose** whether **we** want to smoke and drink or not?

Environmental factors

- Scientists believe **unexplored regions** like remote parts of rainforests might contain **untapped drug** resources. But some people think we shouldn't **exploit** these regions because any interesting finds may lead to **deforestation** and **reduced biodiversity** in these areas.

So there you have it — how science works...

Hopefully these pages have given you a nice intro to how science works, i.e. what scientists do to provide you with 'facts'. Once you've got it sussed, it's time to move on to the really good stuff — the Biology itself.

Planning an Experiment

Experiments are pretty cool — much more exciting than revising anyway. Before you start planning an experiment, you need to be really clear on what you're trying to find out — you should start off with a prediction or hypothesis (see p.2).

A *Good Experiment* Gives *Results* that are:

1) **Precise** — precise results **don't vary** much **from the mean**. Precision is **reduced** by **random error**.

2) **Repeatable and reproducible** — repeatable means if the **same person** repeats the experiment using the same methods and equipment, they will get the same results. Reproducible means if **someone different** does the experiment, using a slightly different method or piece of equipment, the results will be the same.

3) **Valid** — valid results **answer the original question**. To get valid results you need to **control all the variables** to make sure you're only testing the thing you want to.

Repeatable and reproducible results are sometimes called reliable results.

4) **Accurate** — accurate results are **really close** to the **true answer**.

Here are some things you need to consider when designing a good experiment:

1) **Only one variable should be changed** — Variables are **quantities** that have the **potential to change**, e.g. pH. In an experiment you usually **change one variable** and **measure its effect** on another variable.
   - The variable that you **change** is called the **independent variable**.
   - The variable that you **measure** is called the **dependent variable**.

2) **All the other variables should be controlled** — When you're investigating a variable you need to keep everything else that could affect it **constant**. This means you can be sure that **only** your **independent** variable is **affecting** the thing you're measuring (the dependent variable).

3) **Negative controls should be used** — Negative controls are used to **check** that only the independent variable is affecting the dependent variable. Negative controls **aren't expected** to have **any effect** on the experiment.

4) **The experiment should be repeated at least three times and a mean should be calculated** — this reduces the effect of **random error** on your experiment, which makes your results **more precise**. Doing repeats and getting similar results each time also shows that your data is **repeatable** and makes it more likely to be **reproducible**.

> **EXAMPLE:** Investigating the effect of **temperature** on **enzyme activity**.
> 1) Temperature is the **independent** variable.
> 2) Enzyme activity is the **dependent** variable.
> 3) pH, volume, substrate concentration and enzyme concentration should all **stay the same** (and the quantities should be recorded to allow someone else to reproduce the experiment).
> 4) The experiment should be **repeated** at least **three times** at each temperature used.
> 5) A **negative control**, containing everything used **except the enzyme**, should be measured at each temperature used. No enzyme activity should be seen with these controls.

Select Appropriate *Apparatus*, *Equipment* and *Techniques*

1) When you're **planning** an experiment you need to decide what it is you're going to **measure** and **how often** you're going to take measurements. E.g. if you're investigating the **rate of respiration**, you could either measure the volume of **oxygen used** over time or the volume of **carbon dioxide produced** over time. You could take measurements at, e.g. 30 second intervals or 60 second intervals.

2) Then you need to choose the most **appropriate** apparatus, equipment and techniques for the experiment. E.g.

   - The **measuring apparatus** you use has to be **sensitive** enough to measure the changes you're looking for. E.g. if you need to measure changes of **1 cm³** you need to use a **measuring cylinder** that can measure in 1 cm³ increments. It'd be no good trying with one that only measures 10 cm³ increments — it wouldn't be sensitive enough. And if you need to measure **small changes** in pH, a **pH meter** (which can measure pH to several decimal places) would be more sensitive than indicator paper.

   - The **equipment** and **apparatus** you choose has to be **appropriate** for the **function** it needs to perform. E.g. if you are studying the **nuclei** of cells under the microscope you need to **stain** them with a dye that stains nuclei, e.g. methylene blue. It would be no good staining them with eosin, as this doesn't stain the nuclei.

   - The **technique** you use has to be the most **appropriate** one for your **experiment**. E.g. if you want to make a series of solutions for a **calibration curve**, you'd usually use a **serial dilution technique** (see p. 21).

Examiners love getting you to **suggest improvements** to **methods** — for example, how a method could be improved to make the results more valid. So make sure you really know how to **design** a **good experiment**.

Planning an Experiment

Use *Apparatus* and *Techniques Correctly* to Obtain *Precise Results*

1) Once you've chosen the best apparatus and techniques to use in your experiment,
   you need to make sure you can **use them correctly** — make sure you know how to
   use all the ones you've come across in class. Here are just a few examples:

Read volume from here —
at the bottom of the meniscus.

The meniscus is the curved upper surface of the liquid inside the pipette.

- **Pipettes** — Graduated pipettes have a **scale** so you can measure specific volumes — make sure you read the **meniscus** at **eye level**.

- **Water baths** — Make sure you **allow time** for water baths to **heat up** before starting your experiment. Don't forget that your **solutions** will need **time** to get to the **same temperature** as the water before you start the experiment too.

- **Data logger** — Decide **what** you are **measuring** and what **type** of **data logger** you will need, e.g. temperature, pH. Connect an **external sensor** to the data logger if you need to. Decide **how often** you want the data logger to take readings depending on the **length** of the **process** that you are measuring.

2) Make sure you're measuring things using **appropriate units**. E.g. if you're measuring time, it might be better to use seconds rather than minutes — when you come to processing your results, it'll be easier to work with a result of 73 seconds than a result of 1.217 minutes. Also, make sure you **record** your **units properly**, e.g. if you're measuring the length of something and accidently write cm instead of mm, any **calculations** you do will be **affected** and your **conclusions** may be **wrong**.

3) Make sure you **perform** all **techniques carefully** and that any **apparatus** is **set up correctly** — this will help to **minimise errors** which would affect your results.

Risk Assessments Help You to Work Safely

1) When you're planning an experiment, you need to carry out a **risk assessment**. To do this, you need to identify:
   - All the **dangers** in the experiment, e.g. any hazardous chemicals, microorganisms or naked flames.
   - **Who** is at **risk** from these dangers.
   - What can be done to **reduce** the **risk**, such as wearing goggles or gloves or working in a fume cupboard.

2) You also need to consider any **ethical issues** in your experiment. For example, if you're using **living animals** (e.g. insects) you must treat them with **respect**. This means **handling them carefully** and keeping them away from **harmful chemicals**, **extreme heat sources** and other things that might cause them **physical discomfort**.

Record Your Data in a Table

It's a good idea to draw a table to **record** the **results** of your experiment in.

1) When you draw a table, make sure you **include** enough **rows** and **columns** to **record all of the data** you need to. You might also need to include a column for **processing** your data (e.g. working out an average).

2) Make sure each **column** has a **heading** so you know what's going to be recorded where.

3) The **units** should be in the **column** heading, not the table itself.

Farm	Length of hedgerows (km)	Number of species
1	49	21
2	90	28
3	155	30

data   heading   units   column

row

Watch Out for **Anomalous Results**

Doing repeats makes it easier to spot anomalous results.

When you look at all the **data** in your **table**, you may notice that you have a result that **doesn't seem to fit in** with the rest at all. These results are called **anomalous results**. You should **investigate** anomalous results — if you can work out what happened (e.g. you measured something totally wrong) you can **ignore** them when **processing** your results.

My best apparatus is the pommel horse...

It's not really, I just like the word pommel. Scientists are rightfully fussy about methods and equipment — I mean if you're going to bother doing an experiment, you should at least make sure it's going to give you results you can trust.

Processing and Presenting Data

Once you've collected your data you really need to do something with it so you can use it....

Processing the Data Helps You to Interpret it

You Might Need to Calculate Percentage Change

Calculating **percentage change** helps to **quantify** how much something has changed, e.g. the percentage of plants that were killed with a herbicide in a particular year compared to the previous year.
To **calculate** it you use this equation:

$$\text{Percentage change} = \frac{\text{final value} - \text{original value}}{\text{original value}} \times 100$$

A **positive** value shows an **increase** and a **negative** value shows a **decrease**.

Averages and the Range Summarise Your Data

When you've done **repeats** of an experiment you should always calculate the **mean**. To do this **add together** all the data values and **divide** by the **total** number of values in the sample.

You could also be asked to calculate the median (the middle number when you put all your data in numerical order) or the mode (the number that appears most often in a set of data).

Test tube	Repeat (g)			Mean (g)	Range (g)
	1	2	3		
A	28	37	32	$(28 + 37 + 32) \div 3 = 32.3$	$37 - 28 = 9$
B	47	51	60	$(47 + 51 + 60) \div 3 = 52.7$	$60 - 47 = 13$
C	68	70	70	$(68 + 70 + 70) \div 3 = 69.3$	$70 - 68 = 2$

You might also need to calculate the **range** (how **spread out** the data is). To do this find the **largest** data value and **subtract** the **smallest** data value from it.

Standard deviation can be more useful than the **range** because it tells you how **values** are spread about the **mean** rather than just the **total spread** of data. A **small standard deviation** means the repeated results are all **similar** and **close** to the mean, i.e. **precise**. There's more on standard deviation on pages 162-163.

Statistical Tests Are Used to Analyse Data Mathematically

Statistical tests can be used to analyse **quantitative** (numerical) or **qualitative** (non-numerical) results. E.g.

1) The **Student's t-test** — you can use the Student's t-test when you have two sets of **data** that you want to **compare**, e.g. whether males and females performed differently in the same test. It tests whether there is a **significant difference** in the **means** of the two data sets. The value obtained is compared to a **critical value**, which helps you decide **how likely** it is that the results or 'differences in the means' were **due to chance**. If the value obtained from the t-test is **greater than** the critical value at a **probability (P value)** of **5% or less** (≤ 0.05), then you can be 95% confident that the difference is significant and not due to chance.

2) **Spearman's rank correlation coefficient** — this tells you the **degree** to which **two sets** of **data** are **related**. It is given as value between 1 and –1. A value of 1 indicates a **strong positive correlation**, 0 means there is **no correlation** and –1 is a **strong negative correlation**. (There's more on correlations on page 8.) You can compare your result to a critical value to find out whether or not the correlation is **significant**.

Watch Out For Significant Figures

When you're processing your data you may well want to round any **really long numbers** to a certain number of **significant figures**. E.g. **0.6878976** rounds to **0.69** to 2 s.f..

The first significant figure of a number is the first digit that isn't a zero. The second, third and fourth significant figures follow on immediately after the first (even if they're zeros).

When you're doing **calculations** using numbers given to a certain number of significant figures, you should always give your **answer** to the **lowest number** of significant figures that was used in the calculation.
For example:

$$1.2 \div 1.85 = 0.648648648... \quad = 0.65$$

2 s.f.   3 s.f.   Answer should be rounded to 2 s.f.   Round the last digit up to 5.

This is because the **fewer digits** a measurement has, the less **accurate** it is.
Your answer can only be as accurate as the **least accurate measurement** in the calculation.

Processing and Presenting Data

Choose a Suitable **Graph** or **Chart** to Present Your Data

Graphs and charts are a great way of **presenting data** — they can make results much **easier to interpret**.

1) When you have **qualitative** data (non-numerical data, e.g. blood group) or **discrete** data (numerical data that can only take certain values in a range, e.g. shoe size) you can use **bar charts** or **pie charts**.

2) When you have **continuous** data (data that can take any value in a range, e.g. height or weight) you can use **histograms** or **line graphs.**

3) When you want to plot **one variable against the other** you can use a **scatter graph**.

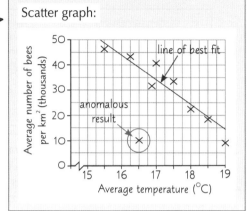

Scatter graph:

Whatever type of graph you use, you should make sure that:

* The **dependent variable** goes on the **y-axis** (the vertical axis) and the **independent** on the **x-axis** (the horizontal axis).

* You always **label** the **axes**, include the quantity and **units**, and choose a **sensible scale**.

* The graph covers **at least half** of the **graph paper**.

If you need to draw a **line** (or curve) **of best fit** on a **scatter graph**, draw the line through or as near to as many points as possible, **ignoring** any **anomalous** results.

Find the **Rate** By Finding the **Gradient**

Rate is a **measure** of how much something is **changing over time**. Calculating a rate can be useful when analysing your data, e.g. you might want to the find the **rate of a reaction**. Rates are easy to work out from a graph:

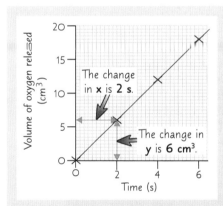

For a **linear** graph you can calculate the **rate** by finding the **gradient of the line**:

$$\text{Gradient} = \frac{\text{Change in Y}}{\text{Change in X}}$$

So in this **example**:

$$\text{rate} = \frac{6 \text{ cm}^3}{2 \text{ s}} = 3 \text{ cm}^3 \text{ s}^{-1}$$

cm³ s⁻¹ means the same as cm³/s (centimetres cubed per second)

The **equation** of a **straight line** can always be written in the form **y = mx + c**, where **m** is the **gradient** and **c** is the **y-intercept** (this is the **value of y** when the line crosses the **y-axis**). In this example, the equation of the line is **y = 3x + 0** (or just **y = 3x**). Knowing the equation of the line allows you to estimate results not plotted on the graph. E.g. in this case, when x (the time) is **20 s**, y (the volume of oxygen released) will be 3x = 3 × 20 = **60 cm³**.

For a **curved** (non-linear) graph you can find the **rate** by drawing a **tangent**:

1) Position a ruler on the graph at the **point** where you want to know the **rate**.

2) **Angle** the **ruler** so there is **equal space** between the **ruler** and the **curve** on **either** side of the point.

3) **Draw** a **line** along the ruler to make the tangent.

   Extend the line right across the graph — it'll help to make your **gradient calculation easier** as you'll have **more points** to choose from.

4) **Calculate** the **gradient** of the **tangent** to find the **rate**.

Gradient = 55 m² ÷ 4.4 years = **12.5 m² year⁻¹**

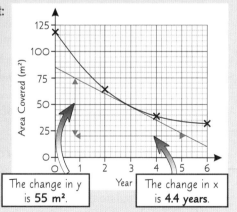

The change in y is **55 m².**   Year   The change in x is **4.4 years**.

Significant figures — a result of far too many cream cakes...

Graphs and charts are great for seeing what's going on in your results. Don't get confused if you need to find the rate of something from a graph — you just have to find the gradient of the line. And if you haven't got a straight line, draw one.

Drawing Conclusions and Evaluating

So once you've processed your data you'll want to see what conclusions you can come to. Evaluations are important too so you can assess your experiment and think about how you could do things differently next time.

You Need to **Draw Conclusions** From Your **Data**

1) Conclusions need to be **valid**. A conclusion can only be considered as valid if it answers the original question (see page 4).

2) You can often draw conclusions by looking at the relationship (**correlation**) between two variables:

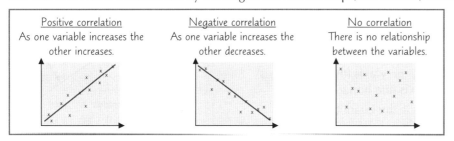

There is no correlation between the colour of your tights and the proportion of your life you spend upside down.

3) You have to be very **careful** when **drawing conclusions** from data like this because a **correlation** between two variables **doesn't** always mean that a **change** in one variable **causes** a **change** in the other (the correlation could be due to **chance** or there could be a **third variable** having an effect).

4) If there's a relationship between two variables and a change in one variable **does** cause a change in the other it's called a **causal relationship**.

5) It can be **concluded** that a **correlation** is a **causal relationship** if every other variable that could possibly affect the result is **controlled**.

In reality this is very hard to do — correlations are generally accepted to be causal relationships if lots of studies have found the same thing, and scientists have figured out exactly how one factor causes the other.

6) When you're making a conclusion you **can't** make broad **generalisations** from data — you have to be very **specific**. You can only **conclude** what the results show and **no more**.

> **Example**
>
> The graph shows the results from a study into the effect of penicillin dosage on the duration of fever in men. The only **conclusion** you can draw is that as the **dosage** of **penicillin increases**, the **duration** of **fever** in **men decreases**. You **can't** conclude that this is true for any other antibiotic, any other symptom or even for female patients — the **results** could be **completely different**.

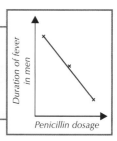

Uncertainty is the Amount of **Error** Your **Measurements** Might Have

1) The results you get from an experiment won't be completely perfect — there'll always be a **degree of uncertainty** in your measurements due to limits in the **sensitivity** of the apparatus you're using.

2) For example, an electronic mass balance might measure to the **nearest 0.01 g**, but the real mass could be up to **0.005 g smaller or larger**. It has an **uncertainty value** of ± **0.005g**.

3) The ± sign tells you the **range** in which the **true value** lies (to within a certain probability). The range is called the **margin of error**.

You Can **Calculate** The **Percentage Error** of Your **Measurements**

If you know the **uncertainty value** of your measurements, you can calculate the **percentage error** using this formula:

$$\text{percentage error} = \frac{\text{uncertainty}}{\text{reading}} \times 100$$

50 cm³ of HCl is measured with an uncertainty value of ± 0.05 cm³.

percentage error = $\frac{0.05}{50}$ × 100 = **0.1%**

Drawing Conclusions and Evaluating

You Can **Minimise** the **Errors** in Your **Measurements**

1) One obvious way to **reduce errors** in your measurements is to buy the most **sensitive equipment** available. In real life there's not much you can do about this one — you're stuck with whatever your school or college has got. But there are other ways to **lower the uncertainty** in experiments.

2) For example, you can plan your experiment so you **measure** a **greater amount** of something:

> If you use a **500 cm³** cylinder that goes up in **5 cm³** increments, each reading has an uncertainty of ± **2.5 cm³**.
>
> So using a 500 cm³ cylinder to measure **100 cm³** of liquid will give you a percentage error of:
>
> But if you measure **200 cm³** in the same cylinder, the percentage error is:
>
> $$\frac{2.5}{100} \times 100 = \mathbf{2.5\%}$$
>
> $$\frac{2.5}{200} \times 100 = \mathbf{1.25\%}$$
>
> Hey presto — you've just **halved** the uncertainty.

You Need to **Sum Up** Your Experiment in an **Evaluation**

1) In an **evaluation** you need to assess the following things about your **experiment** and the **data** you gathered:
   - **Repeatability**: Did you take enough repeat readings of the measurements? Would you do more repeats if you were to do the experiment again? Do you think you'd get similar data if you did the experiment again?
   - **Reproducibility**: Have you compared your results with other people's results? Were your results similar? Could other scientists gain data showing the same relationships that are shown in your data?
   - **Validity**: Does your data answer the question you set out to investigate? Were all the variables controlled?

2) Make sure you **evaluate** your **method**. Is there anything you could have done to make your results more **precise** or **accurate**? Were there any **limitations** in your method, e.g. should you have taken measurements more **frequently**? Were there any **sources** of **error** in your experiment? Could you have used more sensitive **apparatus** or **equipment**? Think about how you could **refine** and **improve** your experiment if you did it again.

3) Once you've thought about these points you can decide how much **confidence** you have in your **conclusion**. For example, if your results are **repeatable, reproducible** and **valid** and they back up your conclusion then you can have a **high degree** of **confidence** in your conclusion.

Practice Questions

Q1 What is a dependent variable?

Q2 Why is it important to repeat an experiment at least three times?

Q3 Describe how you would find the rate at a specific point on a curved graph.

Q4 Give one way that you could minimise error in an experiment.

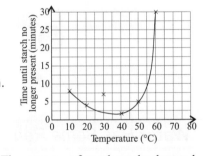

Exam Question

Q1 Amylase is an enzyme that catalyses the breakdown of starch into simple sugars. The presence of starch can be detected with iodine solution — it turns from a browny-orange colour to blue-black when starch is present. An experiment was done to investigate the effect of temperature on the action of amylase. In the experiment amylase solution and starch solution were added to a boiling tube and mixed together. The boiling tube was then placed in a water bath set to the required temperature. At the start of the experiment and every minute afterwards, a small sample of the solution was taken from the boiling tube and added to a spot tile. Iodine solution was added to the sample and the time at which the solution remained browny-orange was recorded. The experiment was repeated at six different temperatures. The graph above shows the results.

   a) Give three variables that should have been controlled in this experiment. [3 marks]

   b) Suggest why the result at 30 °C has not been included on the graph's curve of best fit. [1 mark]

   c) Give two limitations of the method used and suggest how these could be improved. [4 marks]

   d) What conclusions can be drawn from the results of the experiment? [2 marks]

Correlation Street — my favourite programme...

Don't ever, ever assume that correlation means cause. There, I've told you again. No excuses now. A good evaluation is a sign that you really understand what makes a good experiment, so make sure your evaluation-writing-skills are top notch.

Water

Your body needs lots of molecules to stay alive, and these pages cover one of the most important — water.

Water is Vital to Living Organisms

Water makes up about 80% of a cell's contents. It has loads of important **functions**, inside and outside of cells:

1) Water is a **metabolite** in loads of important **metabolic reactions**, including **condensation** and **hydrolysis reactions** (see below).

2) Water helps with **temperature control** because it has a **high latent heat of vaporisation** (see below) and a **high specific heat capacity** (see next page).

3) Water is a **solvent**, which means some substances **dissolve** in it. Most metabolic reactions take place **in solution** (e.g. in the **cytoplasm** of eukaryotic and prokaryotic cells — see pages 38 and 44) so water's pretty essential.

4) Water molecules are very **cohesive** (they stick together), which helps **water transport** in **plants** (see next page) as well as transport in other organisms.

> A metabolic reaction is a chemical reaction that happens in a living organism to keep the organism alive. A metabolite is a substance involved in a metabolic reaction.

Water Molecules Have a Simple Structure

1) A molecule of **water (H_2O)** is **one atom** of **oxygen (O)** joined to **two atoms** of **hydrogen (H_2)** by **shared electrons.**

2) Because the **shared negative** hydrogen electrons are **pulled towards** the oxygen atom, the other side of each hydrogen atom is left with a **slight positive charge**.

3) The **unshared** negative electrons on the oxygen atom give it a **slight negative charge**.

4) This makes water a **polar** molecule — it has a **partial negative (δ–)** charge on one side and a **partial positive (δ+)** charge on the other.

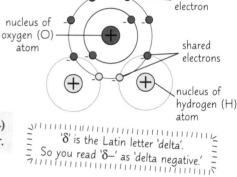

nucleus of oxygen (O) atom

unshared electron

shared electrons

nucleus of hydrogen (H) atom

> '$δ$' is the Latin letter 'delta'. So you read 'δ–' as 'delta negative.'

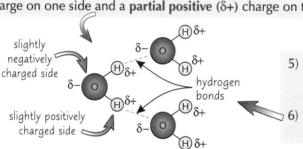

slightly negatively charged side

slightly positively charged side

hydrogen bonds

5) The slightly negatively charged **oxygen atoms attract** the slightly positively charged **hydrogen atoms** of other water molecules.

6) This attraction is called **hydrogen bonding** and it gives water some of its useful properties.

Water Has Some Really Useful Properties

Here's a bit more about some of the **useful properties** of **water**:

Water is an Important Metabolite

1) Many metabolic reactions involve a **condensation** or **hydrolysis** reaction.

2) A **hydrolysis** reaction requires a **molecule of water** to **break** a **bond**. A **condensation** reaction releases a molecule of water as a **new bond** is formed.

3) For example, **amino acids** are **joined** together to make **polypeptides** (proteins) by **condensation** reactions (see page 16). **Energy** from **ATP** is released through a **hydrolysis** reaction (see page 34).

Water has a High Latent Heat of Vaporisation

1) It takes a lot of **energy** (**heat**) to **break** the hydrogen bonds between water molecules.

2) So water has a **high latent heat of vaporisation** — a lot of energy is used up when water **evaporates** (vaporises).

3) This is useful for living organisms because it means they can use water loss through evaporation to **cool down** (e.g. humans **sweat** to cool down) without losing too much water.

Water

Water Can **Buffer** (Resist) Changes in **Temperature**

1) The **hydrogen bonds** between water molecules can **absorb** a **lot** of energy.

2) So water has a **high specific heat capacity** — it takes a lot of energy to heat it up.

3) This is useful for living organisms because it means that water **doesn't** experience **rapid temperature changes**. This makes water a **good habitat** because the temperature **under water** is likely to be **more stable** than on land. The water **inside** organisms also remains at a fairly **stable** temperature — helping them to **maintain** a **constant** internal **body temperature**.

Water is a **Good Solvent**

1) A lot of important substances in metabolic reactions are **ionic** (like **salt**, for example). This means they're made from **one positively charged** atom or molecule and **one negatively charged** atom or molecule (e.g. salt is made from a positive sodium ion and a negative chloride ion).

2) Because water is polar, the **positive end** of a water molecule will be attracted to the **negative ion**, and the **negative end** of a water molecule will be attracted to the **positive ion**.

3) This means the ions will get **totally surrounded** by water molecules — in other words, they'll **dissolve**.

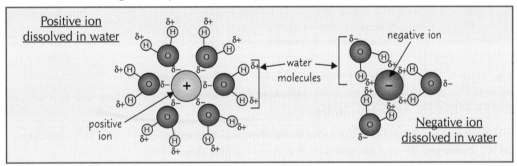

4) So water's **polarity** makes it a useful **solvent**.

There's Strong **Cohesion** Between **Water** Molecules

1) Cohesion is the **attraction** between molecules of the same type (e.g. two water molecules). Water molecules are **very cohesive** (they tend to stick together) because they're **polar**.

2) Strong cohesion helps water to **flow**, making it great for **transporting substances**. For example, it's how water travels in **columns** up the **xylem** (tube-like transport cells) in **plants** (see p. 99).

3) Strong cohesion also means that water has a **high surface tension** when it comes into contact with **air**. This is the reason why sweat forms **droplets**, which evaporate from the skin to cool an organism down. It's also the reason that **pond skaters**, and some other insects, can 'walk' on the surface of a pond.

Practice Questions

Q1 Briefly describe the structure of a water molecule.

Q2 Why is water's high specific heat capacity useful for living organisms?

Q3 Describe how a positive ion dissolves in water.

Exam Question

Q1 In hot temperatures, elephants commonly spray themselves with water.
With reference to the structure and properties of water, explain:

a) why this behaviour acts as a cooling mechanism for the elephant. [3 marks]

b) why water forms droplets when the elephant sprays it from its trunk. [2 marks]

Pssssssssssssssssssssssssssssssssssssssssssssssssss — *need the loo yet?*

Water is pretty darn useful really. It looks so, well, dull — but in fact it's scientifically amazing. It's essential for all kinds of jobs — keeping cool, transporting things, enabling reactions, etc. And it's all to do with its polar structure.

Carbohydrates

Even though there is, and has been, a huge variety of different organisms on Earth, they all share some biochemistry — for example, they all contain a few carbon-based compounds that interact in similar ways.

Carbohydrates are Made from Monosaccharides

1) Most carbohydrates are **polymers**. A polymer is a molecule made up of **many similar, smaller molecules** (called **monomers**) bonded together.

Although most carbohydrates are polymers, single monosaccharides are also called carbohydrates.

2) The monomers that make up carbohydrates are called **monosaccharides**.

3) **Glucose** is a monosaccharide with **six carbon** atoms — this means it's a **hexose** monosaccharide.

4) There are **two isomers** (different forms) of glucose — **alpha** (α) and **beta** (β). They both have a **ring structure**:

5) Glucose's **structure** is related to its **function** as the main **energy source** in animals and plants. Its structure makes it **soluble** so it can be **easily transported**. Its chemical bonds contain **lots of energy**.

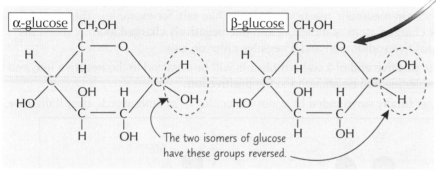

The two isomers of glucose have these groups reversed.

Ribose is the sugar component of RNA nucleotides (see p. 32).

6) **Ribose** is a monosaccharide with **five carbon** atoms — this means it's a **pentose** monosaccharide.

7) Here is its **structure:**

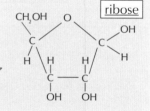

ribose

8) All carbohydrates are made up of the same **three chemical elements** — **carbon (C)**, **hydrogen (H)** and **oxygen (O)**. For every **carbon atom** in the carbohydrate there are usually **two hydrogen atoms** and **one oxygen atom**.

Monosaccharides Join Together to Form Disaccharides and Polysaccharides

1) Monosaccharides are **joined together** by **glycosidic bonds**.

2) During **synthesis**, a **hydrogen** atom on one monosaccharide bonds to a **hydroxyl (OH)** group on the other, **releasing** a molecule of **water**. This is called a **condensation** reaction.

3) The **reverse** of this synthesis reaction is **hydrolysis**. A molecule of water reacts with the glycosidic bond, **breaking it apart**.

Sugar is a general term for monosaccharides and disaccharides.

4) A **disaccharide** is formed when **two monosaccharides** join together:

For example, two α-**glucose** molecules are joined together by a **glycosidic bond** to form **maltose**:

α-glucose   +   α-glucose $\rightleftharpoons$ synthesis / hydrolysis   maltose $+$ H_2O

H_2O is removed   glycosidic bond

Other disaccharides are formed in a similar way. **Sucrose** is a disaccharide formed when α–**glucose** and **fructose** join together. **Lactose** is a disaccharide formed by the joining together of β–**glucose** and **galactose**.

5) A **polysaccharide** is formed when **more than two monosaccharides** join together:

Lots of α-**glucose** molecules are joined together by **glycosidic bonds** to form **amylose**.

glycosidic bonds

α-glucose   α-glucose   α-glucose   α-glucose   α-glucose

Carbohydrates

Starch, Glycogen and Cellulose are Three Important Polysaccharides

There's a close relationship between the **structure** and **function** of all these polysaccharides:

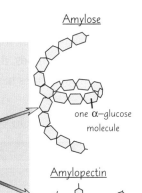
Amylose

one α–glucose molecule

Amylopectin

1 Starch — the main **energy storage material** in **plants**

1) Cells get **energy** from **glucose**. Plants **store** excess glucose as **starch** (when a plant **needs more glucose** for energy it **breaks down** starch to release the glucose).

2) Starch is a mixture of **two** polysaccharides of α–**glucose** — **amylose** and **amylopectin**:
   - **Amylose** — a long, **unbranched chain** of α–glucose. The angles of the glycosidic bonds give it a **coiled structure**, almost like a cylinder. This makes it **compact**, so it's really **good for storage** because you can **fit more** into a small space.
   - **Amylopectin** — a long, **branched chain** of α–glucose. Its **side branches** allow the **enzymes** that break down the molecule to get at the **glycosidic bonds easily**. This means that the glucose can be **released quickly**.

3) Starch is **insoluble** in water, so it **doesn't** cause water to enter cells by **osmosis** (see p. 66) which would make them swell. This makes it good for **storage**.

Glycogen

2 Glycogen — the main **energy storage material** in **animals**

1) Animal cells get **energy** from **glucose** too. But animals **store** excess glucose as **glycogen** — another polysaccharide of α–**glucose**.

2) Its structure is very similar to amylopectin, except that it has **loads** more **side branches** coming off it. Loads of branches means that stored glucose can be **released quickly**, which is **important for energy release** in animals.

3) It's also a very **compact** molecule, so it's good for storage.

3 Cellulose — the major component of **cell walls** in **plants**

1) Cellulose is made of **long, unbranched** chains of β–**glucose**.

2) When β–**glucose** molecules **bond**, they form **straight** cellulose chains.

3) The cellulose chains are linked together by **hydrogen bonds** to form strong fibres called **microfibrils**. The strong fibres mean cellulose provides **structural support** for cells (e.g. in plant cell walls).

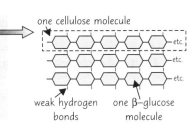
one cellulose molecule

etc.
etc.
etc.

weak hydrogen bonds   one β–glucose molecule

Practice Questions

Q1 What is the structural difference between an α–glucose molecule and a β–glucose molecule?

Q2 Describe how glycosidic bonds are formed and broken in living organisms.

Q3 Briefly describe the structure of starch.

Q4 What is the function of cellulose?

Exam Questions

Q1 Mannose is a hexose monosaccharide.
Which of the following is most likely to give the chemical formula of a mannose molecule?

A $C_5H_{10}O_5$ B $C_6H_{12}O_6$ C $C_6H_{12}N_6$ D $C_5H_5O_{10}$ [1 mark]

Q2 State the function of glycogen and explain how the structure of glycogen is linked to its function.   [3 marks]

Mmmm, starch... Tasty, tasty chips and beans... *dribble*. Ahem, sorry.

Remember that condensation and hydrolysis reactions are the reverse of each other — maltose, sucrose and lactose are all formed and broken down by these reactions. And don't forget that starch is composed of two different polysaccharides... and that glucose exists as two isomers... so many reminders, so little space...

Lipids

On to lipids, or 'fatty oily things' to you and me. Some of them are just straightforward fats, but others have extra bits stuck to them. These pages are about three types of lipid — triglycerides, phospholipids and cholesterol.

Triglycerides are a Kind of Lipid

1) Triglycerides are **macromolecules** — they're **complex molecules** with a relatively **large molecular mass**.

2) Like **all lipids**, they contain the chemical elements **carbon**, **hydrogen** and **oxygen**.

3) Triglycerides have **one** molecule of **glycerol** with **three fatty acids** attached to it.

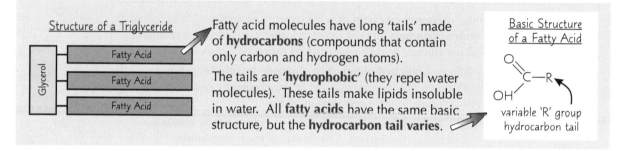

Triglycerides Contain Ester Bonds

1) Triglycerides are **synthesised** by the formation of an **ester bond** between each **fatty acid** and the **glycerol molecule**.

2) Each ester bond is formed by a **condensation reaction** (in which a water molecule is released).

3) The process in which triglycerides are synthesised is called **esterification**.

4) Triglycerides **break down** when the ester bonds are **broken**. Each ester bond is broken in a **hydrolysis reaction** (in which a water molecule is used up).

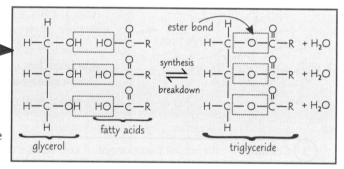

Fatty Acids can be Saturated or Unsaturated

There are **two** kinds of fatty acids — **saturated** and **unsaturated**. The difference is in their **hydrocarbon tails**.

Saturated fatty acids **don't** have any **double bonds** between their **carbon atoms**. The fatty acid is 'saturated' with hydrogen.

Unsaturated fatty acids have **at least one** double bond between **carbon atoms**, which cause the chain to kink.

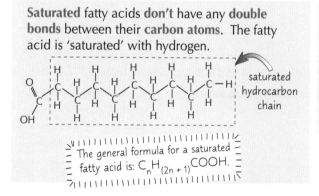

The general formula for a saturated fatty acid is: $C_nH_{(2n+1)}COOH$.

Phospholipids are Similar to Triglycerides

1) **Phospholipids** are also **macromolecules**. They're pretty similar to triglycerides except one of the fatty acid molecules is replaced by a **phosphate group**.

2) The phosphate group is **hydrophilic** (it attracts water molecules) and the fatty acid tails are **hydrophobic**.

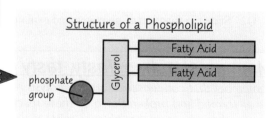

Structure of a Phospholipid

Lipids

The **Structures** of Lipids Relate to Their **Functions**

The properties of **triglycerides**, **phospholipids** and **cholesterol** are all related to their **functions**:

TRIGLYCERIDES

In **animals** and **plants**, triglycerides are mainly used as **energy storage molecules**.
Some **bacteria** (e.g. *Mycobacterium tuberculosis*) use triglycerides to store both **energy** and **carbon**.
Triglycerides are good for storage because:

1) The **long hydrocarbon tails** of the fatty acids contain lots of **chemical energy** — a load of energy is **released** when they're **broken down**. Because of these tails, lipids contain about **twice** as much energy per gram as carbohydrates.

2) They're **insoluble**, so they don't cause water to enter the cells by **osmosis** (see p. 66) which would make them swell. The triglycerides bundle together as **insoluble droplets** in cells because the fatty acid tails are **hydrophobic** (water-repelling) — the tails **face inwards**, shielding themselves from water with their glycerol heads.

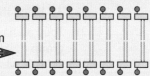

PHOSPHOLIPIDS

Phospholipids are found in the **cell membranes** of all eukaryotes and prokaryotes.
They make up what's known as the **phospholipid bilayer** (see p. 56).
Cell membranes **control** what **enters and leaves** a cell.

1) Phospholipid heads are **hydrophilic** and their tails are **hydrophobic**, so they form a **double** layer with their heads facing **out** towards the water on either side.

2) The **centre** of the bilayer is **hydrophobic**, so water-soluble substances **can't** easily pass through it — the membrane acts as a **barrier** to those substances.

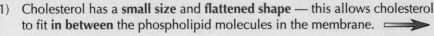

CHOLESTEROL

Cholesterol is another type of lipid — it has a **hydrocarbon ring** structure attached to a hydrocarbon tail. The ring structure has a **polar hydroxyl (OH) group** attached to it. In **eukaryotic cells**, cholesterol molecules help **strengthen** the cell membrane by **interacting** with the **phospholipid bilayer**.

'Polar' means it has a slightly negatively charged bit and a slightly positively charged bit — see p. 10.

1) Cholesterol has a **small size** and **flattened shape** — this allows cholesterol to fit **in between** the phospholipid molecules in the membrane.

2) They bind to the hydrophobic tails of the phospholipids, causing them to **pack more closely together**. This helps to make the membrane **less fluid** and **more rigid**.

cholesterol

Practice Questions

Q1 What are triglycerides composed of?

Q2 What is the difference between a saturated fatty acid and an unsaturated fatty acid?

Q3 Sketch the structure of a phospholipid.

Exam Questions

Q1 Explain how phospholipid molecules arrange themselves in cell membranes and relate this to their structure. [3 marks]

Q2 Explain how each of these features of lipids is important for their function in living things:

a) Cholesterol molecules have a flattened shape. [2 marks]

b) Triglycerides have a hydrophobic tail. [2 marks]

Hydrocarbon tails, phospho-thingies... Whatever happened to just lard?

You don't get far in life without extensive lard knowledge, so learn all the details on these pages good and proper. Understanding lipids is important for lots of things, including our health — so make sure you know about how the structure of lipids gives them some quite groovy properties. Right, this lipids talk is making me hungry — chips time...

Proteins

There are millions of different proteins. They're the most abundant molecules in cells, making up 50% or more of a cell's dry mass — now that's just plain greedy. Like carbohydrates and lipids, proteins are essential for life.

Proteins are Made from *Long Chains* of *Amino Acids*

1) Just like carbohydrates (see page 12), proteins are **polymers**.

2) Amino acids are the **monomers** in proteins.

3) A **dipeptide** is formed when **two** amino acids join together.

4) A **polypeptide** is formed when **more than two** amino acids join together.

5) **Proteins** are made up of **one or more polypeptides**.

Grant's cries of "die peptide, die" could be heard for miles around. He'd never forgiven it for sleeping with his wife.

Different Amino Acids Have *Different Variable Groups*

1) **All living things** share a bank of only **20 amino acids**.

2) They all have the same general structure — a **carboxyl group** (-COOH) and an **amino group** (-NH$_2$) attached to a **carbon** atom. The **only difference** between different amino acids is what makes up their **variable R group**.

<u>Structure of an Amino Acid</u>

R ◄——variable group

H$_2$N — C — COOH

amino group   H   carboxyl group

<u>E.g. Structure of Glycine</u>

H

H$_2$N — C — COOH

H

Glycine is the smallest amino acid — the R group is a hydrogen atom.

3) All amino acids contain the chemical elements **carbon, oxygen, hydrogen** and **nitrogen**. Some also contain **sulfur**.

Amino Acids are Joined Together by *Peptide Bonds*

1) Amino acids are linked together by **peptide bonds** to form dipeptides and polypeptides.

2) A molecule of **water** is **released** during the reaction — it's a **condensation** reaction.

3) The **reverse** of this reaction **adds** a molecule of water to **break** the peptide bond — it's a **hydrolysis** reaction.

amino acid 1   amino acid 2   dipeptide

H   H   H   R   O   H   R
 \   \   condensation   \ | || | |
  N — C—COOH +   N — C—COOH   ⇌   N—C—C—N—C—COOH
 / | / | hydrolysis   / | | |
H   H   H   H   H   H   H   H
      R   R

H$_2$O —— a molecule of water is formed during synthesis.

peptide bond

Proteins

Proteins Have Four Structural Levels

Proteins are **big**, **complicated** molecules. They're much easier to explain if you describe their structure in four 'levels'. These levels are a protein's **primary**, **secondary**, **tertiary** and **quaternary** structures.

Primary Structure — this is the **sequence** of **amino acids** in the **polypeptide chain**. Different proteins have **different sequences** of amino acids in their primary structure. A change in just one amino acid may change the structure of the whole protein.

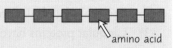
amino acid

Secondary Structure — the polypeptide chain doesn't remain flat and straight. **Hydrogen bonds** form between nearby amino acids in the chain. This makes it automatically **coil** into an **alpha (α) helix** or **fold** into a **beta (β) pleated sheet** — this is the secondary structure.

α-helix   β-pleated sheet

Tertiary Structure — the coiled or folded chain of amino acids is often **coiled** and **folded further**. **More bonds** form between different parts of the polypeptide chain. For proteins made from a **single** polypeptide chain, the tertiary structure forms their **final 3D structure**.

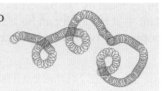

Quaternary Structure — some proteins are made of **several different polypeptide chains** held together by **bonds**. The **quaternary structure** is the way these polypeptide chains are assembled together. E.g. **haemoglobin** is made of **four** polypeptide chains, bonded together. For proteins made from **more than one polypeptide chain, the quaternary structure is** the protein's **final 3D structure**.

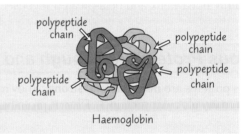
polypeptide chain
polypeptide chain
polypeptide chain
polypeptide chain
Haemoglobin

Computer modelling can create **3D interactive images** of proteins. This is really handy for **investigating** the **different levels of structure** in a protein molecule.

Different Bonds Hold Different Structural Levels Together

The four structural levels of a protein are held together by **different kinds** of **bonds**:

1) **Primary structure** — held together by the **peptide bonds** between amino acids.

2) **Secondary structure** — held together by **hydrogen bonds** (see above).

3) **Tertiary structure** — this is affected by a few different kinds of bonds:

- **Ionic bonds.** These are **attractions** between **negatively-charged** R groups and **positively-charged** R groups on different parts of the molecule.

- **Disulfide bonds.** Whenever two molecules of the amino acid **cysteine** come close together, the **sulfur atom** in one cysteine bonds to the sulfur in the other cysteine, forming a disulfide bond.

- **Hydrophobic** and **hydrophilic interactions.** When **hydrophobic** (water-repelling) R groups are close together in the protein, they tend to **clump together**. This means that **hydrophilic** (water-attracting) R groups are more likely to be pushed to the **outside**, which affects how the protein **folds up** into its final structure.

> *Heating a protein to a high temperature will break up its ionic and hydrophobic/hydrophilic interactions and hydrogen bonds. In turn this will cause a change in the protein's 3D shape.*

- **Hydrogen bonds** — these weak bonds form between slightly **positively-charged hydrogen atoms** in some R groups and **slightly negatively-charged** atoms in other R groups on the polypeptide chain.

4) **Quaternary structure** — this tends to be determined by the **tertiary structure** of the individual polypeptide chains being bonded together. Because of this, it can be influenced by **all the bonds** mentioned above.

Proteins

Globular Proteins Are Round and Compact

1) In a globular protein, the **hydrophilic R groups** on the amino acids tend to be pushed to the **outside** of the molecule. This is caused by the **hydrophobic** and **hydrophilic interactions** in the protein's **tertiary structure** (see previous page).

2) This makes globular proteins **soluble**, so they're **easily transported** in fluids.

3) Globular proteins have a **range of functions** in living organisms. For example:

Dean did a great impression of a globular protein.

> **HAEMOGLOBIN** is a globular protein that carries **oxygen** around the body in **red blood cells** (see page 92). It's known as a **conjugated protein** — this means it's a protein with a **non-protein group** attached. The non-protein part is called a **prosthetic group**. Each of the four polypeptide chains in haemoglobin has a prosthetic group called **haem**. A haem group contains **iron**, which oxygen binds to.

haem group

> **INSULIN** is a **hormone** secreted by the **pancreas**. It helps to regulate the **blood glucose level**. Its **solubility** is important — it means it can be **transported** in the **blood** to the tissues where it acts. An insulin molecule consists of **two polypeptide chains**, which are held together by **disulfide bonds**.

> **AMYLASE** is an **enzyme** (see page 24) that catalyses the breakdown of **starch** in the digestive system. It is made of a **single chain** of amino acids. Its secondary structure contains **both** alpha-helix and beta-pleated sheet sections. **Most enzymes** are **globular proteins**.

Fibrous Proteins Are Tough and Rope-Shaped

Fibrous proteins are **insoluble** and **strong**. They're **structural** proteins and are fairly **unreactive** (unlike many globular proteins). Fibrous proteins include:

- **Collagen** — found in animal **connective tissues**, such as bone, skin and muscle. It is a very **strong** molecule. **Minerals** can bind to the protein to increase its **rigidity**, e.g. in bone.

The Structure of a Collagen Molecule

- **Keratin** — found in many of the **external structures** of animals, such as skin, hair, nails, feathers and horns. It can either be **flexible** (as it is in skin) or **hard and tough** (as it is in nails).

- **Elastin** — found in **elastic connective tissue**, such as skin, large blood vessels and some ligaments. It is **elastic**, so it allows tissues to return to their original shape after they have been stretched.

Practice Questions

Q1 Describe the general structure of an amino acid.

Q2 Name the bond that joins amino acids together in proteins.

Q3 What is a conjugated protein?

Exam Questions

Q1 Suggest which of the following proteins is most abundant in a tortoise's shell.

A Collagen   B Elastin   C Alpha-amylase   D Keratin   [1 mark]

Q2* HSA is a globular protein, which transports other molecules such as fatty acids around the bloodstream. The molecule consists of 585 amino acids, several of which are cysteine.

Describe the bonds that could be present in the tertiary structure of HSA and suggest how its structure makes it suited for its role of transporting molecules in the blood. [6 marks]

* You will be assessed on the quality of your written response in this question.

The name's Bond — Peptide Bond...

Proteins are annoyingly complicated. Not happy with one, or even two structural levels, they can have four of the things. And as for all that nasty stuff about disulfide bonds and ionic interactions... Urgh.

Inorganic Ions

Inorganic ions are just teeny tiny little things, but they're essential for many biological processes.

Inorganic Ions Have an Electric Charge

1) An **ion** is an atom (or group of atoms) that has an **electric charge**.
2) An ion with a **positive charge** is called a **cation**.
3) An ion with a **negative charge** is called an **anion**.
4) An **inorganic** ion is one which **doesn't contain carbon** (although there are a few exceptions to this rule).
5) Inorganic ions are really important in **biological processes**. Here are some you might come across:

	Name of ion	Chemical Symbol	Example(s) of roles in biological processes
Cations	Calcium	Ca^{2+}	Involved in the transmission of **nerve impulses** and the release of **insulin** from the pancreas. Acts as a **cofactor** for many **enzymes** (see p. 29).
	Sodium	Na^+	Important for generating **nerve impulses**, for **muscle contraction** and for **regulating fluid balance** in the body.
	Potassium	K^+	Important for generating **nerve impulses**, for **muscle contraction** and for **regulating fluid balance** in the body.
	Hydrogen	H^+	Affects the **pH** of substances (**more H^+ ions** than OH^- ions in a solution creates an **acid**).
	Ammonium	NH_4^+	Absorbed from the **soil** by **plants** and is an important source of **nitrogen** (which is then used to make, e.g. amino acids, nucleic acids).
	Iron	Fe^{2+} / Fe^{3+}	Allows **haemoglobin** in **red blood cells** to transport **oxygen**. Fe^{2+} ions in haemoglobin **bind** to oxygen, temporarily becoming Fe^{3+} until oxygen is released.
Anions	Nitrate	NO_3^-	Absorbed from the **soil** by **plants** and is an important source of **nitrogen** (which is then used to make, e.g. amino acids, nucleic acids).
	Hydrogencarbonate	HCO_3^-	Acts as a **buffer**, which helps to maintain the **pH** of the blood.
	Chloride	Cl^-	Acts as a **cofactor** for the enzyme **amylase** (see p. 29). Also involved in some **nerve impulses**.
	Phosphate	PO_4^{3-}	Involved in **photosynthesis** and **respiration** reactions. Needed for the synthesis of many biological molecules, such as **nucleotides** (including **ATP**), **phospholipids**, and **calcium phosphate** (which strengthens bones).
	Hydroxide	OH^-	Affects the **pH** of substances (**more OH^- ions** than H^+ ions in a solution creates an **alkali**).

Practice Questions

Q1 What is the difference between a cation and an anion?

Q2 Write the chemical symbols for the following ions: calcium, ammonium, nitrate, phosphate, hydroxide.

Exam Question

Q1 Carbonic acid (H_2CO_3) is a weak acid present in the blood.
A reaction with water causes a hydrogen ion to dissociate from the carbonic acid molecule.
Name the anion that's formed in this reaction and write its chemical symbol. [2 marks]

Stop all that texting and get revising — I've got my ion you...

Well, who doesn't love a big table to brighten up Biology? I do, that's for sure. You'll definitely meet some of these inorganic ions again in your Biology studies, so it's a good idea to make friends with them now. Better get cracking.

Biochemical Tests for Molecules

Here's a bit of light relief for you — two pages on how you test for the different molecules you've read about...

Use the **Benedict's Test** for **Sugars**

Sugar is a general term for **monosaccharides** and **disaccharides**. All sugars can be classified as **reducing** or **non-reducing**. The **Benedict's test** tests for sugars — it **differs** depending on the **type** of sugar you are testing for.

REDUCING SUGARS

1) Reducing sugars include **all monosaccharides** (e.g. glucose) and **some disaccharides** (e.g. maltose and lactose).
2) You add **Benedict's reagent** (which is **blue**) to a sample and **heat it** in a water bath that's been brought to the **boil**.

   The colour of the precipitate changes from:

   Always use an excess of Benedict's solution — this makes sure that all the sugar reacts.

3) If the test's **positive** it will form a **coloured precipitate** (solid particles suspended in the solution).
4) The higher the concentration of reducing sugar, the further the colour change goes — you can use this to **compare** the amount of reducing sugar in different solutions. A more accurate way of doing this is to **filter** the solution and **weigh the precipitate**.

NON-REDUCING SUGARS

1) If the result of the reducing sugars test is **negative**, there could still be a non-reducing sugar present. To test for **non-reducing sugars**, like sucrose, first you have to break them down into monosaccharides.
2) You do this by getting a new sample of the test solution, adding **dilute hydrochloric acid** and carefully heating it in a water bath that's been brought to the **boil**. You then **neutralise** it with **sodium hydrogencarbonate**. Then just carry out the **Benedict's test** as you would for a reducing sugar.
3) If the test's **positive** it will form a **coloured precipitate** (as for the reducing sugars test). If the test's **negative** the solution will **stay blue**, which means it **doesn't contain any sugar** (either reducing or non-reducing).

Use **Test Strips** for **Glucose**

Glucose can also be tested for using **test strips** coated in a **reagent**. The strips are dipped in a test solution and **change colour** if glucose is **present**. The colour change can be compared to a **chart** to give an indication of the concentration of glucose present. The strips are useful for testing a person's **urine** for glucose, which may indicate they have **diabetes**.

Use the **Iodine Test** for **Starch**

Just add **iodine dissolved in potassium iodide solution** to the test sample.
- If starch **is present**, the sample changes from **browny-orange** to a dark, **blue-black** colour.
- If there's **no starch**, it stays browny-orange.

Make sure you always talk about iodine in potassium iodide solution, not just iodine.

Use the **Biuret Test** for **Proteins**

There are **two stages** to this test.
1) The test solution needs to be **alkaline**, so first you add a few drops of **sodium hydroxide solution**.
2) Then you add some **copper(II) sulfate solution**.
   - If protein **is** present the solution turns **purple**.
   - If there's **no protein**, the solution will stay blue.

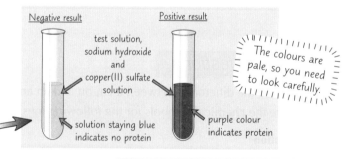

The colours are pale, so you need to look carefully.

Use the **Emulsion Test** for **Lipids**

Shake the test substance with **ethanol** for about a minute, then **pour** the solution into **water**.
- If lipid **is present**, the solution will turn **milky**.
- The **more lipid** there is, the **more noticeable** the milky colour will be.
- If there's **no lipid**, the solution will **stay clear**.

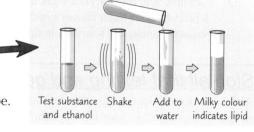

Biochemical Tests for Molecules

Colorimetry is Used to Determine the Concentration of a Glucose Solution

1) You can use **Benedict's reagent** and a **colorimeter** to get a **quantitative estimate** of **how much** glucose (or other reducing sugar) there is in a solution.

2) A colorimeter is a device that measures the **strength** of a **coloured solution** by seeing how much **light** passes through it.

3) A colorimeter measures **absorbance** (the amount of light absorbed by the solution). The **more concentrated** the **colour** of the solution, the **higher** the **absorbance** is.

4) It's easiest to measure the concentration of the **blue Benedict's solution** that's left after the test (the **paler** the solution, the **more glucose** there was). So, the **higher** the glucose concentration, the **lower** the absorbance.

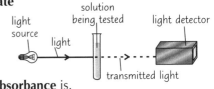

This is How You Do it:

Initially you need to make up several glucose solutions of **different, known concentrations**. You can do this using a **serial dilution** technique:

> You don't have to dilute solutions by a factor of 2. E.g. to dilute by a factor of 10, take 1 cm³ from your original sample and add it to 9 cm³ of water.

This is how you'd make **five serial dilutions** with a **dilution factor of 2**, starting with an initial glucose concentration of **40 mM**...

1) Line up five **test tubes** in a rack.

2) Add **10 cm³** of the initial **40 mM glucose solution** to the first test tube and **5 cm³ of distilled water** to the other four test tubes.

3) Then, using a pipette, draw **5 cm³** of the solution from the **first** test tube, add it to the distilled water in the **second** test tube and **mix** the solution **thoroughly**. You now have **10 cm³** of solution that's **half as concentrated** as the solution in the first test tube (it's **20 mM**).

4) Repeat this process **three more times** to create solutions of **10 mM**, **5 mM** and **2.5 mM**.

Once you've got your glucose solutions, you need to make a **calibration curve**. Here's how:

1) Do a **Benedict's test** on each solution (plus a **negative control** of **pure water**). Use the **same amount** of Benedict's solution in each case.

2) **Remove** any **precipitate** — either leave for **24 hours** (so that the precipitate **settles out**) or **centrifuge** them.

3) Use a **colorimeter** (with a **red filter**) to measure the **absorbance** of the Benedict's solution **remaining** in each tube.

4) Use the results to make the **calibration curve**, showing absorbance against glucose concentration.

Then you can test the **unknown solution** in the same way as the known concentrations and use the calibration curve to find its concentration.

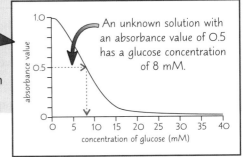

An unknown solution with an absorbance value of 0.5 has a glucose concentration of 8 mM.

Practice Questions

Q1 Describe how you would test a solution for starch.

Q2 Describe how you would test for lipids in a solution.

Exam Question

Q1 Equal volumes of three different sugar solutions (A, B and C) were each tested with the same large volume of Benedict's solution. Later, the concentrations of Benedict's solution in each test tube were compared, using a colorimeter. The table shows the absorbance of each solution.

solution	absorbance
A	1.22
B	0.68
C	0.37

   a) Which original solution contained the highest concentration of reducing sugar? [1 mark]

   b) Suggest two factors that should be kept constant when carrying out this test. [2 marks]

The Anger Test — annoy test subject. If it goes red, anger is present...

There are lots of different biochemical tests on the previous page — don't get mixed up between the different colour changes and what they mean. At least this colorimetry thingy-me-bob is a bit more exciting. Sort of.

Biochemical Tests and Separating Molecules

If you haven't had enough of finding out what biochemical molecules solutions contain, you're in luck. Biosensors and chromatography now. You've probably tried chromatography before with a spot of ink on a piece of filter paper.

Biosensors Can Detect Chemicals in a Solution

1) A **biosensor** is a device that uses a **biological molecule**, such as an **enzyme** (see page 24) to detect a **chemical**.

2) The biological molecule produces a **signal** (e.g. a **chemical** signal), which is converted to an **electrical signal** by a **transducer** (another part of the **biosensor**).

3) The electrical signal is then **processed** and can be used to work out other information.

Example: Glucose Biosensors

1) A **glucose biosensor** is used to determine the **concentration** of **glucose** in a solution.

2) It does this using the enzyme **glucose oxidase** and **electrodes**.

3) The enzyme catalyses the **oxidation** of **glucose** at the electrodes — this creates a **charge**, which is converted into an **electrical signal** by the electrodes (the transducer).

4) The electrical signal is then **processed** to work out the **initial glucose concentration**.

Chromatography is Good for Separating and Identifying Things

1) Chromatography is used to **separate** stuff in a mixture — once it's separated out, you can often **identify** the components.

2) For example, chromatography can be used to separate out and identify biological molecules such as **amino acids**, **carbohydrates**, **vitamins** and **nucleic acids**.

3) There are quite a few different types of chromatography — **paper chromatography** and **thin-layer chromatography** are the two you're most likely to come across.

Here's How Chromatography Works

1) All types of chromatography (including paper and thin-layer) have the same **basic set up**:

> 1) A **MOBILE PHASE** — where the molecules **can move**.
>   - In both paper and thin-layer chromatography the mobile phase is a **liquid solvent**, such as ethanol or water.
> 2) A **STATIONARY PHASE** — where the molecules **can't move**.
>   - In paper chromatography the stationary phase is a piece of **chromatography paper**.
>   - In thin-layer chromatography the stationary phase is a **thin** (0.1-0.3 mm) **layer of solid**, e.g. silica gel, on a **glass or plastic plate**.

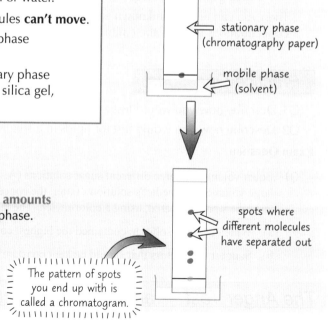

Example: paper chromatography

stationary phase (chromatography paper)

mobile phase (solvent)

spots where different molecules have separated out

2) And they all use the same basic principle:
- The mobile phase **moves through** or **over** the stationary phase.
- The components in the mixture spend **different amounts of time** in the mobile phase and the stationary phase.
- The components that spend longer in the **mobile phase** travel **faster** or **further**.
- The time spent in the different phases is what **separates out** the components of the mixture.

The pattern of spots you end up with is called a chromatogram.

Biochemical Tests and Separating Molecules

Paper Chromatography is used to Identify Unknown Amino Acids

Chromatography can be used to identify the **biological molecules in a mixture**. Below is an example of how **paper chromatography** can be used to identify **amino acids** in a **mixture**. If you're trying to identify **different biological molecules**, the **method** will **vary slightly** (e.g. a different solvent might be used) but the basic principle will be the same.

Here's what you'd do:

1) Draw a **pencil line** near the bottom of a piece of **chromatography paper** and put a **concentrated spot** of the mixture of amino acids on it. It's best to carefully roll the paper into a **cylinder** with the spot on the outside so it'll stand up.

2) Add a small amount of prepared **solvent** (a mixture of **butan-1-ol**, **glacial ethanoic acid** and **water** is usually used for amino acids) to a beaker and dip the **bottom** of the **paper** into it (not the spot). This should be done in a **fume cupboard**. Cover with a **lid** to stop the solvent evaporating.

3) As the solvent spreads up the paper, the different amino acids move with it, but at **different rates**, so they separate out.

4) When the solvent's **nearly** reached the top, take the paper out and **mark** the solvent front with pencil. Then you can leave the paper to **dry out** before you analyse it (see below).

5) Amino acids **aren't coloured**, which means you **won't be able to see them** on the paper. So before you can analyse them, you have to spray the paper with **ninhydrin solution** to turn the amino acids **purple**. This should also be done in a **fume cupboard** and **gloves** should be worn. (Note: you can't use ninhydrin to detect all biological molecules, only proteins and amino acids.)

6) You can then use R_f **values** to **identify** the separated molecules:

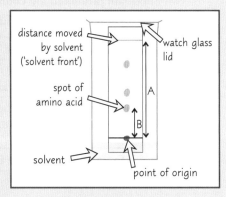

An R_f **value** is the ratio of the distance travelled by a spot to the distance travelled by the solvent. You can calculate it using this formula:

$$R_f \text{ value of amino acid} = \frac{B}{A} = \frac{\text{distance travelled by spot}}{\text{distance travelled by solvent}}$$

When you're measuring how far a spot has travelled, you measure from the **point of origin** to the **vertical centre** of the spot.

You can work out what was in a mixture by calculating an R_f value for each spot and looking each R_f value up in a **database**, or table, of **known values**.

You could also compare your chromatogram to the chromatogram of a known mixture and identify the components that way — if two spots have travelled the same distance in the solvent, they will be the same molecule.

Practice Questions

Q1 What is a biosensor?
Q2 What is chromatography used for?
Q3 Why would you use ninhydrin solution when using chromatography to identify amino acids in a mixture?

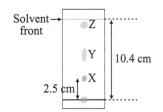

Sugar	R_f value
Glucose	0.20
Fructose	0.24
Xylose	0.30

Exam Question

Q1 The paper chromatogram above shows the separation of three sugars from a solution.
a) Briefly describe the method used to produce this chromatogram. [3 marks]
b) Explain why the spots have ended up in different positions on the chromatogram. [1 mark]
c) Calculate the R_f value of spot X and use your answer to identify the sugar it contains. [3 marks]

I'm afraid you can't read anymore of this page — it's been bio-censored...

Well, these two pages aren't that bad really. There's all that clever, technical biosensor gubbins at the beginning and then the rest is fun stuff about spots appearing in chromatography. And even better, it's the end of a section.

Action of Enzymes

Enzymes crop up loads in Biology — they're really useful 'cos they make reactions work more quickly.

Enzymes are Biological Catalysts

> A catalyst is a substance that speeds up a chemical reaction without being used up in the reaction itself.

1) Enzymes **speed up chemical reactions** by acting as **biological catalysts**. They catalyse **metabolic reactions** — both at a **cellular level** (e.g. **respiration**) and for the **organism** as a **whole** (e.g. **digestion** in mammals).

2) Enzymes can affect **structures** in an organism (e.g. enzymes are involved in the production of **collagen**, an important protein in the **connective tissues** of animals) as well as **functions** (like **respiration**).

3) Enzyme action can be **intracellular** — **within** cells, or **extracellular** — **outside** cells.

> **Intracellular Enzyme Example — Catalase**
>
> 1) **Hydrogen peroxide** (H_2O_2) is the **toxic by-product** of several cellular reactions. If left to build up, it can **kill cells**.
>
> 2) **Catalase** is an enzyme that works **inside cells** to catalyse the breakdown of hydrogen peroxide to **harmless oxygen** (O_2) and **water** (H_2O).

> **Extracellular Enzyme Examples — Amylase and Trypsin**
>
> 1) Amylase and trypsin both work **outside cells** in the human **digestive system**.
>
> 2) **Amylase** is found in **saliva**. It's **secreted** into the **mouth** by cells in the **salivary glands**. It catalyses the **hydrolysis** (breakdown, see p. 10) of **starch** into **maltose** (a sugar) in the mouth.
>
> 3) **Trypsin** catalyses the hydrolysis of **peptide bonds** — turning **big polypeptides** into **smaller ones** (which then get broken down into amino acids by other enzymes). Trypsin is produced by cells in the **pancreas** and secreted into the **small intestine**.

4) Enzymes are **globular proteins** (see p. 18).

5) Enzymes have an **active site**, which has a **specific shape**. The active site is the part of the enzyme that the **substrate** molecules (the substance that the enzyme interacts with) **bind to**.

6) The specific shape of the active site is determined by the enzyme's **tertiary structure** (see p. 17).

7) For the enzyme to work, the substrate has to **fit into** the **active site** (its shape has to be **complementary**). If the substrate shape doesn't match the active site, the reaction won't be catalysed. This means that enzymes work with very few substrates — usually only one.

Enzymes Reduce Activation Energy

1) In a chemical reaction, a certain amount of energy needs to be supplied to the chemicals before the reaction will start. This is called the **activation energy** — it's often provided as **heat**.

2) Enzymes **reduce** the amount of activation energy that's needed, often making reactions happen at a **lower temperature** than they could without an enzyme. This **speeds** up the **rate of reaction**.

3) When a substance binds to an enzyme's active site, an **enzyme-substrate complex** is formed. It's the formation of the enzyme-substrate complex that **lowers** the **activation energy**. Here are two reasons why:

> 1) If two substrate molecules need to be **joined**, attaching to the enzyme holds them **close together**, **reducing** any **repulsion** between the molecules so they can bond more easily.
>
> 2) If the enzyme is catalysing a **breakdown reaction**, fitting into the active site puts a **strain** on bonds in the substrate. This strain means the substrate molecule **breaks up** more easily.

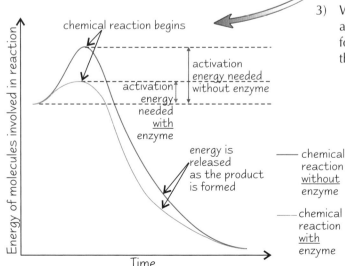

SECTION 2 — ENZYMES

Action of Enzymes

The 'Lock and Key' Model is a Good Start...

Enzymes are a bit picky. They only work with **substrates** that fit their active site. Early scientists studying the action of enzymes came up with the '**lock and key**' model. This is where the **substrate fits** into the **enzyme** in the same way that a **key fits** into a **lock**.

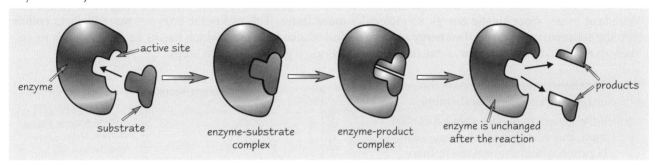

Scientists soon realised that the lock and key model didn't give the full story. The enzyme and substrate do have to fit together in the first place, but new evidence showed that the **enzyme-substrate complex changed shape** slightly to complete the fit. This **locks** the substrate even more tightly to the enzyme. Scientists modified the old lock and key model and came up with the '**induced fit**' model.

...but the 'Induced Fit' Model is a Better Theory

The '**induced fit**' model helps to explain why enzymes are so **specific** and only bond to one particular substrate.

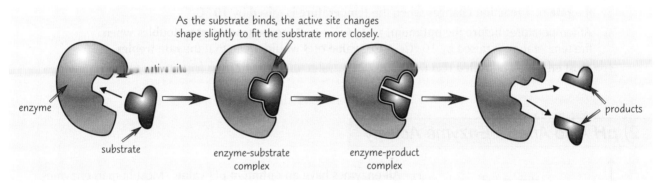

The substrate doesn't only have to be the right shape to fit the active site, it has to make the active site **change shape** in the right way as well. This is a prime example of how a widely accepted theory can **change** when **new evidence** comes along. The 'induced fit' model is still widely accepted — for now, anyway.

Practice Questions

Q1 What is an enzyme?
Q2 What is the name given to the amount of energy needed to start a reaction?
Q3 What is an enzyme-substrate complex?
Q4 Explain why enzymes are specific.

Exam Question

Q1 Dextranase is an enzyme that catalyses the breakdown of specific bonds in dextran (a polysaccharide).

Use the induced fit model of enzyme action to explain why dextranase catalyses the breakdown of dextran, but not amylose (another polysaccharide). [3 marks]

But why is the enzyme-substrate complex?

OK, nothing too tricky here. The main thing to remember is that every enzyme has a specific shape, so it only works with specific substrates that fit the active site. The induced fit model is a newer theory that explains this.

Factors Affecting Enzyme Activity

Now you know what enzymes are and how they work, it's time to take a look at what makes them tick. These pages cover the four main factors affecting enzyme activity and also how you can measure the rate of enzyme reactions.

1) Temperature has a Big Influence on Enzyme Activity

Like any chemical reaction, the **rate** of an enzyme-controlled reaction **increases** when the **temperature's increased**. More heat means **more kinetic energy**, so molecules **move faster**. This makes the enzymes **more likely** to **collide** with the substrate molecules. The **energy** of these collisions also **increases**, which means each collision is more likely to **result** in a **reaction**. But, if the temperature gets too high, the **reaction stops**.

1) The rise in temperature makes the enzyme's molecules **vibrate more**.

2) If the temperature goes above a certain level, this vibration **breaks** some of the **bonds** that hold the enzyme in shape.

3) The **active site changes shape** and the enzyme and substrate **no longer fit together**.

4) At this point, the enzyme is **denatured** — it no longer functions as a catalyst.

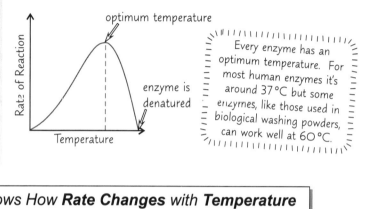

Every enzyme has an optimum temperature. For most human enzymes it's around 37 °C but some enzymes, like those used in biological washing powders, can work well at 60 °C.

The Temperature Coefficient (Q_{10}) Shows How Rate Changes with Temperature

1) The **temperature coefficient** or Q_{10} value for a reaction shows **how much** the **rate** of a **reaction changes** when the **temperature** is **raised** by **10 °C**.

2) At temperatures **before** the **optimum**, a Q_{10} value of **2** means that the **rate doubles** when the temperature is raised by 10 °C. A Q_{10} value of **3** would mean that the **rate trebles**.

3) Most **enzyme-controlled reactions** have a Q_{10} value of **around 2**.

2) pH Also Affects Enzyme Activity

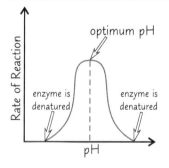

1) All enzymes have an **optimum pH value**. Most human enzymes work best at pH 7 (neutral), but there are exceptions. **Pepsin**, for example, works best at acidic pH 2, which is useful because it's found in the stomach.

2) Above and below the optimum pH, the H^+ and OH^- ions found in acids and alkalis can mess up the **ionic bonds** and **hydrogen bonds** that hold the enzyme's tertiary structure in place. This makes the active site change shape, so the enzyme is **denatured**.

3) Enzyme Concentration Affects the Rate of Reaction

1) The **more enzyme molecules** there are in a solution, the more likely a substrate molecule is to **collide** with one and form an **enzyme-substrate complex**. So increasing the concentration of the enzyme **increases** the **rate of reaction**.

2) But, if the amount of **substrate** is **limited**, there comes a point when there's more than enough enzyme molecules to deal with all the available substrate, so adding more enzyme has **no further effect**.

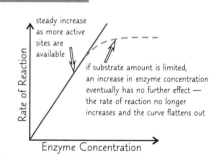

steady increase as more active sites are available

if substrate amount is limited, an increase in enzyme concentration eventually has no further effect — the rate of reaction no longer increases and the curve flattens out

Factors Affecting Enzyme Activity

4) *Substrate Concentration* Affects the Rate of Reaction *Up to a Point*

1) The **higher** the substrate concentration, the **faster** the reaction — more substrate molecules means a **collision** between substrate and enzyme is **more likely** and so more active sites will be used.

2) This is only true up until a **'saturation'** point though. After that, there are so many substrate molecules that the enzymes have about as much as they can cope with (all the **active sites are full**), and adding more substrate **makes no difference** to the rate of reaction.

3) Substrate concentration **decreases** with **time** during a reaction (unless more substrate is added to the reaction mixture), so if no other variables are changed, the **rate of reaction will decrease over time** too. This makes the **initial** rate of reaction (the reaction rate right at the start of the reaction, close to **time 0**) the **highest** rate of reaction.

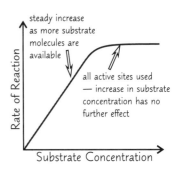

steady increase as more substrate molecules are available

all active sites used — increase in substrate concentration has no further effect

Rate of Reaction

Substrate Concentration

You can calculate the initial rate of an enzyme-controlled reaction from a graph — see next page for more.

You can *Measure* the *Rate* of an *Enzyme-Controlled* Reaction

Here are two ways of measuring the **rate** of an enzyme-controlled reaction:

1) You Can Measure *How Fast* the *Product* of the Reaction is *Made*

Catalase catalyses the breakdown of hydrogen peroxide into water and oxygen. It's easy to measure the volume of oxygen produced and to work out **how fast** it's given off. The diagram below shows the **apparatus** you'll need. The oxygen released **displaces** the water from the measuring cylinder. (A **stand** and **clamp** would also be pretty useful to hold the cylinder upside down, as would a **stopwatch** and a **water bath**.) Here's how to carry out the experiment:

1) Set up boiling tubes containing the **same volume** and **concentration** of **hydrogen peroxide**. To keep the pH constant, add **equal volumes** of a suitable **buffer solution** to each tube. (A buffer solution is able to resist changes in pH when small amounts of acid or alkali are added.)

2) Set up the rest of the **apparatus** as shown in the diagram.

3) Put each boiling tube in a **water bath** set to a different temperature (e.g. 10 °C, 20 °C, 30 °C and 40 °C) along with another tube containing **catalase** (wait 5 minutes before moving onto the next step so the enzyme gets up to temperature).

4) Use a pipette to add the **same volume** and **concentration** of **catalase** to each boiling tube. Then **quickly attach** the **bung** and **delivery tube**.

5) **Record** how much oxygen is produced in the **first minute** (60 s) of the reaction. Use a **stopwatch** to measure the time.

6) **Repeat** the experiment at each temperature three times, and use the results to find an **average volume of oxygen produced**.

7) **Calculate** the **average rate of reaction** at each temperature by dividing the volume of oxygen produced by the time taken (i.e. 60 s). The units will be cm^3 s^{-1}.

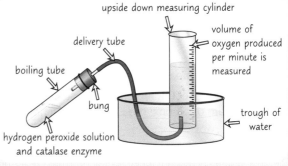

upside down measuring cylinder

delivery tube

volume of oxygen produced per minute is measured

boiling tube

bung

hydrogen peroxide solution and catalase enzyme

trough of water

A negative control reaction, i.e. a boiling tube not containing catalase, should also be carried out at each temperature.

Factors Affecting Enzyme Activity

2) You Can Measure How Fast the Substrate is Broken Down

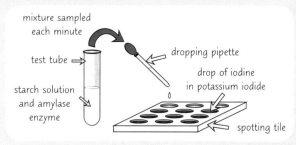

mixture sampled each minute

test tube

dropping pipette

drop of iodine in potassium iodide

starch solution and amylase enzyme

spotting tile

The enzyme **amylase** catalyses the breakdown of **starch** to **maltose**. To measure the rate, you'll need a **stopwatch** and the **apparatus** shown in the diagram. A drop of **iodine in potassium iodide** is put into each well on a **spotting tile**. A known concentration of **amylase** and **starch** are then mixed together in a test tube. A **dropping pipette** is used to put a drop of this mixture into one of the wells containing the iodine solution on the spotting tile at **regular intervals** and the resulting colour is observed. The iodine solution goes **dark blue-black** when **starch** is **present** but remains its normal **browny-orange** colour when there's **no starch** around. You can see how fast **amylase** is working by **recording** how long it takes for the iodine solution to **no longer** turn blue-black when starch/amylase mixture is added. **Repeat** the experiment using **different concentrations** of **amylase**. Make sure you **repeat** the experiment three times at **each** amylase concentration.

These experiments show you how to investigate the effects of **temperature** and **enzyme concentration** on the rate of enzyme-controlled reactions. You can **alter** these experiments to investigate the effect of a **different variable**, e.g. **pH** (by adding a **buffer solution** with a **different pH** to each test tube) or **substrate concentration** (you could use **serial dilutions** to make substrate solutions with **different** concentrations). The key is to **only** change **one variable**.

You Can Use a Tangent to Calculate the Initial Rate of Reaction

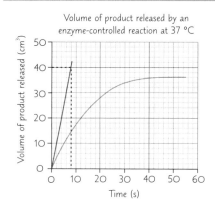

Volume of product released by an enzyme-controlled reaction at 37 °C

Volume of product released (cm³) — Time (s)

To work out the initial rate of reaction carry out the following steps:

1) **Draw** a **tangent** to the curve at **t = 0**, using a ruler. Do this by positioning the ruler so it's an **equal distance** from the curve at **both sides** of where it's touching it. Here you'll have to **estimate** where the curve would **continue** if it carried on **below zero**. Then draw a **line** along the ruler.

2) Then calculate the **gradient** of the **tangent** — this is the **initial rate of reaction**.
Gradient = change in y-axis ÷ change in x-axis
In this graph it's: 40 cm³ ÷ 8 s = **5 cm³ s⁻¹**

Practice Question

Q1 What does it mean if an enzyme is denatured?

Q2 Explain the effect of increasing substrate concentration on the rate of an enzyme-catalysed reaction.

Exam Questions

Q1 A student carries out an enzyme-controlled reaction at 37 °C and 65 °C. Her results are shown in the graph.
Draw a tangent to find the initial rate of reaction at 65 °C. [1 mark]

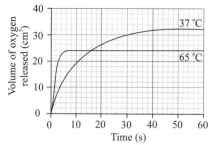

Volume of oxygen released (cm³) — Time (s) — 37 °C — 65 °C

Q2 Casein is a protein found in milk powder. A student wants to investigate the effect of varying pH on the rate of casein breakdown by the enzyme trypsin. She intends to add trypsin to a series of solutions containing milk powder at different pHs and time how long it takes for each solution to turn from cloudy to translucent.

a) Suggest how the student could vary the pH of the milk powder solutions. [1 mark]

b) Give one variable that the student will need to control in this experiment. [1 mark]

c) The student has read that the optimum pH for trypsin is pH 8.
Describe and explain what will happen to the rate of the reaction above this pH. [4 marks]

My rate of reaction depends on what time of day it is...

It's worth making sure that you understand what each of the different graphs on these pages show. You should also make sure you know how you could investigate the different factors that affect enzyme activity.

Cofactors and Enzyme Inhibition

Cofactors are substances that enzymes need to work. Enzyme inhibitors, yep you guessed it, inhibit their action.
Some inhibitors are poisons, but they're not all bad — we use some of them as medicinal drugs.

Cofactors and Coenzymes are Essential for Enzymes to Work

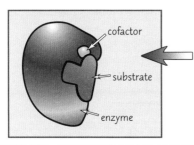

Some enzymes will only work if there is another **non-protein** substance bound to them. These non-protein substances are called **cofactors**.

1) Some cofactors are **inorganic** molecules or ions. They work by helping the enzyme and substrate to **bind together**. They don't directly participate in the reaction so aren't **used up** or **changed** in any way. For example, **chloride ions (Cl⁻)** are **cofactors** for the enzyme **amylase**.

2) Some cofactors are **organic** molecules — these are called **coenzymes**. They participate in the reaction and are **changed** by it (they're just like a second substrate, but they aren't called that). They often act as **carriers**, moving **chemical groups** between different enzymes. They're **continually recycled** during this process. **Vitamins** are often **sources** of coenzymes.

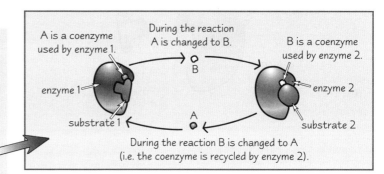

During the reaction B is changed to A (i.e. the coenzyme is recycled by enzyme 2).

3) If a cofactor is **tightly bound** to the enzyme, it's known as a **prosthetic group**. For example, **zinc ions (Zn²⁺)** are a prosthetic group for **carbonic anhydrase** (an enzyme in red blood cells, which catalyses the production of carbonic acid from water and carbon dioxide). The zinc ions are a **permanent part** of the enzyme's **active site**.

Enzyme Activity can be Inhibited

Enzyme activity can be prevented by **enzyme inhibitors** — molecules that **bind to the enzyme** that they inhibit. Inhibition can be **competitive** (see below) or **non-competitive** (see next page).

COMPETITIVE INHIBITION

1) **Competitive inhibitor** molecules have a **similar shape** to that of the **substrate** molecules.
2) They **compete** with the substrate molecules to **bind** to the **active site**, but **no reaction** takes place.
3) Instead they **block** the active site, so **no substrate** molecules can **fit** in it.

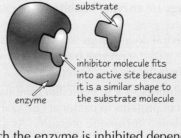

inhibitor molecule fits into active site because it is a similar shape to the substrate molecule

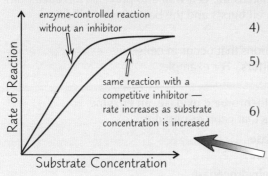

4) How much the enzyme is inhibited depends on the **relative concentrations** of the inhibitor and the substrate.
5) If there's a **high concentration** of the **inhibitor**, it'll take up **nearly all** the **active sites** and hardly any of the substrate will get to the enzyme.
6) But if there's a **higher concentration** of **substrate**, then the substrate's chances of getting to an active site before the inhibitor **increase**. So **increasing** the concentration of **substrate** will **increase** the **rate of reaction** (up to a point).

Cofactors and Enzyme Inhibition

NON-COMPETITIVE INHIBITION

1) **Non-competitive inhibitor** molecules bind to the enzyme **away from its active site**. The site they bind to is known as the enzyme's **allosteric site**.

2) This causes the active site to **change shape** so the substrate molecules can **no longer bind** to it.

3) They **don't 'compete'** with the substrate molecules to bind to the active site because they are a **different shape**.

4) **Increasing** the concentration of **substrate won't** make any difference to the reaction rate — enzyme activity will still be inhibited.

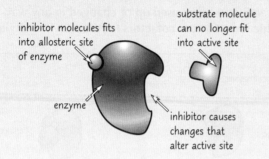

inhibitor molecules fits into allosteric site of enzyme

substrate molecule can no longer fit into active site

enzyme

inhibitor causes changes that alter active site

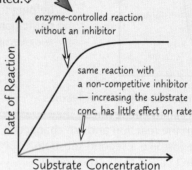

enzyme-controlled reaction without an inhibitor

same reaction with a non-competitive inhibitor — increasing the substrate conc. has little effect on rate

Rate of Reaction

Substrate Concentration

Inhibitors Can Be Reversible or Non-Reversible

Which one they are depends on the **strength of the bonds** between the enzyme and the inhibitor.

1) If they're **strong, covalent bonds**, the inhibitor can't be removed easily and the inhibition is **irreversible**.

2) If they're **weaker hydrogen bonds** or weak **ionic bonds**, the inhibitor can be removed and the inhibition is **reversible**.

The hockey team had strong bonds. Especially after they accidentally glued their kits together.

Some Drugs and Metabolic Poisons are Enzyme Inhibitors

Some **medicinal drugs** are **enzyme inhibitors**, for example:

1) Some **antiviral** drugs (drugs that stop **viruses** like **HIV**) — e.g. **reverse transcriptase inhibitors** inhibit the enzyme **reverse transcriptase**, which catalyses the **replication** of **viral DNA**. This **prevents** the virus from **replicating**.

2) Some **antibiotics** — e.g. **penicillin** inhibits the enzyme **transpeptidase**, which **catalyses** the **formation** of **proteins** in bacterial cell walls. This **weakens the cell wall** and prevents the bacterium from regulating its osmotic pressure. As a result the cell **bursts** and the bacterium is **killed**.

Metabolic **poisons interfere** with **metabolic reactions** (the reactions that occur in cells), causing **damage**, **illness** or **death** — they're often **enzyme inhibitors**. For example:

1) **Cyanide** is an **irreversible** inhibitor of **cytochrome c oxidase**, an enzyme that catalyses **respiration** reactions. Cells that can't respire **die**.

2) **Malonate** inhibits **succinate dehydrogenase** (which also catalyses respiration reactions).

3) **Arsenic** inhibits the action of **pyruvate dehydrogenase**, another enzyme that catalyses **respiration** reactions.

Cofactors and Enzyme Inhibition

Metabolic Pathways are *Regulated* by *End-Product Inhibition*

1) A **metabolic pathway** is a series of **connected metabolic reactions**. The **product** of the **first reaction** takes part in the **second reaction** — and so on. Each reaction is catalysed by a **different enzyme**.

2) Many enzymes are **inhibited** by the **product** of the reaction they catalyse. This is known as **product inhibition**.

3) **End-product inhibition** is when the **final product** in a **metabolic pathway** inhibits an enzyme that acts **earlier on** in the pathway.

4) End-product inhibition is a nifty way of **regulating** the pathway and **controlling** the amount of end-product that gets made. For example:

Substance 4 inhibits Enzyme 1

Enzyme 1 — Enzyme 2 — Enzyme 3

Substance 1 → Substance 2 → Substance 3 → Substance 4

- **Phosphofructokinase** is an enzyme involved in the metabolic pathway that **breaks down glucose** to make **ATP**.
- ATP **inhibits** the action of phosphofructokinase — so a **high level** of ATP **prevents** more ATP from being made.

5) Both product and end-product inhibition are **reversible**. So when the level of product starts to **drop**, the level of inhibition will start to fall and the enzyme can start to **function again** — this means that **more product** can be made.

Enzyme Inhibition Can Help to *Protect Cells*

1) Enzymes are sometimes synthesised as **inactive precursors** in **metabolic pathways** to prevent them causing damage to cells. For example, some **proteases** (which **break down proteins**) are synthesised as inactive precursors to stop them **damaging proteins** in the cell in which they're made.

2) Part of the precursor molecule **inhibits** its action as an enzyme. Once this part is **removed** (e.g. via a chemical reaction) the enzyme becomes **active**.

A sense of inhibition might have protected Dan from his dress sense.

Practice Questions

Q1 What are cofactors, coenzymes and prosthetic groups?

Q2 What's the difference between competitive and non-competitive enzyme inhibitors?

Q3 Name one metabolic poison and describe how it works.

Q4 Why are some enzymes synthesised as inactive precursors?

Exam Questions

Q1 In bacteria, lactose is broken down into glucose and galactose by the enzyme ß-galactosidase. Galactose inhibits ß-galactosidase by binding to the active site. Which one of the following statements is correct?

A Galactose is a cofactor of ß-galactosidase.   C Galactose binds to ß-galactosidase via weak hydrogen bonds.

B The inhibition of ß-galactosidase by galactose is irreversible.   D Galactose is a non-competitive inhibitor of ß-galactosidase. [1 mark]

Q2 During an experiment hexokinase (an enzyme that catalyses reactions important in respiration) was found to work only in the presence of magnesium ions and to work slower when aluminium ions were also present.

a) Suggest a possible reason why hexokinase only works when magnesium ions are present. [2 marks]

b) Suggest a possible reason why hexokinase works slower when aluminium ions are present. [2 marks]

c) Explain why aluminium ions are a metabolic poison. [1 mark]

Q3 HIV uses protease enzymes to catalyse the breakdown of proteins. It uses the products of the reaction to replicate new viruses. Ritonavir is a drug used to treat HIV. Its molecules have a similar shape to the protein molecules which are the substrate for HIV protease. Suggest how Ritonavir will affect HIV. Explain your answer. [3 marks]

Enzymes are easily inhibited — they're very shy you know...

Remember, coenzymes help enzymes do their job, while inhibitors get them to stop, and the products of a reaction catalysed by one enzyme may be the inhibitors of another one. If you can follow the ins, outs, ups and downs of some crazy soap opera then you can follow this. Everybody needs good en-zymes...

DNA, RNA and ATP

DNA, RNA and ATP are all important molecules — in fact, they're pretty vital for life.

DNA and RNA Carry Important Information

DNA and RNA are both types of **nucleic acid**. They're found in **all living cells** and they both carry **information**.

1) **DNA** (deoxyribonucleic acid) is used to store **genetic information** — that's **all the instructions** an organism needs to **grow and develop** from a fertilised egg to a fully grown adult.

2) **RNA** (ribonucleic acid) is similar in structure to DNA. One of its main functions is to **transfer** genetic information from the **DNA** to the **ribosomes**. Ribosomes are the body's **'protein factories'** — they read the RNA to make **polypeptides** (proteins) in a process called **translation** (see p. 139). Ribosomes themselves are made from **RNA** and **proteins**.

DNA and RNA are Polymers of Nucleotides

1) A **nucleotide** is a type of biological molecule. It's made from:

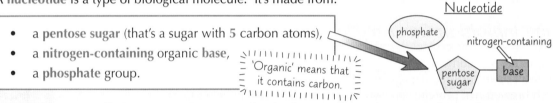

- a **pentose sugar** (that's a sugar with 5 carbon atoms),
- a **nitrogen-containing** organic **base**,
- a **phosphate** group.

'Organic' means that it contains carbon.

2) Nucleotides are really **important**. For a start, they're the **monomers** (see p. 12) that make up **DNA** and **RNA**.

The Sugar in DNA is Called Deoxyribose

1) The **pentose sugar** in a **DNA nucleotide** is called **deoxyribose**.

2) Each DNA nucleotide has the **same sugar** and a **phosphate group**. The **base** on each nucleotide can **vary** though.

3) There are **four** possible bases — adenine (**A**), thymine (**T**), cytosine (**C**) and guanine (**G**).

4) **A**denine and **g**uanine are a type of base called a **purine**. **C**ytosine and **t**hymine are a type of base called a **pyrimidine**.

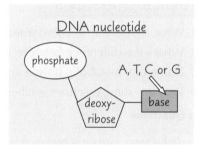

- A **purine** base contains **two carbon-nitrogen rings** joined together.
- A **pyrimidine** base only has **one carbon-nitrogen ring**. So a pyrimidine base is **smaller** than a purine base.

Remember: the pyrimidines in DNA are cytosine and thymine.

The Sugar in RNA is Called Ribose

1) **RNA** contains nucleotides with a **ribose sugar** (not deoxyribose).

2) Like DNA, an RNA nucleotide also has a **phosphate group** and one of **four** different **bases**.

3) In RNA though, **uracil** (**U**) replaces **thymine** as a base.

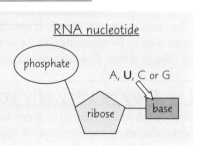

Mary didn't care if it was ribose or deoxyribose, she just wanted her cuppa.

DNA, RNA and ATP

DNA and RNA Nucleotides Join Together to Form Polynucleotides

1) A **polynucleotide** is a **polymer** of **nucleotides**.
Both DNA and RNA nucleotides form polynucleotides.

2) The nucleotides join up via a **condensation reaction** (see p. 10) between the **phosphate** group of one nucleotide and the **sugar** of another.

3) This forms a **phosphodiester bond** (consisting of the phosphate group and two ester bonds).

4) The chain of sugars and phosphates is known as the **sugar-phosphate backbone**.

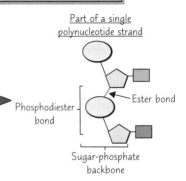

Part of a single polynucleotide strand

Phosphodiester bond

Ester bond

Sugar-phosphate backbone

DNA is Made of Two Polynucleotide Chains in a Double-Helix Structure

1) **Two DNA** polynucleotide strands join together by **hydrogen bonding** between the bases.

2) Each base can only join with one particular partner — this is called **complementary base pairing** (or specific base pairing).

3) **Adenine** always pairs with **thymine** (**A - T**) and **cytosine** always pairs with **guanine** (**C - G**). This means that there are always **equal amounts** of adenine and thymine in a DNA molecule and **equal amounts** of cytosine and guanine.

4) **Two** hydrogen bonds form between **A and T**, and **three** hydrogen bonds form between **C and G**.

5) Two **antiparallel** (running in opposite directions) polynucleotide strands **twist** to form the **DNA double-helix**.

6) DNA was first observed in the 1800s, but lots of scientists at the time **doubted** that it could carry the **genetic code** because it has a **relatively simple chemical composition**. Some argued that genetic information must be carried by **proteins** — which are much more **chemically varied**.

7) By 1953, experiments had shown that DNA was the carrier of the genetic code. This was also the year in which the **double-helix structure**, which helps DNA to carry out its function, was determined by **Watson** and **Crick**.

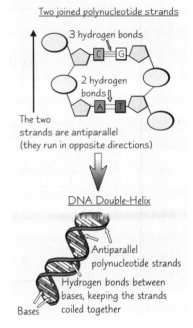

Two joined polynucleotide strands

3 hydrogen bonds

2 hydrogen bonds

The two strands are antiparallel (they run in opposite directions)

DNA Double-Helix

Antiparallel polynucleotide strands

Hydrogen bonds between bases, keeping the strands coiled together

Bases

RNA is a Relatively Short Polynucleotide Chain

RNA is made from a **single** polynucleotide chain (not a double one).
It's much **shorter** than most DNA polynucleotides.

ATP is the Immediate Source of Energy in a Cell

1) Plant and animal cells **release energy** from **glucose** — this process is called **respiration**.

2) A cell **can't** get its energy **directly** from glucose.

3) So, in respiration, the **energy released** from glucose is used to **make ATP** (adenosine triphosphate).

4) ATP is made from the nucleotide base **adenine**, combined with a **ribose sugar** and **three phosphate groups**. It's what's known as a **nucleotide derivative** because it's a **modified** form of a nucleotide:

5) Once made, ATP **diffuses** to the **part** of the **cell** that needs **energy**.

6) The **energy** in ATP is stored in **high energy bonds** between the **phosphate groups**. It's released via **hydrolysis** reactions (see next page).

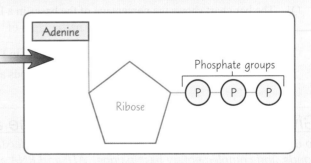

Adenine

Phosphate groups

Ribose

DNA, RNA and ATP

ATP is Quickly Made and Used

1) When **energy** is needed by a cell, **ATP** is **broken down** into **ADP** (adenosine diphosphate) and P_i (inorganic phosphate).

Inorganic phosphate (P_i) is just the fancy name for a single phosphate.

2) This is a **hydrolysis reaction**. A **phosphate bond** is **broken** and **energy** is **released**. The reaction is **catalysed** by the enzyme **ATP hydrolase**.

ATP hydrolase is sometimes known as ATPase.

3) **ATP hydrolysis** can be 'coupled' to other **energy-requiring reactions** in the cell — this means the energy released can be **used directly** to make the **coupled reaction** happen, rather than being **lost** as heat.

4) The released **inorganic phosphate** can also be put to use — it can be **added** to another **compound** (this is known as **phosphorylation**), which often makes the compound **more reactive**.

5) **ATP** can be **re-synthesised** in a **condensation reaction** between **ADP** and P_i. This happens during both **respiration** and **photosynthesis**, and is **catalysed** by the enzyme **ATP synthase**.

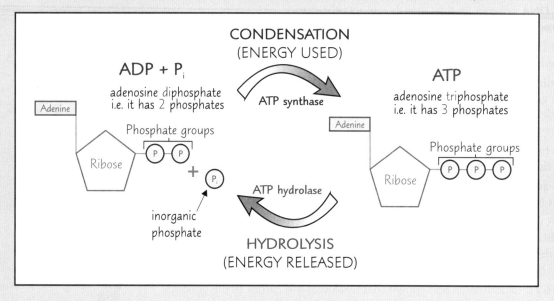

Practice Questions

Q1 What sugar is found in DNA nucleotides?

Q2 Name the bases in RNA.

Q3 What is the name of the base in ATP?

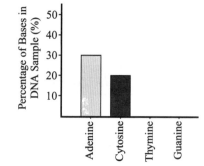

Exam Questions

Q1 The bar chart shows the percentage of the bases in a DNA sample that are adenine and cytosine.
On the chart, sketch bars to show the percentages of thymine and guanine in the sample. [2 marks]

Q2 a) Describe how nucleotides are joined together in DNA. [3 marks]

b) Describe how two single polynucleotide strands are joined to make a double helix. [3 marks]

Give me a D, give me an N, give me an A! What do you get? — confused...

To understand the next few pages, make sure you understand the structure of DNA — polynucleotide strands, hydrogen bonds, and complementary base pairing. ATP and RNA are also important molecules that come up a lot in Biology.

DNA Replication and Purification

DNA has the amazing ability to replicate (copy) itself. These pages cover the facts behind the replication mechanism, as well as some of the history behind its discovery. Oh and there's a bit on purifying DNA too...

DNA *Replicates by* Semi-Conservative *Replication*

DNA **copies** itself **before** cell division (see p. 50) so that each **new** cell has the **full** amount of **DNA**. The method is called **semi-conservative replication** because **half** of the strands in **each new DNA molecule** are from the **original** DNA molecule. This means that there's **genetic continuity** between generations of cells (i.e. the cells produced by cell division inherit their genes from their parent cells).

1) The enzyme **DNA helicase** **breaks** the **hydrogen bonds** between bases on the two **polynucleotide** DNA strands. This makes the helix **unwind** to form two single strands.

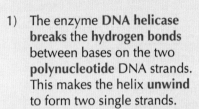
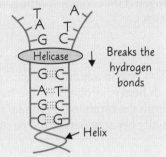

Gerald doesn't need helicase to unwind. He just needs a beach full of seals.

2) Each **original** single strand acts as a **template** for a new strand. **Complementary base pairing** means that **free-floating DNA nucleotides** are attracted to their complementary **exposed bases** on each original template strand — A with T and C with G.

Bases match up using complementary base pairing.

There's more on complementary base pairing on page 33.

3) **Condensation reactions** join the nucleotides of the new strands together — catalysed by the enzyme **DNA polymerase**. Hydrogen bonds **form** between the bases on the original and new strands.

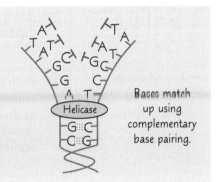
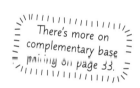

DNA polymerase joins the nucleotides. Hydrogen bonds form between the strands.

4) Each new DNA molecule contains **one strand** from the **original** DNA molecule and one **new strand**.

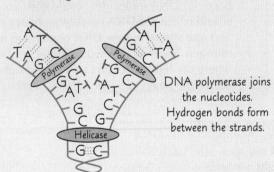
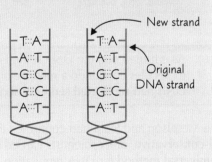

New strand
Original DNA strand

DNA Replication and Purification

Meselson and Stahl Provided Evidence for Semi-Conservative Replication

1) You might remember from page 33 that **Watson** and **Crick** determined the structure of DNA. They also came up with the theory of **semi-conservative DNA replication**.

2) It wasn't until **Meselson** and **Stahl's** experiment a few years **later** that this theory was **validated**. Before that, people were unsure whether DNA replication was **semi-conservative** or **conservative**. If the method was **conservative**, the original DNA strands would **stay together** and the new DNA molecules would contain **two new strands**.

3) Meselson and Stahl showed that DNA is replicated using the **semi-conservative method**. Their experiment used two **isotopes** of **nitrogen** (DNA contains nitrogen) — **heavy** nitrogen (^{15}N) and **light** nitrogen (^{14}N).

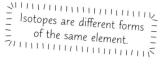
Isotopes are different forms of the same element.

4) Here's how it worked:

1) Two samples of bacteria were grown — one in a nutrient broth containing **light** nitrogen, and one in a broth with **heavy** nitrogen. As the **bacteria reproduced**, they **took up nitrogen** from the broth to help make nucleotides for new DNA. So the nitrogen gradually became part of the bacteria's DNA.

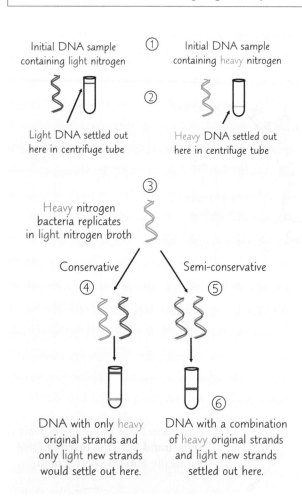

① Initial DNA sample containing light nitrogen / Initial DNA sample containing heavy nitrogen

② Light DNA settled out here in centrifuge tube / Heavy DNA settled out here in centrifuge tube

③ Heavy nitrogen bacteria replicates in light nitrogen broth

Conservative ④ / Semi-conservative ⑤

⑥ DNA with only heavy original strands and only light new strands would settle out here. / DNA with a combination of heavy original strands and light new strands settled out here.

2) A **sample of DNA** was taken from each batch of bacteria, and spun in a **centrifuge**. The DNA from the **heavy** nitrogen bacteria settled **lower** down the **centrifuge tube** than the DNA from the **light** nitrogen bacteria — because it's **heavier**.

3) Then the bacteria grown in the **heavy** nitrogen broth were **taken out** and put in a broth containing only **light nitrogen**. The bacteria were left for **one round of DNA replication**, and then **another DNA sample** was taken out and spun in the centrifuge.

4) If replication was **conservative**, the original **heavy** DNA, which would still be together, would settle at the bottom and the new **light** DNA would settle at the top.

5) If replication was **semi-conservative**, the new bacterial DNA molecules would contain **one strand** of the **old** DNA containing **heavy** nitrogen and **one strand** of new DNA containing **light** nitrogen. So the DNA would settle out **between** where the **light** nitrogen DNA settled out and where the **heavy** nitrogen DNA settled out.

6) As it turned out, the DNA settled out in the **middle**, showing that the DNA molecules contained a **mixture** of **heavy** and **light** nitrogen. The bacterial DNA had **replicated semi-conservatively** in the **light** nitrogen.

Once Meselson and Stahl had confirmed that **DNA replication** in **bacteria** was **semi-conservative**, other scientists carried out experiments to show that it was the **universal method** for DNA replication in **all living things**.

DNA Replication and Purification

DNA Polymerase Moves in Opposite Ways Along Antiparallel DNA Strands

Each end of a DNA strand is slightly **different** in its structure.
One end is called the **3'** (pronounced 'three prime') end and one end is called the **5'** (five prime) end.
In a DNA helix, the strands run in **opposite** directions — they're **antiparallel**.

The **active site** of **DNA polymerase** is only **complementary** to the **3' end** of the newly forming DNA strand — so the enzyme can **only add nucleotides** to the new strand at the **3' end**.

This means that the **new strand** is made in a **5' to 3'** direction and that DNA polymerase moves down the **template strand** in a **3' to 5'** direction. Because the strands in the double-helix are **antiparallel**, the DNA polymerase working on **one** of the template strands **moves** in the **opposite direction** to the DNA polymerase working on the **other** template strand.

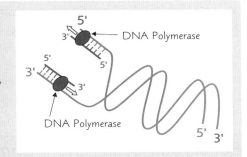

You Can Purify DNA Using a Precipitation Reaction

I really like this investigation. It's **proper science**, with **green bubbly stuff** (detergent) and everything...

1) **Break up the cells** in your sample (probably a bit of **onion** or something). You can do this using a **blender**.

2) Make up a solution of **detergent** (a dilute washing-up liquid will do), **salt** (sodium chloride) and **distilled water**.

3) Add the broken-up cells to a beaker containing the detergent solution. Incubate the beaker in a water bath at 60 °C for 15 minutes.

4) Once incubated, put your beaker in an **ice bath** to **cool** the mixture down. When it's cooled, **filter** the mixture. Transfer a sample of your mixture to a clean boiling tube.

5) Add **protease enzymes** to the filtered mixture. These will **break down** some **proteins** in the mixture, e.g. proteins bound to the DNA. Adding **RNase enzymes** will break down any **RNA** in the mixture.

6) Slowly dribble some **cold ethanol** down the side of the tube, so that it forms a **layer** on top of the DNA-detergent mixture.

7) If you leave the tube for a few minutes, the DNA will form a **white precipitate** (solid), which you can remove from the tube using a glass rod.

- The detergent in the mixture breaks down the cell membranes.
- The salt binds to the DNA and causes it to clump together.
- The temperature of the water bath should stop enzymes in the cells from working properly and breaking down the DNA.

There's more on enzymes on pages 24 - 31.

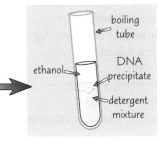

Practice Questions

Q1 What is the role of DNA helicase in DNA replication?
Q2 Why do you need to use detergent when extracting DNA from cells?

Exam Question

Q1 Describe the process of semi-conservative DNA replication. [5 marks]

DNA DNA Replication Replication is is Semi-Conservative Semi-Conservative

DNA precipitation is some clever science that you can do yourself in the lab. Those lads Watson, Crick, Meselson and Stahl all probably started off just like you, messing about with detergent and bits of onion — so get mixing...

Eukaryotic Cells and Organelles

There are two types of cell — prokaryotic and eukaryotic. The next few pages are about eukaryotic cells and their organelles (all the tiny bits and bobs that you can only see in detail with a fancy microscope)...

Organisms can be **Prokaryotes** or **Eukaryotes**

1) Prokaryotic organisms are **prokaryotic cells** (i.e. they're single-celled organisms) and eukaryotic organisms are made up of **eukaryotic cells**.

2) Both types of cells contain **organelles**. Organelles are **parts** of cells — each one has a **specific function**.

1) Eukaryotic cells are **complex** and include all **animal** and **plant** cells, as well as all cells in **algae** and **fungi**.

2) Prokaryotic cells are **smaller** and **simpler**, e.g. bacteria. See page 44 for more.

Eukaryotic Cells Have a *Complex* Internal *Structure*

Eukaryotic cells are generally a **bit more complicated** than prokaryotic cells. You've probably been looking at **animal** and **plant cell** diagrams for years, so hopefully you'll be familiar with some of the bits and pieces...

Animal Cell

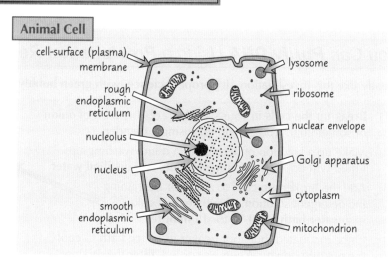

Plant Cell

Plant cells have all the **same organelles** as animal cells, but with a few **added extras**:

- a **cellulose cell wall** with **plasmodesmata** ('channels' for exchanging substances with adjacent cells),
- a **vacuole** (compartment that contains cell sap),
- and of course good old **chloroplasts**.

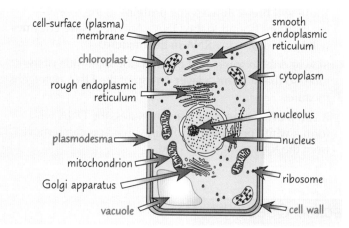

Algal and Fungal Cells

1) **Algal** cells are a lot like **plant cells** — they have all the **same** organelles, including a **cell wall** and **chloroplasts**.

2) **Fungal** cells are also a lot like plant cells, but with two key **differences**:
   - their cell walls are made of **chitin**, not cellulose.
   - they **don't have chloroplasts** (because they don't photosynthesise).

Algae carry out photosynthesis, like plants, but can be single-celled or multicellular. Fungi include mushrooms and yeast.

Eukaryotic Cells and Organelles

Different Organelles have Different Functions

This giant table contains a big list of organelles and describes their **structure** and **function**.
Most organelles are surrounded by **membranes**, which sometimes causes confusion — don't make the mistake of thinking that a diagram of an organelle is a diagram of a whole cell. They're not cells — they're **parts of** cells.

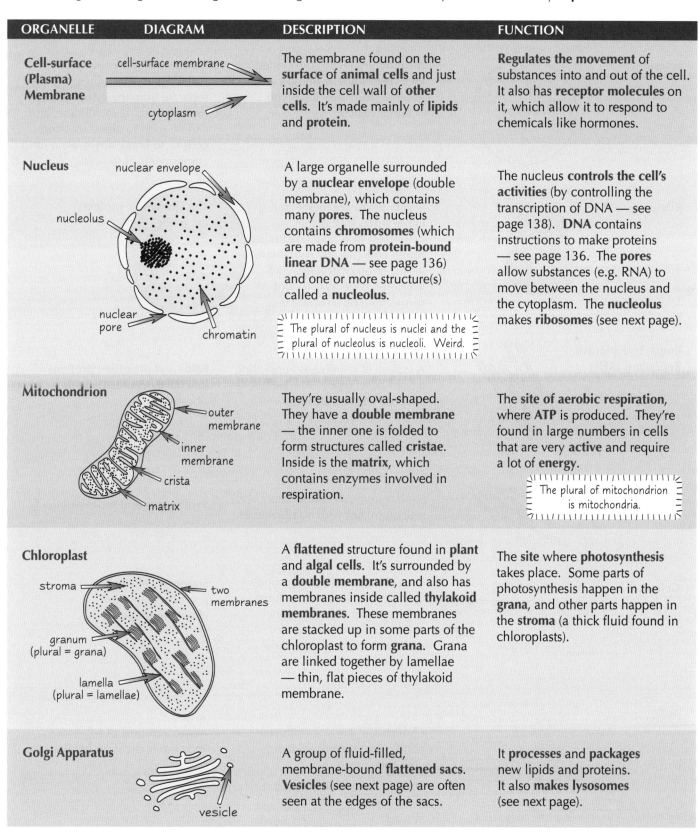

ORGANELLE	DIAGRAM	DESCRIPTION	FUNCTION
Cell-surface (Plasma) Membrane	cell-surface membrane / cytoplasm	The membrane found on the **surface** of **animal cells** and just inside the cell wall of **other cells**. It's made mainly of **lipids** and **protein**.	**Regulates the movement** of substances into and out of the cell. It also has **receptor molecules** on it, which allow it to respond to chemicals like hormones.
Nucleus	nuclear envelope / nucleolus / nuclear pore / chromatin	A large organelle surrounded by a **nuclear envelope** (double membrane), which contains many **pores**. The nucleus contains **chromosomes** (which are made from **protein-bound linear DNA** — see page 136) and one or more structure(s) called a **nucleolus**. *The plural of nucleus is nuclei and the plural of nucleolus is nucleoli. Weird.*	The nucleus **controls the cell's activities** (by controlling the transcription of DNA — see page 138). **DNA** contains instructions to make proteins — see page 136. The **pores** allow substances (e.g. RNA) to move between the nucleus and the cytoplasm. The **nucleolus** makes **ribosomes** (see next page).
Mitochondrion	outer membrane / inner membrane / crista / matrix	They're usually oval-shaped. They have a **double membrane** — the inner one is folded to form structures called **cristae**. Inside is the **matrix**, which contains enzymes involved in respiration.	The **site of aerobic respiration**, where **ATP** is produced. They're found in large numbers in cells that are very **active** and require a lot of **energy**. *The plural of mitochondrion is mitochondria.*
Chloroplast	stroma / two membranes / granum (plural = grana) / lamella (plural = lamellae)	A **flattened** structure found in **plant** and **algal cells**. It's surrounded by a **double membrane**, and also has membranes inside called **thylakoid membranes**. These membranes are stacked up in some parts of the chloroplast to form **grana**. Grana are linked together by lamellae — thin, flat pieces of thylakoid membrane.	The **site** where **photosynthesis** takes place. Some parts of photosynthesis happen in the **grana**, and other parts happen in the **stroma** (a thick fluid found in chloroplasts).
Golgi Apparatus	vesicle	A group of fluid-filled, membrane-bound **flattened sacs**. **Vesicles** (see next page) are often seen at the edges of the sacs.	It **processes and packages** new lipids and proteins. It also **makes lysosomes** (see next page).

Eukaryotic Cells and Organelles

ORGANELLE	DIAGRAM	DESCRIPTION	FUNCTION
Golgi Vesicle		A small **fluid-filled sac** in the cytoplasm, surrounded by a membrane and produced by the **Golgi apparatus**.	**Stores** lipids and proteins made by the Golgi apparatus and **transports** them out of the cell (via the cell-surface membrane).
Lysosome		A **round organelle** surrounded by a **membrane**, with no clear internal structure. It's a type of **Golgi vesicle**.	Contains **digestive enzymes** called **lysozymes**. These are kept separate from the cytoplasm by the surrounding membrane, and can be used to **digest invading cells** or to **break down** worn out components of the cell.
Ribosome		A **very small organelle** that either **floats free** in the cytoplasm or is attached to the **rough endoplasmic reticulum**. It's made up of **proteins** and **RNA** (see page 32). It's **not** surrounded by a membrane.	The **site** where **proteins** are made.
Rough Endoplasmic Reticulum (RER)		A system of membranes enclosing a fluid-filled space. The surface is **covered with ribosomes**.	**Folds** and **processes proteins** that have been made at the ribosomes.
Smooth Endoplasmic Reticulum (SER)		Similar to rough endoplasmic reticulum, but with no **ribosomes**.	**Synthesises** and **processes lipids**.
Cell Wall		A rigid structure that surrounds cells in **plants**, **algae** and **fungi**. In plants and algae it's made mainly of the carbohydrate **cellulose**. In fungi, it's made of **chitin**.	**Supports** cells and prevents them from **changing shape**.
Plasmodesmata		**Channels** in the cell walls of plant cells that **link** adjacent cells together.	Allow **transport** of **substances** and **communication** between cells.

Electron microscopes (see page 47) are often used to see the details of organelle structure.

Eukaryotic Cells and Organelles

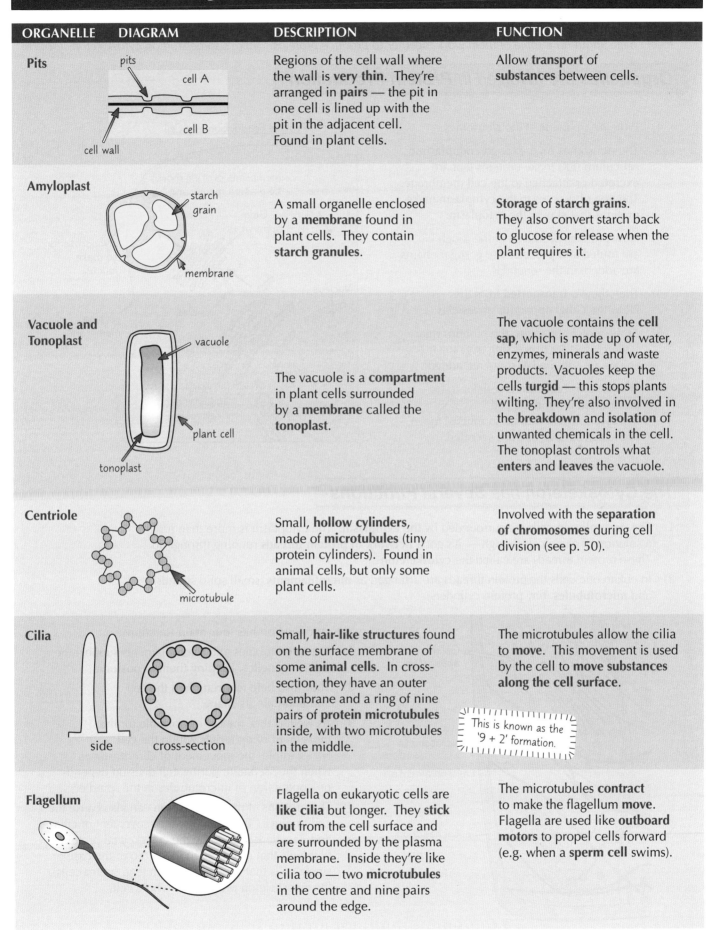

ORGANELLE	DIAGRAM	DESCRIPTION	FUNCTION
Pits	pits / cell A / cell wall / cell B	Regions of the cell wall where the wall is **very thin**. They're arranged in **pairs** — the pit in one cell is lined up with the pit in the adjacent cell. Found in plant cells.	Allow **transport** of **substances** between cells.
Amyloplast	starch grain / membrane	A small organelle enclosed by a **membrane** found in plant cells. They contain **starch granules**.	**Storage** of **starch grains**. They also convert starch back to glucose for release when the plant requires it.
Vacuole and Tonoplast	vacuole / plant cell / tonoplast	The vacuole is a **compartment** in plant cells surrounded by a **membrane** called the **tonoplast**.	The vacuole contains the **cell sap**, which is made up of water, enzymes, minerals and waste products. Vacuoles keep the cells **turgid** — this stops plants wilting. They're also involved in the **breakdown** and **isolation** of unwanted chemicals in the cell. The tonoplast controls what **enters** and **leaves** the vacuole.
Centriole	microtubule	Small, **hollow cylinders**, made of **microtubules** (tiny protein cylinders). Found in animal cells, but only some plant cells.	Involved with the **separation of chromosomes** during cell division (see p. 50).
Cilia	side / cross-section	Small, **hair-like structures** found on the surface membrane of some **animal cells**. In cross-section, they have an outer membrane and a ring of nine pairs of **protein microtubules** inside, with two microtubules in the middle. *This is known as the '9 + 2' formation.*	The microtubules allow the cilia to **move**. This movement is used by the cell to **move substances along the cell surface**.
Flagellum		Flagella on eukaryotic cells are **like cilia** but longer. They **stick out** from the cell surface and are surrounded by the plasma membrane. Inside they're like cilia too — two **microtubules** in the centre and nine pairs around the edge.	The microtubules **contract** to make the flagellum **move**. Flagella are used like **outboard motors** to propel cells forward (e.g. when a **sperm cell** swims).

Eukaryotic Cells and Organelles

After that endless list of organelles, you might need a few minutes to regain consciousness... Then you can read this lovely page about how some of them work together to produce proteins. There's some stuff on cytoskeletons too...

Organelles are Involved in Protein Production

1) Proteins are made at the **ribosomes**.

2) The ribosomes on the **rough endoplasmic reticulum (ER)** make proteins that are **excreted** or attached to the **cell membrane**. The free ribosomes in the **cytoplasm** make proteins that **stay in the cytoplasm**.

3) New proteins produced at the rough ER are **folded** and **processed** (e.g. sugar chains are added) in the rough ER.

4) Then they're **transported** from the ER to the **Golgi apparatus** in **vesicles**.

5) At the Golgi apparatus, the proteins may undergo **further processing** (e.g. sugar chains are trimmed or more are added).

6) The proteins enter more **vesicles** to be transported around the cell. E.g. glycoproteins (found in **mucus**) move to the cell surface and are **secreted**.

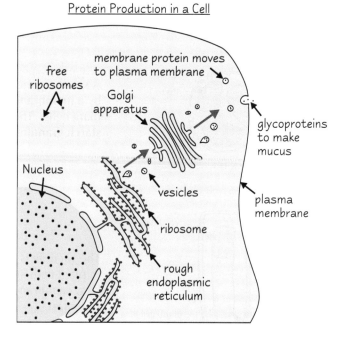

Protein Production in a Cell

The Cytoskeleton has Several Functions

1) The organelles in cells are surrounded by the **cytoplasm**. The cytoplasm is more than just a solution of chemicals though — it's got a **network of protein threads** running through it. These protein threads are called the **cytoskeleton**.

2) In eukaryotic cells the protein threads are arranged as **microfilaments** (small solid strands) and **microtubules** (tiny protein cylinders).

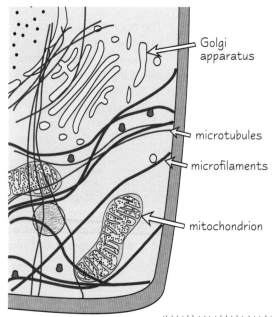

The cytoskeleton has **four main functions**:

1) The microtubules and microfilaments **support** the cell's organelles, keeping them **in position**.

2) They also help to **strengthen** the cell and **maintain its shape**.

3) As well as this, they're responsible for the **movement of materials** within the cell. For example, the movement of **chromosomes** when they separate during cell division depends on contraction of microtubules in the spindle.

4) The proteins of the cytoskeleton can also cause the cell to **move**. For example, the movement of **cilia** and **flagella** is caused by the cytoskeletal protein filaments that run through them. So in the case of single cells that have a flagellum (e.g. sperm cells), the cytoskeleton propels the **whole cell**.

The assembly of microtubules and microfilaments, and the movement of materials along them, requires energy from respiration.

Eukaryotic Cells and Organelles

Practice Questions

Q1 What is the function of chloroplasts?

Q2 Describe the function of Golgi vesicles.

Q3 How does the structure of rough endoplasmic reticulum differ from that of smooth endoplasmic reticulum?

Q4 What is a plant cell wall made of? What about a fungal cell wall?

Q5 Which two organelles allow transport of substances between plant cells?

Q6 Describe the structure of pits in a plant cell.

Q7 Name the membrane that surrounds a vacuole.

Q8 What is the function of centrioles?

Exam Questions

Q1 Which of the following describes a structure found in plant cells but not in animal cells?

A A system of membranes enclosing a fluid-filled space.

B A flattened structure surrounded by a double membrane. Internal membranes are stacked up in places to form grana.

C A small organelle consisting of two subunits. It is not surrounded by a membrane.

D A round, membrane-bound organelle containing digestive enzymes.　[1 mark]

Q2 a) Identify these two organelles from their descriptions as seen in an electron micrograph.

　　i) An oval-shaped organelle surrounded by a double membrane. The inner membrane is folded and projects into the inner space, which is filled with a grainy material.　[1 mark]

　　ii) A collection of flattened membrane 'sacs' arranged roughly parallel to one another. Small, circular structures are seen at the edges of these 'sacs'.　[1 mark]

　　b) State the function of the two organelles that you have identified.　[2 marks]

Q3 The image on the right shows a plant organelle as seen under an electron microscope. Which of the following describes its function?

A It keeps the cell turgid and is involved in the breakdown and isolation of unwanted chemicals in the cell.

B It transports substances between cells.

C It is the site where photosynthesis takes place.

D It stores starch grains and converts starch back to glucose for release when the plant requires it.　[1 mark]

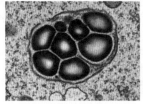

Q4 The image on the right shows a plant organelle as seen under an electron microscope.

　　a) Identify the organelle.　[1 mark]

　　b) State the function of the organelle.　[1 mark]

Q5 Pancreatic cells make and secrete hormones (made of protein) into the blood. From production to secretion, list, in order, four organelles involved in making hormones.　[4 marks]

Q6 Give three functions of a cell's cytoskeleton.　[3 marks]

Organelles — not a church girl band...

Not the most exciting pages in the world, but these organelles will keep popping up throughout the rest of the book, so it's good to learn them now — mitochondria are needed for respiration, the cell-surface membrane is essential for controlling the movement of things in and out of the cell, and all the DNA stuff happens in the nucleus.

Prokaryotic Cells and Viruses

Now we're on to prokaryotic cells and viruses. They're much smaller than eukaryotic cells — and, luckily for both of us, so is the bit about them in this book. No ridiculously long tables here...

The Structure of **Prokaryotic** Cells is Different to **Eukaryotic** Cells

Remember, prokaryotic cells are **smaller** and **simpler** than eukaryotic cells (see page 38). **Bacteria** are examples of prokaryotic cells. This diagram illustrates the **structure** of a prokaryotic cell and what all the different organelles do:

The **cytoplasm** of a prokaryotic cell has **no membrane-bound organelles** (unlike a eukaryotic cell). It has **ribosomes** — but they're **smaller** than those in a eukaryotic cell.

Just like in a eukaryotic cell, the **cell-surface membrane** is mainly made of lipids and proteins. It controls the movement of substances into and out of the cell.

See pages 39-41 for more on organelles.

The **cell wall supports** the cell and prevents it from changing shape. It's made of a polymer called **murein**. Murein is a **glycoprotein** (a protein with a carbohydrate attached).

The **flagellum** (plural **flagella**) is a long, hair-like structure that rotates to make the prokaryotic cell **move**. **Not all** prokaryotes have a flagellum. **Some** have **more than one**.

Unlike a eukaryotic cell, a prokaryotic cell **doesn't** have a nucleus. Instead, the **DNA** floats free in the cytoplasm. It's **circular DNA**, present as one long coiled-up strand. It's **not attached** to any **histone proteins** (see p. 136).

Plasmids are **small loops of DNA** that aren't part of the main circular DNA molecule. Plasmids contain genes for things like **antibiotic resistance**, and can be passed between prokaryotes. Plasmids are **not always** present in prokaryotic cells. **Some** prokaryotic cells have **several**.

Some prokaryotes, e.g. bacteria, also have a **capsule** made up of secreted **slime**. It helps to **protect** bacteria from attack by cells of the immune system.

Theo went the wrong way about getting practical experience in understanding cell structure.

Viruses are Acellular — They're Not Cells

Viruses are just **nucleic acids** surrounded by **protein** — they're **not even alive**.

- They're even **smaller** than bacteria.
- **Unlike** bacteria, viruses have **no** cell-surface membrane, **no** cytoplasm and **no** ribosomes.
- **All** viruses invade and reproduce **inside** the cells of **other** organisms. These cells are known as **host cells**.

Viruses contain a **core** of **genetic material** — either **DNA** or **RNA**.

See pages 32-33 for more on DNA and RNA.

The **protein coat** around the core is called the **capsid**.

Attachment proteins stick out from the edge of the capsid. These let the virus cling on to a suitable host cell.

Prokaryotic Cells and Viruses

Prokaryotic Cells Replicate by Binary Fission

In binary fission, the cell **replicates** (makes copies of) its genetic material,
before physically **splitting** into **two daughter cells**:

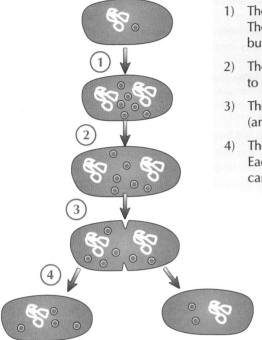

1) The circular DNA and plasmid(s) **replicate**. The main **DNA loop** is only replicated **once**, but **plasmids** can be replicated **loads of times**.

2) The cell gets bigger and the **DNA loops** move to **opposite 'poles'** (ends) of the cell.

3) The **cytoplasm** begins to **divide** (and **new cell walls** begin to form).

4) The cytoplasm **divides** and two **daughter cells** are produced. Each daughter cell has **one copy** of the **circular DNA**, but can have a **variable** number of copies of the **plasmid(s)**.

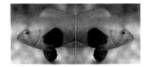

Binary fishin'

Viruses Use Host Cells to Replicate Themselves

1) Viruses use their **attachment proteins** to bind to **complementary receptor proteins** on the surface of **host cells**.

2) Different viruses have different attachment proteins and therefore require **different** receptor proteins on host cells. As a result, some viruses can only infect **one type of cell** (others can infect lots of different cells).

3) Because they're not alive, viruses **don't** undergo cell division. Instead, they **inject** their **DNA** or **RNA** into the host cell — this hijacked cell then uses its own 'machinery' (e.g. enzymes, ribosomes) to do the virus's dirty work and **replicate the viral particles**.

Remember — viruses are acellular — they're not cells.

Practice Questions

Q1 What is a flagellum?
Q2 What is a plasmid?
Q3 What is the protein coat around the core of a virus called?

Exam Question

Q1 Cholera is a disease caused by the prokaryotic organism *Vibrio cholerae*.
a) Name the polymer that makes up the cell wall of *Vibrio cholerae*. [1 mark]
b) Outline the process by which *Vibrio cholerae* replicates. [3 marks]
c) There are different strains of *Vibrio cholerae*. One strain has a capsule. Another does not. Suggest how having a capsule might benefit *Vibrio cholerae*. [1 mark]

Viruses and binary fission — nothing to do with computers...

The key things to remember about prokaryotic cells is that they're smaller and simpler than eukaryotic cells and they have no nucleus or other membrane-bound organelles. Only prokaryotic cells replicate by binary fission. Eukaryotic cells divide using different processes and viruses don't divide at all — they replicate inside host cells.

Analysis of Cell Components

If you were born over a century ago then you wouldn't have had to learn all this stuff about organelles because people wouldn't have known anything about them. But then better microscopes were invented and here we are.

Magnification is Size, Resolution is Detail

We all know that microscopes produce a **magnified image** of a sample, but **resolution** is just as important...

1) MAGNIFICATION is how much **bigger** the image is than the specimen (the sample you're looking at). It can be calculated using this formula:

$$\text{magnification} = \frac{\text{image size}}{\text{object size}}$$

There are several, slightly different versions of this formula, but don't worry — they all mean the same thing.

2) RESOLUTION is how **detailed** the image is. More specifically, it's how well a microscope **distinguishes** between **two points** that are **close together**. If a microscope lens can't separate two objects, then increasing the magnification won't help.

Georgina didn't believe in the need for microscopes – she had her trusty varifocals.

You Can Rearrange the Magnification Formula

You can calculate the **magnification** of an image using the **formula** above. Here's an example...

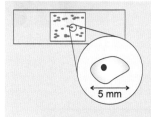

5 mm

You have a magnified image that's 5 mm wide. Your specimen is 50 micrometers (μm) wide. First, get everything into the same units:
   1 mm = 1000 μm
   so 50 μm ÷ 1000 = 0.05 mm
Now calculate the magnification:
   5 ÷ 0.05 = **× 100**

You can also **rearrange** the formula to work out the **image size** or **object size**. You can use this handy **formula triangle** to help you. All you have to do is put your finger over what you want to know and read off the formula. E.g. if you want to know the object size, cover up object size. That leaves image size ÷ magnification.

$$\frac{\text{image size}}{\text{magnification} \times \text{object size}}$$

Different Types of Microscopes Have Different Properties

1) Light microscopes

1) **Light microscopes** use light (no surprises there).

Light microscopes are also known as optical microscopes.

2) They have a **lower resolution** than electron microscopes — they have a maximum resolution of about **0.2 μm**. So they're usually used to look at **whole cells or tissues**.

3) The maximum useful **magnification** of a light microscope is about × **1500**.

2) Laser Scanning Confocal Microscopes (a special type of light microscope)

1) **Laser Scanning Confocal Microscopes** use **laser beams** (intense beams of light) to **scan** a specimen, which is usually tagged with a **fluorescent** dye.

2) The laser causes the dye to **fluoresce** — **give off light**. This light is then **focused** through a **pinhole** onto a **detector**. The detector is hooked up to a computer, which generates an image. The image can be **3D**.

3) The pinhole means that any **out-of-focus light** is **blocked**, so these microscopes produce a much **clearer image** than a normal light microscope.

4) They can be used to look at objects at **different depths** in **thick specimens**.

This is not how a Laser Scanning Confocal Microscope works. Sadly.

Analysis of Cell Components

3) Electron microscopes

Electron microscopes use **electrons** instead of light to form an image. They have a **higher resolution** than light microscopes so give **more detailed images**. There are two kinds of electron microscope:

1) **Transmission electron microscope (TEM)** — use **electromagnets** to focus a **beam of electrons**, which is then transmitted **through** the specimen. **Denser** parts of the specimen absorb **more electrons**, which makes them look **darker** on the image you end up with. TEMs are good because they provide **high resolution images** (so they can be used to look at a range of **organelles**) but they can only be used on **thin specimens**. A TEM image of a mitochondrion is shown above on the right.

2) **Scanning electron microscope (SEM)** — **scan** a beam of electrons across the specimen. This **knocks off** electrons from the specimen, which are gathered in a **cathode ray tube** to form an **image**. The images produced show the **surface** of the specimen and can be **3D**. But they give **lower resolution images** than TEMs. Here's an SEM image of a mitochondrion.

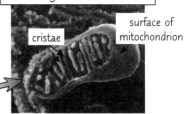

TEM image of a mitochondrion

cristae

matrix

K.R. PORTER/SCIENCE PHOTO LIBRARY

SEM image of a mitochondrion

surface of mitochondrion

cristae

PROFESSORS P. MOTTA & T. NAGURO/ SCIENCE PHOTO LIBRARY

The angle at which specimens are cut can affect how they appear (e.g. a mitochondrion cut at a different angle might appear circular).

You Can **Compare Magnification** and **Resolution**

Here's a lovely little table with all of the important numbers about the **magnification** and **resolution** of **light microscopes** and both types of **electron microscope**. I made it just for you, 'cos I'm nice like that.

	light microscope	TEM	SEM
maximum resolution	0.2 µm	0.0002 µm	0.002 µm
maximum magnification	× 1500	can be more than × 1 000 000	usually less than × 500 000

TEMs have the highest resolution because they can distinguish between the smallest objects (or objects that are only 0.0002 µm apart).

Practice Questions

Q1 What is the formula for calculating the magnification of an image?

Q2 What is meant by a microscope's resolution?

Q3 Which has a higher resolution: a light microscope, TEM or SEM?

Exam Questions

Q1 An insect is 0.5 mm long. In a book, a picture of the insect is 8 cm long. Calculate the magnification of the image. [2 marks]

Q2 A light micrograph shows a human cheek cell at × 100 magnification. The actual diameter of the cell is 59 µm. What is the diameter of the cell in the image? [2 marks]

Q3 The table shows the dimensions of some different organelles found in animal cells.

a) Name those organelles in the table that would be visible using a good quality light microscope. Explain your answer. [3 marks]

b) Which organelles would be visible using an SEM? Explain your answer. [2 marks]

organelle	diameter / µm
lysosome	0.1
mitochondrion	2
nucleus	5
ribosome	0.02
vesicle	0.05

A light microscope is better than a heavy one — for your back anyway...

OK, there's quite a bit of info on these pages, but the whole magnification thing isn't all that bad once you've given it a go. If you're doing a calculation involving the magnification formula, make sure you convert all your figures into the same units before you start. Resolution's a bit trickier to get your head round, but take your time and you'll be fine.

Analysis of Cell Components

Cells, organelles and other specimens have to be prepared before they can be viewed under a microscope.
And that's what these two pages are all about. You're in for a treat, let me tell you...

Samples Need to be Stained

1) In light microscopes and TEMs, the beam of light (or electrons) **passes through the object** being viewed. An image is produced because some parts of the object **absorb more light** (or electrons) than others.

2) Sometimes the object being viewed is completely **transparent**. This makes the whole thing look **white** because the light rays (or electrons) just pass **straight through**.

3) To get round this, the object can be **stained**:

Staining samples for light microscopes:

- For the light microscope, this means using some kind of **dye**. Common stains include **methylene blue** and **eosin**.

- The stain is taken up by some parts of the object more than others — the **contrast** makes the different parts show up.

- **Different stains** are used to make **different things** show up. For example, **eosin** is used to stain **cell cytoplasms**. **Methylene blue** stains **DNA**.

- **More than one** stain can be used at once.

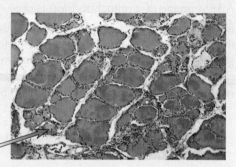

An eosin stained specimen, as seen through a light microscope.

Staining samples for electron microscopes:

For the electron microscope, objects are dipped in a solution of **heavy metals** (like **lead**). The metal ions scatter the electrons, again creating **contrast** — some parts of the object show up **darker** than others.

Electron micrograph images are always black and white even when stained, but colour can be added artificially after the image has been made.

Here's How to Prepare a Microscope Slide

1) If you want to look at a specimen under a **light microscope**, you need to stick it on a **slide** first.

2) A slide is a strip of **clear glass** or **plastic**. Slides are usually **flat**, but some of them have a small **dip** or **well** in the centre (useful if your specimen's particularly big or a liquid).

3) There are **two main ways** of preparing a microscope slide:

Dry Mount

- Your specimen needs to let **light** through it for you to be able to see it clearly under the microscope. So if you've got quite a **thick specimen**, you'll need to take a **thin slice** to use on your slide.
- Use **tweezers** to pick up your specimen and put it in the **middle** of a clean slide.
- Pop a **cover slip** (a square of thin, transparent plastic or glass) **on top**.

Cover slip
Specimen
Slide

Wet Mount

- Start by pipetting a small **drop of water** onto the slide. Then use **tweezers** to place your specimen on top of the water drop.
- To put the **cover slip** on, stand the slip **upright** on the slide, next to the water droplet. Then carefully **tilt** and lower it so it covers the specimen. Try **not** to get any **air bubbles** under there — they'll obstruct your view of the specimen.
- Once the cover slip is in position, you can add a **stain**. Put a drop of stain next to one edge of the cover slip. Then put a bit of **paper towel** next to the opposite edge. The stain will get **drawn** under the slip, **across** the **specimen**.

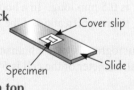

Cover slip
Water droplet

Wet mounts are good for looking at tiny organisms that live in water.

Analysis of Cell Components

Cell Fractionation Separates Organelles

Suppose you wanted to look at some **organelles** under an **electron microscope**. First you'd need to **separate** them from the **rest of the cell** — you can do this by **cell fractionation**. There are **three** steps to this technique:

1) Homogenisation — Breaking Up the Cells

Homogenisation can be done in several **different ways**, e.g. by vibrating the cells or by grinding the cells up in a blender. This **breaks up** the **plasma membrane** and **releases** the **organelles** into solution. The solution must be kept **ice-cold**, to reduce the activity of enzymes that break down organelles. The solution should also be **isotonic** — this means it should have the **same concentration** of **chemicals** as the cells being broken down, to prevent damage to the organelles through **osmosis**. A **buffer solution** should be added to **maintain** the **pH**.

2) Filtration — Getting Rid of the Big Bits

Next, the homogenised cell solution is **filtered** through a **gauze** to separate any **large cell debris** or **tissue debris**, like connective tissue, from the organelles. The organelles are much **smaller** than the debris, so they pass through the gauze.

3) Ultracentrifugation — Separating the Organelles

After filtration, you're left with a solution containing a **mixture** of organelles. To separate a particular organelle from all the others you use **ultracentrifugation**.

1) The cell fragments are poured into a **tube**. The tube is put into a **centrifuge** (a machine that separates material by spinning) and is spun at a **low speed**. The **heaviest organelles**, like nuclei, get flung to the bottom of the tube by the centrifuge. They form a **thick sediment** at the bottom — the **pellet**. The rest of the organelles stay suspended in the fluid above the sediment — the **supernatant**.

2) The supernatant is **drained off**, poured into **another tube**, and spun in the centrifuge at a **higher speed**. Again, the **heaviest organelles**, this time the mitochondria, form a pellet at the bottom of the tube. The supernatant containing the rest of the organelles is drained off and spun in the centrifuge at an **even higher speed**.

3) This process is **repeated** at higher and higher speeds, until all the organelles are **separated out**. Each time, the pellet at the bottom of the tube is made up of lighter and lighter organelles.

As the ride got faster, everyone felt their nuclei sink to their toes

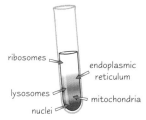

The organelles are <u>separated in order of mass</u> (from heaviest to lightest) — this order is usually: nuclei, then mitochondria, then lysosomes, then endoplasmic reticulum, and finally ribosomes.

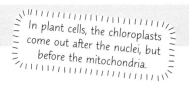

In plant cells, the chloroplasts come out after the nuclei, but before the mitochondria.

Practice Question

Q1 Why is it sometimes necessary to stain an object before viewing it through a microscope?

Q2 Describe how to prepare a wet mount slide.

Exam Question

Q1 Explain why a homogenised cell solution should be kept ice-cold and isotonic. [2 marks]

Cell fractionation — sounds more like maths to me...

So, if you fancy getting up close and personal with mitochondria remember to homogenise, filter and ultracentrifuge first. It's useful to learn how to prepare a microscope slide now too — it's going to crop again later in this book...

Cell Division — Mitosis

If it wasn't for cell division, we'd still only be one cell big. If it wasn't for pies, my favourite jeans would still fit.

Mitosis is Cell Division that Produces Genetically Identical Cells

There are two types of cell division in **eukaryotes** — **mitosis** and **meiosis** (see pages 144-145 for more on meiosis).

1) In **mitosis** a **parent cell** divides to produce **two genetically identical daughter cells** (they contain an **exact copy** of the **DNA** of the parent cell).

2) Mitosis is needed for the **growth** of multicellular organisms (like us) and for **repairing damaged tissues**. It's also a method of **asexual reproduction** for some plants, animals and fungi.

3) In multicellular organisms, not all cells keep their ability to divide (see next page). The ones that do, follow a **cell cycle**. Mitosis is part of the cell cycle:

> The cell cycle consists of a period of **cell growth** and **DNA replication** called **interphase**. **Mitosis** happens after that. Interphase (cell growth) is subdivided into three separate growth stages. These are called G_1, **S** and G_2.

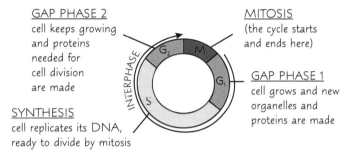

GAP PHASE 2
cell keeps growing and proteins needed for cell division are made

SYNTHESIS
cell replicates its DNA, ready to divide by mitosis

MITOSIS
(the cycle starts and ends here)

GAP PHASE 1
cell grows and new organelles and proteins are made

Mitosis has Four Division Stages

Mitosis is one **continuous process**, but it's described as a series of **division stages** — prophase, metaphase, anaphase and telophase. **Interphase** comes **before** mitosis in the cell cycle.

To find out more about chromosomes — see page 136.

> **Interphase** — The cell carries out normal functions, but also prepares to divide. The cell's **DNA** is **unravelled** and **replicated**, to double its genetic content. The **organelles** are also **replicated** so it has spare ones, and its ATP content is increased (ATP provides the energy needed for cell division).

Interphase

Cell
Chromosome
Cytoplasm
Nucleus
Centriole

Unravelled DNA containing two copies of each chromosome

1) <u>Prophase</u> — The **chromosomes** **condense**, getting **shorter** and **fatter**. Tiny bundles of protein called **centrioles** start moving to opposite ends of the cell, forming a network of protein fibres across it called the **spindle**. The **nuclear envelope** (the membrane around the nucleus) **breaks down** and chromosomes lie free in the cytoplasm.

Centrioles move to opposite ends of the cell

Nuclear envelope starts to break down

Centromere

As mitosis begins, the chromosomes are made of two strands joined in the middle by a <u>centromere</u>. The separate strands are called <u>chromatids</u>. There are two strands because each chromosome has already made an <u>identical copy</u> of itself during <u>interphase</u>. When mitosis is over, the chromatids end up as one-strand chromosomes in the daughter cells.

One chromatid — Centromere
Sister chromatids

2) <u>Metaphase</u> — The chromosomes (each with two chromatids) **line up** along the middle of the cell and become **attached** to the **spindle** by their **centromere**.

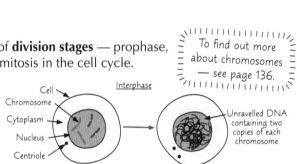

Spindle fibres

Centromeres on spindle equator

3) <u>Anaphase</u> — The **centromeres divide**, separating each pair of sister **chromatids**. The **spindles contract**, pulling chromatids to **opposite poles** (ends) of the **spindle**, centromere first. This makes the chromatids appear **v-shaped**.

Sister chromatids moving to opposite poles of the spindle

4) <u>Telophase</u> — The chromatids reach the **opposite poles** on the spindle. They **uncoil** and become **long** and **thin** again. They're now called **chromosomes** again. A **nuclear envelope** forms around each group of chromosomes, so there are now **two nuclei**. The **cytoplasm divides** (cytokinesis) and there are now **two daughter cells** that are **genetically identical** to the original cell and to each other. Mitosis is finished and each daughter cell starts the **interphase** part of the cell cycle to get ready for the next round of mitosis.

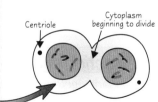

Centriole

Cytoplasm beginning to divide

Cell Division — Mitosis

The *Time Taken* for Each *Stage* of Mitosis *Varies*

You can **calculate** how long each stage of mitosis lasts if you're given the right information.

> **Example:** A scientist observes a section of growing tissue under the microscope. He counts 100 cells undergoing mitosis. Of those, 10 cells are in metaphase. One complete cell cycle of the tissue lasts 15 hours. How long do the cells spend in metaphase? Give your answer in minutes.

1) The scientist has observed that **10 out of 100 cells** are in **metaphase**. This suggests that the **proportion** of time the cells spend in metaphase must be **10/100th** of the **cell cycle**.
2) You're told that the cell cycle in these cells lasts **15 hours**. That's (15 × 60 =) **900 minutes**.
3) So the cells spend: $\frac{10}{100} \times 900 = $ **90 minutes** in metaphase.

Cancer is the Result of *Uncontrolled Cell Division*

1) **Mitosis** and the **cell cycle** are **controlled by genes**.
2) Normally, when cells have divided enough times to make **enough new cells**, they stop. But if there's a **mutation** in a gene that controls cell division, the cells can **grow out of control**.
3) The cells **keep on dividing** to make more and more cells, which form a **tumour**.
4) **Cancer** is a tumour that **invades** surrounding tissue.

Mutations are changes in the base sequence of an organism's DNA (see p. 146).

Some *Cancer Treatments* Target the *Cell Cycle*

Some treatments for cancer are designed to **control** the **rate of cell division** in tumour cells by **disrupting** the **cell cycle**. This **kills** the **tumour cells**. These treatments don't **distinguish** tumour cells from normal cells though — they also **kill normal body cells** that are dividing. However, tumour cells **divide much more frequently** than normal cells, so the treatments are **more likely** to kill tumour cells. Some cell cycle **targets** of cancer treatments include:

1) **G1 (cell growth and protein production)** — Some chemical drugs (chemotherapy) prevent the **synthesis of enzymes** needed for DNA replication. If these aren't produced, the cell is unable to enter the **synthesis phase** (S), disrupting the cell cycle and forcing the cell to **kill itself**.
2) **S phase (DNA replication)** — **Radiation** and some drugs **damage DNA**. At several points in the cell cycle (including just before and during S phase) the DNA in the cell is **checked** for damage. If severe damage is detected, the **cell will kill itself** — **preventing** further **tumour growth**.

Practice Questions

Q1 Give the two main functions of mitosis.
Q2 List the four stages of mitosis.
Q3 Describe how tumours are formed.
Q4 Give one example of how a cancer treatment can target the cell cycle.

Exam Question

Q1 The diagrams show cells at different stages of mitosis.
  a) For each of the cells A, B and C, name the stage of mitosis. [3 marks]
  b) Name the structures labelled X, Y and Z in cell A. [3 marks]

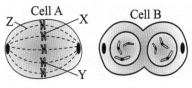

Doctor, I'm getting short and fat — don't worry, it's just a phase...

Quite a lot on these pages — but the process of mitosis is important stuff, so no slacking. Mitosis is vital — it's how cells multiply and how organisms like us grow. Don't forget — the best way to learn is to get drawing those diagrams.

Cell Division — Investigating Mitosis

It's time to dust off your lab coat and get out your safety specs. Here are all the techniques you need to study mitosis. Look over pages 46 and 48 to remind yourself about how a light microscope works and staining cells.

Root Tips Can be Stained and Squashed to Observe Mitosis

You can **prepare** and **stain** a **root tip** in order to observe the **stages of mitosis**. Make sure you're wearing **safety goggles** and a **lab coat** before you start. You should also wear **gloves** when using **stains**.

1) **Cut** 1 cm from the **tip** from a **growing root** (e.g. of an onion). It needs to be the **tip** because that's where **growth** occurs (and so that's where **mitosis** takes place).
   If you're using ethano-orcein to stain the cells, the tips will also need to be fixed in ethanoic acid.

2) **Prepare** a boiling tube containing **1 M hydrochloric acid** and put it in a **water bath at 60 °C**.

3) **Transfer** the root tip into the **boiling tube** and incubate for about **5 minutes**.

4) Use a pipette to **rinse** the **root tip** well with **cold water**. Leave the tip to **dry** on a **paper towel**.

5) Place the root tip on a **microscope slide** and cut **2 mm** from the **very tip** of it. Get **rid** of the **rest**.

6) Use a **mounted needle** to **break** the tip **open** and **spread** the cells out thinly.

7) **Add** a few drops of **stain** and leave it for a few minutes. The stain will make the **chromosomes easier to see** under a microscope. There are loads of different stains, all with crazy names (**toluidine blue O, ethano-orcein, Feulgen stain**...
   If you're using the Feulgen stain, you'll need an extra rinse.

8) **Place** a **cover slip** over the cells and **push** down firmly to **squash** the tissue. This will make the tissue **thinner** and allow **light** to pass through it. **Don't smear** the cover slip sideways (or you'll damage the chromosomes).

9) Now you can look at all the stages of mitosis under an **light microscope** (see below). You should see something that looks like the photograph on the right.

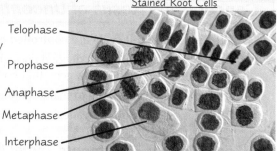

Stained Root Cells

Telophase
Prophase
Anaphase
Metaphase
Interphase

HERVE CONGE, ISM/SCIENCE PHOTO LIBRARY

See p. 50 for more on how to recognise the different stages of mitosis in cells.

You Can Observe Cells Using a Light Microscope

Here's how to use a light microscope to **observe** your prepared root tip cells:

1) Start by clipping the **slide** you've prepared onto the **stage**.

2) Select the **lowest-powered objective lens** (i.e. the one that produces the lowest magnification).

3) Use the **coarse adjustment knob** to move the objective lens down to just above the slide.

4) Look down the **eyepiece** (which contains the ocular lens) and adjust the **focus** with the **fine adjustment knob**, until you get a **clear image** of what's on the slide.

5) If you need to see the slide with **greater magnification**, swap to a **higher-powered objective lens** and refocus.

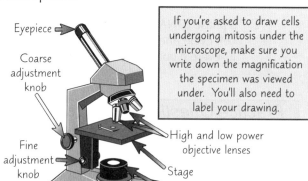

Eyepiece
Coarse adjustment knob
Fine adjustment knob
High and low power objective lenses
Stage
Light

If you're asked to draw cells undergoing mitosis under the microscope, make sure you write down the magnification the specimen was viewed under. You'll also need to label your drawing.

The Mitotic Index Is the Proportion of Cells Undergoing Mitosis

You can **calculate** the **mitotic index** of your cells using this **formula**:

$$\text{mitotic index} = \frac{\text{number of cells with visible chromosomes}}{\text{total number of cells observed}}$$

This lets you work out how quickly the **tissue** is growing and if there's anything **weird** going on. A **plant root tip** is constantly **growing**, so you'd expect a **high mitotic index** (i.e. **lots** of cells in **mitosis**). In other tissue samples, a high mitotic index could mean that **tissue repair** is taking place or that there is **cancerous growth** in the tissue.

Cell Division — Investigating Mitosis

You Can Use A *Graticule* and *Micrometer* to Calculate the *Size* of *Cells...*

1) To calculate the **size** of the cells you're looking at, you can use the **eyepiece graticule** and **stage micrometer** — they're a bit like **rulers**.

2) An **eyepiece graticule** is fitted onto the **eyepiece**. It's like a transparent ruler with **numbers**, but **no units**.

3) The **stage micrometer** is placed on the **stage** — it is a microscope slide with an **accurate scale** (it has units) and it's used to work out the **value** of the divisions on the **eyepiece graticule** at a **particular magnification**.

4) This means that when you take the stage micrometer away and replace it with the slide containing your tissue sample, you'll be able to **measure** the size of the cells. Here's an **example**:

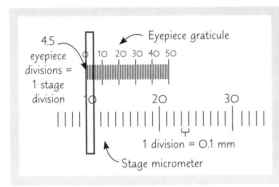

1) Line up the **eyepiece** graticule and the **stage** micrometer.

2) Each **division** on the stage micrometer is **0.1 mm** long.

3) At this magnification, **1 division** on the **stage micrometer** is the same as **4.5 divisions** on the **eyepiece graticule**.

4) To work out the size of **1 division** on the **eyepiece graticule**, you need to divide 0.1 by 4.5:
1 division on eyepiece graticule = 0.1 ÷ 4.5 = **0.022 mm**

5) So if you look at a cell under the microscope at this magnification and it's **4 eyepiece divisions** long, you know it measures:
4 × 0.022 = **0.088 mm**.

The eyepiece graticule will need to be re-calibrated at different magnifications.

...Or You Can Use This *Formula*...

If you're given an **image** of cells under the microscope in the exam, you can calculate their **actual size** using this **formula**:

$$\text{actual size} = \frac{\text{size of image}}{\text{magnification}}$$

Example: If the image of a cell measures **5 mm** and the magnification is × 100, then the **actual** size of the cell will be: 5 ÷ 100 = **0.05 mm**.

Artefacts Can Get in the Way of Your *Observations*

1) Artefacts are things that you can see down the microscope that **aren't** part of the **cell or specimen** that you're looking at.

2) They can be anything from bits of **dust**, **air bubbles** and **fingerprints**, to inaccuracies caused by **squashing** and **staining** your sample.

3) Artefacts are usually made during the **preparation** of your slides and **shouldn't** really be there at all — you'll need to prepare your root tip cells **carefully** to avoid creating artefacts.

The new organelle Steve had discovered looked just like his thumb print.

Artefacts are especially common in **electron micrographs** because specimens need a lot of preparation before you can **view** them under an electron microscope. The first scientists to use these microscopes could only **distinguish** between **artefacts** and **organelles** by **repeatedly** preparing specimens in **different ways**. If an object could be seen with **one** preparation technique, but **not another**, it was more likely to be an **artefact** than an **organelle**.

Practice Questions

Q1 Why do you need to squash the tissue when preparing a slide of plant root tip cells?

Exam Question

Q1 A sample of cells was prepared to observe mitosis. In total, 42 cells were observed. 32 of those had visible chromosomes. Calculate the mitotic index for this sample. Give your answer to 2 decimal places. [2 marks]

'Staining your samples' — *a common problem at the start of exams...*

Wow — I bet you never realised there was so much to know about using a microscope. Still, staining root tips is pretty straightforward and so's preparing a slide. Using a graticule is tricky, but once you get your head round it you'll be fine.

Cellular Organisation

Multicellular organisms have specialised cells, which are organised into tissues and organs, so that they can carry out all of the necessary functions that they need to survive.

Cells are **Specialised** for their Particular Function

In **multicellular** eukaryotic organisms, cells become **specialised** to carry out **specific functions** — so depending on what job it does, a specialised cell can look very different to the cells you saw on page 38. Here are some examples:

Animal Cells

Neutrophil
Flexible shape
Lots of lysosomes
Nucleus

1) **Neutrophils** (a type of white blood cell) defend the body against disease. Their **flexible shape** allows them to **engulf** foreign particles or pathogens (see p. 122). The many **lysosomes** in their cytoplasm contain **digestive enzymes** to **break down** the engulfed particles.

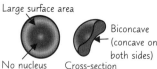
Erythrocyte
Large surface area
Biconcave (concave on both sides)
No nucleus   Cross-section

2) **Erythrocytes** (red blood cells) carry oxygen in the blood. The **biconcave** disc shape provides a **large surface area** for gas exchange. They have **no nucleus** so there's more room for **haemoglobin** (see p. 92), the protein that carries oxygen.

3) **Epithelial cells** cover the surfaces of organs. The cells are **joined** by **interlinking** cell membranes and a membrane at their base. **Ciliated** epithelia (e.g. in the **airways**) have **cilia** that beat to move particles away. **Squamous** epithelia (e.g. in the **lungs**) are very thin to allow **efficient diffusion** of gases.

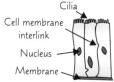
Ciliated epithelial cells
Cilia
Cell membrane interlink
Nucleus
Membrane

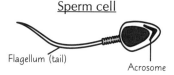
Sperm cell
Flagellum (tail)
Acrosome

4) **Sperm cells** (male sex cells) have a **flagellum** (tail) so they can **swim** to the egg (female sex cell). They also have lots of **mitochondria** to provide the **energy** to swim. The **acrosome** contains **digestive enzymes** to enable the sperm to **penetrate** the surface of the egg.

Plant Cells

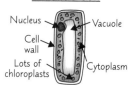
Palisade cell
Nucleus   Vacuole
Cell wall
Lots of chloroplasts   Cytoplasm

1) **Palisade mesophyll cells** in leaves do most of the **photosynthesis**. They contain **many chloroplasts**, so they can absorb a lot of sunlight. The walls are **thin**, so carbon dioxide can **easily diffuse** into the cell.

2) **Root hair cells** absorb water and mineral ions from the soil. They have a **large surface area** for absorption and a **thin**, permeable cell wall, for entry of water and ions. The cytoplasm contains **extra mitochondria** to provide the **energy** needed for **active transport** (see p. 63).

Root hair cell
Thin cell wall   Nucleus

Guard cells
Cells turgid, stoma opens   Cells flaccid, stoma closes

3) **Guard cells** are found in pairs, with a gap between them to form a **stoma**. This is one of the tiny **pores** in the surface of the leaf used for **gas exchange**. In the **light**, guard cells **take up water** and become **turgid**. Their **thin outer walls** and **thickened inner walls** force them to bend outwards, **opening** the stomata. This allows the leaf to exchange gases for photosynthesis.

Cellular Organisation

Specialised Cells are Organised into Tissues and Organs

1) In multicellular eukaryotic organisms, **specialised cells** are grouped together to form **tissues**. For example, **squamous epithelial cells** form **squamous epithelium** — a tissue that lines many surfaces in the body.
2) A tissue is a group of cells **working together** to perform a particular **function**.
3) Different **tissues** work together to form **organs**.

Different Organs Make up an Organ System

Organs work together to form **organ systems** — each system has a **particular function**. For example:

The **respiratory system** is made up of all the organs, tissues and cells involved in **breathing**. The lungs, trachea, larynx, nose, mouth and diaphragm are all part of the respiratory system.

The alveoli are where gas exchange takes place in the lungs. For more information on gas exchange and the respiratory system in mammals, see pages 68-69 and 72-75.

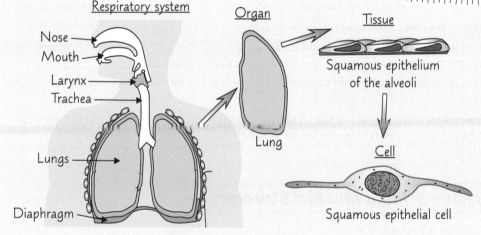

John and Fido — working together as part of an organ system.

Practice Questions

Q1 Briefly describe the structure of erythrocytes.

Q2 Define what is meant by a tissue.

Q3 Name one organ found in animals.

Exam Questions

Q1 Describe how a palisade cell is adapted for its role in photosynthesis. [2 marks]

Q2 The liver is made of hepatocyte cells that form the main tissue, blood vessels to provide nutrients and oxygen, and connective tissue that holds the liver together. Is the liver best described as a tissue, organ or an organ system? Explain your answer. [2 marks]

Soft and quilted — the best kind of tissues...

It's amazing to think that even though some cells in the same organism look radically different to each other, they all contain the same DNA. Cell specialisation is what allows an organism to become more efficient at performing different tasks — like exchanging gases with the environment. Without it, we'd be big uniform lumps which didn't get up to much.

Cell Membranes

As you saw on pages 39-41 it's not just cells that have membranes, lots of organelles have them too.
Now it's time to delve a little deeper and see exactly what membranes do — lucky you.

Membranes Control What Passes Through Them

Cells, and many of the **organelles** inside them, are surrounded by **membranes**, which have a **range of functions**:

Membranes at the **surface of cells** (PLASMA membranes)

1) They are a **barrier** between the **cell** and its **environment**, controlling **which substances enter and leave** the cell. They're **partially permeable** — they let some molecules through but not others. Substances can move across the plasma membrane by **diffusion, osmosis** or **active transport** (see pages 60-67).

2) They allow **recognition** by other cells, e.g. the cells of the **immune system** (see p.122-123).

3) They allow **cell communication** (sometimes called **cell signalling**) — see p. 58.

Partially permeable membranes can be useful at sea.

Membranes **within cells**

1) The membranes around **organelles divide** the cell into different **compartments** — they act as a **barrier** between the **organelle** and the **cytoplasm**. This makes different **functions more efficient**, e.g. the substances needed for **respiration** (like enzymes) are kept together inside **mitochondria**.

2) They can form **vesicles** to **transport** substances between different areas of the cell (see p. 40).

3) They control **which substances enter and leave** the organelle, e.g. RNA (see p. 32) leaves the nucleus via the nuclear membrane. They are also **partially permeable**.

4) You can also get membranes **within organelles** — these act as **barriers** between the membrane contents and the rest of the organelle, e.g. thylakoid membranes in chloroplasts (see p. 39).

5) Membranes within cells can be the **site** of **chemical reactions**, e.g. the **inner membrane** of a mitochondrion contains **enzymes** needed for **respiration**.

Cell Membranes have a 'Fluid Mosaic' Structure

The **structure** of all membranes is basically the same. They're composed of **lipids** (mainly phospholipids), **proteins** and **carbohydrates** (usually attached to proteins or lipids).

See pages 12-18 for more about lipids, proteins and carbohydrates.

1) In 1972, the **fluid mosaic model** was suggested to describe the **arrangement** of **molecules** in the membrane.

2) In the model, **phospholipid molecules** form a continuous, double layer (**bilayer**).

3) This bilayer is '**fluid**' because the phospholipids are **constantly moving**.

4) **Cholesterol** molecules are present within the bilayer (see next page).

5) **Protein molecules** are scattered through the bilayer, like tiles in a **mosaic**.

6) Some **proteins** have a **polysaccharide** (carbohydrate) chain attached — these are called **glycoproteins**.

7) Some **lipids** also have a **polysaccharide chain** attached — these are called **glycolipids**.

The phospholipid bilayer is about 7 nm thick.

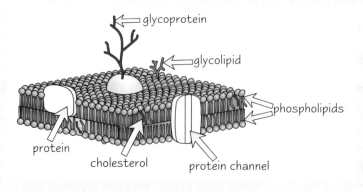

Cell Membranes

The **Different Components** of Cell Membranes have **Different Roles**

Phospholipids Form a Barrier to Dissolved Substances

1) **Phospholipid molecules** have a 'head' and a 'tail'.
2) The head is hydrophilic — it **attracts water**.
3) The tail is hydrophobic — it **repels water**.
4) The molecules automatically **arrange** themselves into a **bilayer** — the **heads face out** towards the water on either side of the membrane.
5) The **centre** of the bilayer is **hydrophobic** so the membrane **doesn't** allow **water-soluble substances** (like ions) through it — it acts as a **barrier** to these dissolved substances. (But **fat-soluble substances**, e.g. fat-soluble vitamins, can **dissolve** in the bilayer and pass directly through the membrane.)

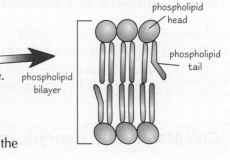

Cholesterol Gives the Membrane Stability

1) **Cholesterol** is a type of lipid.
2) It's present in **all** cell membranes (except bacterial cell membranes).
3) Cholesterol molecules fit **between** the phospholipids. They bind to the hydrophobic tails of the phospholipids, causing them to pack **more closely together**. This makes the membrane **less fluid** and **more rigid**.

See p. 15 for more on phospholipids and cholesterol.

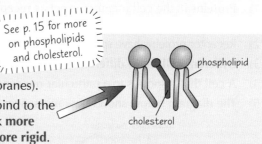

Proteins Control What Enters and Leaves the Cell

1) Some proteins form **channels** in the membrane (see p. 60) — these allow **small** or **charged** particles **through**.
2) Other proteins (called **carrier proteins**) transport molecules and ions across the membrane by **active transport** and **facilitated diffusion** (see pages 60 and 63).
3) Proteins also act as **receptors** for molecules (e.g. hormones) in **cell signalling** (see next page). When a molecule **binds** to the protein, a **chemical reaction** is triggered inside the cell.

Glycolipids and Glycoproteins act as Receptors for Messenger Molecules

1) Glycolipids and glycoproteins **stabilise** the membrane by forming **hydrogen bonds** with surrounding **water molecules**.
2) They're also sites where **drugs**, **hormones** and **antibodies** bind.
3) They act as **receptors** for **cell signalling**.
4) They're also **antigens** — cell surface molecules involved in the immune response (see p. 122).

Practice Questions

Q1 Give two functions of membranes at the cell surface and two functions of membranes within the cell.
Q2 Give three molecules that are present in animal cell membranes.

Exam Questions

Q1 Explain why the plasma membrane can be described as having a fluid mosaic structure. [2 marks]

Q2 State two functions of proteins in cell membranes. [2 marks]

Fluid Mosaic Model — think I saw one being sold at a craft fair...

It's weird to think that cells are surrounded by a layer that's 'fluid' — it's a good job it is though, 'cause if cell membranes were rigid a cell wouldn't be able to change shape or stretch without bursting. It's also a good job that the membrane's partially permeable — so that it can let oxygen into the cell and carbon dioxide out of the cell. Phew.

Cell Membranes

Cells like to have a good chat with one another every so often. To do this they use a process called cell signalling.

Cell Signalling is How Cells Communicate with Each Other

Cells need to communicate with each other to **control processes** inside the body and to **respond** to **changes** in the **environment**.

Cells communicate with each other using **messenger molecules**:

1) One cell **releases** a messenger molecule (e.g. a **hormone**).
2) This molecule **travels** (e.g. in the blood) to another cell.
3) The messenger molecule is detected by the cell because it **binds** to a **receptor** on its **cell membrane**.

Cell Membrane Receptors Play an Important Role in Cell Signalling

1) **Proteins** in the cell membrane act as **receptors** for messenger molecules. These are called 'membrane-bound receptors'.
2) Receptor proteins have **specific shapes** — only **messenger molecules** with a **complementary shape** can **bind** to them.
3) **Different cells** have **different types** of receptors — they respond to **different messenger molecules**.
4) A cell that responds to a particular messenger molecule is called a **target cell**.
5) The diagram below shows how messenger molecules bind to target cells.

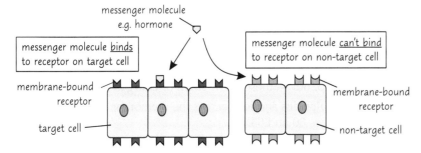

Example: Glucagon

Glucagon is a **hormone** that's **released** when there **isn't enough glucose** in the **blood**. It **binds** to **receptors** on **liver cells**, causing the liver cells to **break down** stores of **glycogen** to glucose.

Drugs Also Bind to Cell Membrane Receptors

1) Many **drugs** work by **binding** to **receptors** in cell membranes.
2) They either **trigger** a **response** in the cell, or **block** the receptor and **prevent** it from **working**.

Example: Antihistamines

Cell damage causes the release of **histamine**. Histamine binds to receptors on the surface of other cells and causes **inflammation**. **Antihistamines** work by **blocking histamine receptors** on cell surfaces. This **prevents** histamine from binding to the cell and **stops inflammation**.

The Permeability of the Cell Membrane can be Investigated in the Lab

The permeability of cell membranes is affected by **different conditions**, e.g. **temperature**, **solvent type** and **solvent concentration**. You can investigate how these things affect permeability by doing an experiment using **beetroot**. Beetroot cells contain a **coloured pigment** that **leaks out** — the **higher** the **permeability** of the membrane, the **more pigment** leaks out of the cell.

Here's how you could investigate how **temperature** affects **beetroot membrane permeability**:

1) Cut five **equal sized** pieces of beetroot and **rinse** them to remove any pigment released during cutting.
2) Place the five pieces in five different **test tubes**, each with **5 cm³ of water**.
3) Place each test tube in a **water bath** at a **different temperature**, e.g. 10 °C, 20 °C, 30 °C, 40 °C, 50 °C, for the **same length of time**.
4) **Remove** the pieces of beetroot from the tubes, leaving just the **coloured liquid**.
5) Now you need to use a **colorimeter** — a machine that passes **light** through the liquid and measures how much of that light is **absorbed** (see p. 21). The **higher** the **permeability** of the membrane, the **more pigment** is **released**, so the **higher** the absorbance of the liquid.

Cell Membranes

Increasing *the* Temperature Increases Membrane Permeability

Experiments like the one on the previous page have shown that membrane permeability **changes** with temperature:

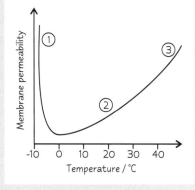

1. **Temperatures below 0 °C**
   The phospholipids don't have much energy, so they can't move very much. They're **packed closely together** and the membrane is **rigid**. But **channel proteins** and **carrier proteins** in the membrane **deform**, **increasing** the **permeability** of the membrane. **Ice crystals** may form and **pierce** the membrane making it **highly permeable** when it thaws.

2. **Temperatures between 0 and 45 °C**
   The phospholipids can **move** around and **aren't** packed as tightly together — the membrane is **partially permeable**. As the temperature **increases** the phospholipids **move more** because they have more energy — this **increases** the **permeability** of the membrane.

3. **Temperatures above 45 °C**
   The phospholipid bilayer starts to **melt** (break down) and the membrane becomes more **permeable**. **Water** inside the cell **expands**, putting pressure on the membrane. **Channel proteins** and **carrier proteins** **deform** so they can't control what enters or leaves the cell — this increases the **permeability** of the membrane.

Changing the Solvent Affects Membrane Permeability

Different solvents and their **concentration** can affect the **permeability** of cell membranes.

1) Surrounding cells in a **solvent** (such as ethanol) **increases** the **permeability** of their cell membranes.

2) This is because solvents **dissolve** the **lipids** in a cell membrane, so the membrane loses its structure.

3) Some solvents **increase** cell **permeability** more than others, e.g. **ethanol** increases cell permeability more than **methanol**.

4) You could **investigate** the effects of different solvents by doing an experiment using **beetroot** like the one on the previous page.

5) **Increasing** the **concentration** of the solvent will also **increase** membrane **permeability**. For example, this graph shows the effect of alcohol concentration on membrane permeability.

Practice Questions

Q1 Describe, using an example, how cells communicate with one another.

Q2 Describe how the permeability of a cell membrane changes as the temperature increases.

Exam Question

Q1 The table on the right shows the results of an investigation into the effect of alcohol concentration on the permeability of beetroot cell membranes.

Alcohol concentration / %	Absorbance
0	0.14
25	0.22
50	0.49
75	1.03
100	1.28

a) Suggest a suitable method that could have been used to obtain these results. [4 marks]

b) What conclusion can be drawn from the results? [2 marks]

c) Suggest an explanation for the results. [1 mark]

Perm-eability — it's definitely decreased since the 80s...

Messenger molecules are released by different cells in your body. They travel round and bind to receptors on other cells, causing some kind of response. This signalling fine-tunes all the body's processes and keeps us working properly.

Diffusion and Facilitated Diffusion

Ooooh it's starting to get a bit more exciting... here's how some substances can get across cell membranes without using energy. Just what you've always wanted to know, I bet.

Diffusion is the Passive Movement of Particles

1) Diffusion is the net movement of particles (molecules or ions) from an area of **higher concentration** to an area of **lower concentration**.

2) Molecules will diffuse **both ways**, but the **net movement** will be to the area of **lower concentration**. This continues until particles are **evenly distributed** throughout the liquid or gas.

3) The **concentration gradient** is the path from an area of higher concentration to an area of lower concentration. Particles diffuse **down** a concentration gradient.

4) Diffusion is a **passive process** — **no energy** is needed for it to happen.

5) Particles can diffuse **across cell membranes**, as long as they can **move freely** through the membrane.

> Polar molecules have partial positive and negative charges (see p. 10). Non-polar molecules don't.

> E.g. **oxygen** and **carbon dioxide** can diffuse easily through cell membranes because they're **small**, so they can pass through spaces between the phospholipids. They're also **non-polar**, which makes them **soluble** in **lipids**, so they can **dissolve** in the **hydrophobic bilayer**.

6) When molecules diffuse **directly** through a cell membrane, it's also known as **simple diffusion**.

Facilitated Diffusion uses Carrier Proteins and Channel Proteins

1) Some **larger molecules** (e.g. amino acids, glucose) would **diffuse extremely slowly** through the phospholipid bilayer because they're so **big**.

2) **Charged particles**, e.g. **ions** and **polar molecules**, would also diffuse slowly — that's because they're **water soluble**, and the **centre** of the **bilayer** is **hydrophobic** (see page 57).

3) So to **speed things up**, large or charged particles diffuse through **carrier proteins** or **channel proteins** in the membrane instead — this is called **facilitated diffusion**.

4) Like diffusion, facilitated diffusion moves particles **down** a **concentration gradient**, from a higher to a lower concentration.

5) It's also a passive process — it **doesn't** use **energy**.

Andy needed all his concentration for this particular gradient...

Carrier proteins move **large molecules** across membranes, down their concentration gradient. **Different carrier proteins** facilitate the diffusion of **different molecules**.

1) First, a large molecule **attaches** to a carrier protein in the membrane.

2) Then, the protein **changes shape**.

3) This **releases** the molecule on the **opposite side** of the membrane.

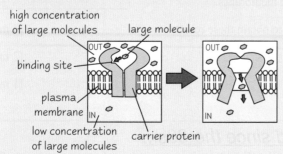

Channel proteins form **pores** in the membrane for **charged particles** to diffuse through (down their concentration gradient). **Different channel proteins** facilitate the diffusion of **different charged particles**.

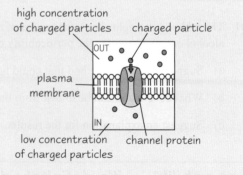

Diffusion and Facilitated Diffusion

The **Rate of Diffusion** Depends on **Several Factors**

The **rate** of **diffusion** across both **external** and **internal cell membranes** can **vary**. Some cells are **adapted** for **rapid diffusion** across their membranes.

Internal cell membranes are ones surrounding organelles, e.g. the mitochondria.

Simple diffusion depends on...

1) The **concentration gradient** — the **higher** it is, the **faster** the rate of diffusion. As diffusion takes place, the **difference in concentration** between the two sides of the membrane **decreases** until it reaches an **equilibrium** (i.e. the concentration on both sides is equal). This means that diffusion **slows down** over time.

2) The **thickness** of the **exchange surface** — the **thinner** the exchange surface (i.e. the **shorter** the **distance** the particles have to travel), the **faster** the rate of diffusion.

3) The **surface area** — the **larger** the surface area (e.g. of the cell-surface membrane), the **faster** the rate of diffusion.

Microvilli increase the surface area for faster diffusion

Some cells (e.g. epithelial cells in the small intestine) have **microvilli** — projections formed by the cell-surface membrane folding up on itself. Microvilli give the cell a **larger surface area** — in human cells, microvilli can increase the surface area by about **600 times**. A larger surface area means that **more particles** can be **exchanged** in the same amount of time — **increasing** the **rate of diffusion**.

Temperature also affects the rate of simple diffusion — the **warmer** it is, the **faster** the rate of diffusion because the particles have **more kinetic energy**, so they move faster.

Facilitated diffusion depends on...

1) The **concentration gradient** — the **higher** the **concentration gradient**, the **faster** the **rate** of **facilitated diffusion** (**up to a point**, see point 2 below). As **equilibrium** is reached, the **rate** of facilitated diffusion will **level off**.

2) The **number** of **channel** or **carrier proteins** — once **all** the **proteins** in a membrane are **in use**, facilitated diffusion **can't happen any faster**, even if you increase the concentration gradient. So the **greater the number** of channel or carrier proteins in the cell membrane, the **faster the rate** of facilitated diffusion.

Having more channel proteins increases the rate of facilitated diffusion

Aquaporins are special **channel proteins** that allow the **facilitated diffusion** of **water** through cell membranes. Some **kidney cells** are **adapted** to have **lots of aquaporins**. The aquaporins allow the cells to **reabsorb** a lot of the water that would otherwise be **excreted** by the body — about **180 litres** need re-absorbing every day.

Water can also diffuse directly through the membrane, even though it's polar. That's because it's relatively small.

Fick's Law Describes the **Rate of Diffusion**

Fick's Law relates the rate of diffusion to the **concentration gradient**, the **surface area** and the **thickness** of the **exchange surface**. It states that:

$$\text{rate of diffusion} \propto \frac{\text{area of diffusion surface} \times \text{difference in concentration}}{\text{thickness of diffusion surface}}$$

'∝' means 'is proportional to'.

A fast rate of diffusion — not good in a swimming pool.

The 'proportional to' bit means that the **rate of diffusion** will **double** if:
- the **surface area** or the **difference in concentration** <u>doubles</u>, OR
- the **thickness** of the surface <u>halves</u>.

Diffusion and Facilitated Diffusion

You Can **Investigate Diffusion** in **Model Cells**

Phenolphthalein is a **pH indicator** — it's **pink** in alkaline solutions and **colourless** in acidic solutions. You can use it to investigate **diffusion** in **agar jelly**:

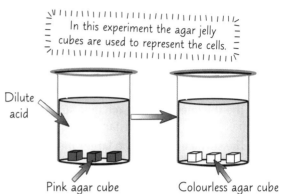

In this experiment the agar jelly cubes are used to represent the cells.

1) First, make up some agar jelly with **phenolphthalein** and dilute **sodium hydroxide**. This will make the jelly a lovely shade of **pink**.

2) Then fill a **beaker** with some dilute **hydrochloric acid**. Using a **scalpel**, cut out a few **cubes** from the jelly and put them in the beaker of acid.

3) If you **leave** the cubes for a while they'll eventually turn **colourless** as the **acid diffuses into** the agar jelly and **neutralises** the sodium hydroxide.

Dilute acid

Pink agar cube   Colourless agar cube

Using this experiment you can **investigate factors** that affect the **rate of diffusion**. For example:

SURFACE AREA — Cut the agar jelly into **different sized** cubes and work out their **surface area to volume ratio** (see p. 68). Time how long it takes each cube to go **colourless** when placed in the **same concentration** of hydrochloric acid. You would expect the cubes with the **largest surface area to volume ratio** to go colourless **fastest**.

CONCENTRATION GRADIENT — Prepare test tubes containing **different concentrations** of hydrochloric acid. Put an equal-sized cube of the agar jelly in each test tube and time how long it takes each one to turn **colourless**. You would expect the cubes in the **highest concentration** of hydrochloric acid to go colourless **fastest**.

TEMPERATURE — Prepare several boiling tubes containing the same concentration of hydrochloric acid and put the tubes into water baths of **varying temperatures**. Put an equal-sized cube of the agar jelly into each boiling tube and time how long it takes each cube to go **colourless**. You would expect the cubes in the **highest temperature** to go colourless **fastest**.

Don't increase the temperature above 65 °C or the agar jelly will start to melt.

Practice Questions

Q1 Diffusion is a passive transport process. What does this mean?

Q2 Other than concentration gradient, give three factors that affect the rate of simple diffusion.

Q3 What is Fick's Law?

Exam Question

Q1 A student carried out an experiment with gelatine blocks containing cresol red, a pH indicator that changes from red to yellow when it comes into contact with acid. She cut cubes into three different sizes and placed each cube into a hydrochloric acid solution. She observed when each cube turned yellow and recorded the time taken. She repeated the experiment four times for each size of cube. Her results are shown in the table.

Size of cube (mm)	Surface area to volume ratio	Time taken for cube to become yellow (s)			
		Trial 1	Trial 2	Trial 3	Trial 4
5 × 5 × 5	1.2:1	174	167	177	182
7 × 7 × 7	0.9:1	274	290	284	292
10 × 10 × 10	0.6:1	835	825	842	838

a) Give two variables that should have been controlled during the experiment. [2 marks]

b) What conclusion about the rate of diffusion can be drawn from the results of the experiment? [1 mark]

c) Suggest one reason why the results of the experiment might not be very precise. [1 mark]

All these molecules moving about — you'd think they'd get tired...

Diffusion is simple really — it's just particles spreading themselves out evenly. Make sure you learn the different factors that can affect the rate of diffusion and know how you can investigate the rate of diffusion in the lab.

Active Transport and Endocytosis

Diffusion and osmosis are passive processes — they don't require energy. So, for those of you feeling a bit more active, here's some stuff all about... you guessed it... active transport.

Active Transport Needs Energy

Active transport uses **energy** to move **molecules** and **ions** across membranes, usually **against** a **concentration gradient**.

Carrier proteins are involved in active transport. The process is pretty **similar** to **facilitated diffusion** (see p. 60) — a molecule **attaches** to the carrier protein, the protein **changes shape** and this moves the molecule **across** the membrane, **releasing it** on the other side.

There are **two main differences** between active transport and facilitated diffusion though:

1) Active transport usually moves solutes from a **low** to a **high** concentration — in facilitated diffusion, they **always** move from a **high** to a **low** concentration.

2) Active transport requires **energy** — facilitated diffusion **does not**.

   • **ATP** is a common **source of energy** in the cell. It's produced by **respiration**.
   • ATP undergoes a **hydrolysis reaction**, splitting into **ADP** and P_i (inorganic phosphate). This **releases energy** so that the solutes can be transported.

The diagram shows the active transport of **calcium**.

Unlike facilitated diffusion, active transport doesn't use channel proteins.

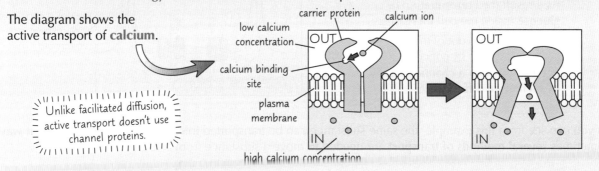

Co-transporters are a type of **carrier protein**.

1) They bind **two** molecules at a time.

2) The concentration gradient of one of the molecules is used to move the other molecule **against** its own concentration gradient.

The diagram shows the co-transport of **sodium ions** and **glucose**. Sodium ions move into the cell **down** their concentration gradient. This moves glucose into the cell too, **against** its concentration gradient.

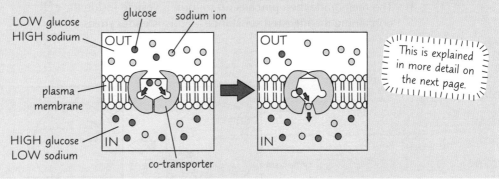

This is explained in more detail on the next page.

These Factors Affect the Rate of Active Transport

When **active transport** moves molecules and ions **against** their concentration gradient, a **decreasing** concentration gradient **doesn't** affect the **rate** of **active transport**. The rate of active transport is affected by:

1) The **speed** of **individual** carrier **proteins** — the **faster** they **work**, the **faster** the **rate** of active transport.

2) The **number** of **carrier proteins** present — the **more proteins** there are, the **faster** the **rate** of active transport.

3) The rate of **respiration** in the cell and the availability of **ATP**. If respiration is **inhibited**, active transport **can't** take place.

Active Transport and Endocytosis

Glucose is Absorbed by Co-transport in the Mammalian Ileum

1) **Glucose** is absorbed into the **bloodstream** in the **small intestine**.

2) In the **ileum** (the final part of the small intestine) the **concentration** of glucose is **too low** for glucose to diffuse out into the blood. So glucose is absorbed from the **lumen** (middle) of the **ileum** by **co-transport**.

Glucose enters the **ileum epithelium** with **sodium ions**

1) **Sodium ions** are **actively transported out** of the ileum epithelial **cells**, into the **blood**, by the **sodium-potassium pump**. This creates a **concentration gradient** — there's now a higher concentration of sodium ions in the lumen of the ileum than inside the cell.

2) This causes sodium ions to **diffuse** from the lumen of the ileum **into the epithelial cell**, down their concentration gradient. They do this via the **sodium-glucose co-transporter proteins**.

3) The co-transporter carries **glucose** into the cell with the sodium. As a result the concentration of **glucose** inside the cell **increases**.

4) Glucose diffuses out of the cell, into the blood, down its concentration gradient through a channel protein, by **facilitated diffusion**.

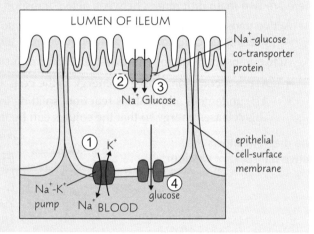

As you can see from this example, the same substance can be transported into or out of a cell in **different ways**. Sometimes **several methods of transport** are needed to move a substance from A to B.

Cells can Take in Substances by Endocytosis

1) Some molecules are way too **large** to be taken into a cell by carrier proteins, e.g. proteins, lipids and some carbohydrates.

2) Instead a cell can **surround** a substance with a **section** of its **cell-surface membrane**.

3) The membrane then **pinches off** to form a **vesicle** inside the cell containing the **ingested substance** — this is **endocytosis**.

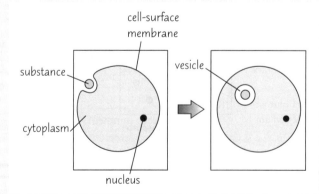

4) Some cells also take in much **larger objects** by endocytosis — for example, some **white blood cells** (mainly phagocytes, see p. 122) use endocytosis to take in things like **microorganisms** and **dead cells** so that they can destroy them.

5) Like active transport, this process also uses **ATP** for **energy**.

Active Transport and Endocytosis

Cells can **Secrete** Substances by **Exocytosis**

1) Some substances **produced** by the cell (e.g. **digestive enzymes, hormones, lipids**) need to be **released** from the cell — this is done by **exocytosis**.

2) **Vesicles** containing these substances **pinch off** from the sacs of the **Golgi apparatus** (see p. 40) and **move towards** the cell-surface membrane.

3) The vesicles **fuse** with the **cell-surface membrane** and **release** their contents **outside** the cell.

4) Some substances (like membrane proteins) **aren't** released outside the cell — instead they are **inserted** straight into the cell-surface membrane.

5) Exocytosis uses **ATP** as an **energy source**.

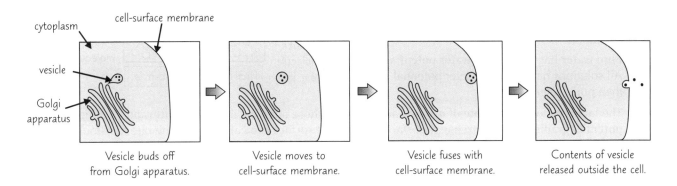

Vesicle buds off from Golgi apparatus.

Vesicle moves to cell-surface membrane.

Vesicle fuses with cell-surface membrane.

Contents of vesicle released outside the cell.

Practice Questions

Q1 What is active transport?

Q2 Which molecule provides the energy for active transport?

Q3 Describe how carrier proteins actively transport substances across the cell membrane.

Q4 Explain how sodium ions are used to transport glucose into ileum epithelial cells.

Exam Questions

Q1 The graph shows the results from an experiment into the uptake of two different solutes (X and Y) by simple bacterial cells.

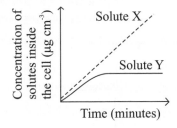

a) Which solute, X or Y, entered the cells by active transport? Give a reason for your answer. [1 mark]

b) Why is energy needed for the active transport of this solute? [1 mark]

c) Describe the process by which energy is released by the cell for active transport. [2 marks]

Q2 Explain the difference between endocytosis and exocytosis. [4 marks]

Revision — like working against a concentration gradient...

Don't worry if it takes you a while to get these pages — there's quite a lot to cover. It's a good idea to go through them bit by bit and don't move on to co-transport until you fully understand active transport in normal carrier proteins.

Osmosis

Here is the last bit on molecules crossing cell membranes. These pages are entirely about the movement of water molecules. Don't worry though — if you've mastered diffusion (see p. 60) you'll nail this in no time.

Osmosis is the *Diffusion* of *Water Molecules*

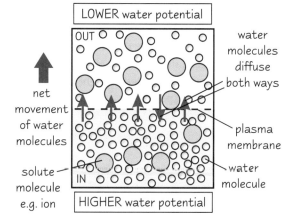

1) Osmosis is the **diffusion** of **water molecules** across a **partially permeable membrane** down a **water potential gradient**. This means water molecules move from an area of **higher water potential** (i.e. higher concentration of water molecules) to an area of **lower water potential** (i.e. lower concentration of water molecules).

2) **Water potential** is the potential (likelihood) of water molecules to diffuse out of or into a solution.

3) **Pure water** has the **highest water potential**. All solutions have a **lower** water potential than pure water.

4) The **factors** affecting the **rate of osmosis** are similar to those affecting the **rate of diffusion** — a **high water potential gradient**, a **thin exchange surface** and a **large surface area** all **increase** the rate of osmosis.

Cells are *Affected* by the *Water Potential* of the *Surrounding Solution*

Water moves **in** or **out** of a cell by osmosis. **How much** moves in or out depends on the **water potential** of the **surrounding solution**. Animal and plant cells behave differently in different solutions.

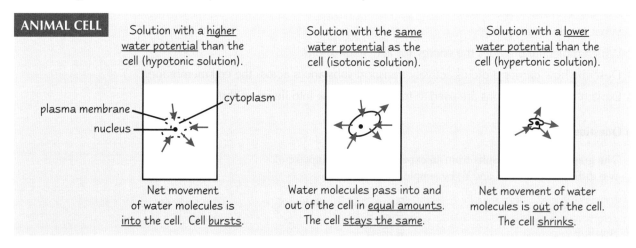

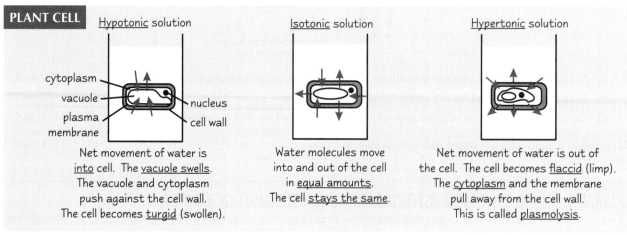

Osmosis

You can do **Experiments** to Investigate **Water Potential**

You can do a simple **experiment**, using potato cylinders, to find out the **water potential** of **plant tissue**. This experiment involves putting potato cylinders into **different concentrations** of sucrose solution — remember, the **higher** the sucrose **concentration**, the **lower** the water **potential**.

1) Prepare **sucrose solutions** of the following concentrations:
0.0 M, 0.2 M, 0.4 M, 0.6 M, 0.8 M, 1.0 M.

2) Use a cork borer or chip maker to cut **potatoes** into **the same sized** pieces. (They need to be about 1 cm in diameter.)

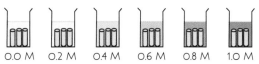

You might also see M written as mol dm⁻³.

3) Divide the chips into **groups of three** and use a **mass balance** to measure the **mass** of each **group**.

4) Place **one group** in each solution.

5) **Leave** the chips in the solution for **as long as possible** (making sure that they all get the **same amount of time**). Try to leave them for at least 20 minutes.

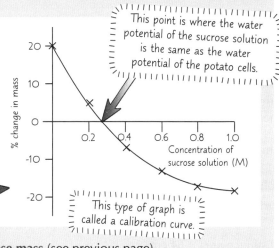

This point is where the water potential of the sucrose solution is the same as the water potential of the potato cells.

6) **Remove** the chips and pat dry **gently** with a paper towel.

7) **Weigh** each **group** again and record your results.

8) Calculate the **% change in mass** for each group.

9) Plot your results on a **graph** like this:

This type of graph is called a calibration curve.

10) If you could see the **potato cells** under a **microscope**, you'd see them becoming **turgid** as the chips **gain mass** and **plasmolysed** as the chips **lose mass** (see previous page).

You can do a **Similar Experiment** with **Eggs**

You can carry out a **similar experiment** using chickens' eggs that have had their **shells dissolved**. The remaining **membrane** is **partially permeable**, so it's a good **model** for showing the effects of **osmosis** in **animal tissue**.

Practice Questions

Q1 Define osmosis.

Q2 What happens to an animal cell if it is placed in a solution with the same water potential as the cell?

Q3 What happens to a plant cell if it is placed in a solution with a higher water potential than the cell?

Exam Question

Q1 Pieces of potato of equal mass were put into different concentrations of sucrose solution for 24 hours. The difference in mass for each is recorded in the table.

Concentration of sucrose / %	1	2	3	4
Mass difference / g	0.4	0.2	0	− 0.2

a) Explain why the pieces of potato in 1% and 2% sucrose solutions gained mass. [3 marks]

b) Suggest a reason why the mass of the piece of potato in 3% sucrose solution stayed the same. [1 mark]

c) What would you expect the mass difference for a potato in a 5% solution to be? Explain your answer. [2 marks]

I always knew that glass of water had potential...

Osmosis is just a fancy name for the diffusion of water molecules. But whether water moves in or out of a cell depends on the water potential of the surrounding solution. Water potential can be pretty confusing — if you can't make head nor tail of an exam question about it try replacing the word 'potential' with 'concentration' and it'll become clearer.

Specialised Exchange Surfaces

Exchanging things with the environment is pretty easy if you're a single-celled organism, but if you're multicellular it all gets a bit more complicated... and it's all down to this 'surface area to volume ratio' malarkey.

Organisms Need to **Exchange Substances** with their **Environment**

Every organism, whatever its size, needs to exchange things with its environment.
Otherwise there'd be no such thing as poop scoops...

1) Cells need to take in **oxygen** (for aerobic respiration) and **nutrients**.

2) They also need to excrete **waste products** like **carbon dioxide** and **urea**.

3) Most organisms need to stay at roughly the **same temperature**, so **heat** needs to be exchanged too.

Raj was glad he'd exchanged his canoe for a bigger boat.

How easy the exchange of substances is depends on the organism's **surface area to volume ratio**.

Smaller Animals have *Higher Surface Area : Volume Ratios*

A mouse has a bigger surface area **relative to its volume** than a hippo. This can be hard to imagine, but you can prove it mathematically. Imagine these animals as cubes:

The hippo could be represented by a block measuring
2 cm × 4 cm × 4 cm.
Its **volume** is 2 × 4 × 4 = **32 cm³**
Its **surface area** is 2 × 4 × 4 = 32 cm² (top and bottom surfaces of cube)
                  + 4 × 2 × 4 = 32 cm² (four sides of the cube)
Total surface area = **64 cm²**
So the hippo has a **surface area:volume ratio** of 64:32 or **2:1**.

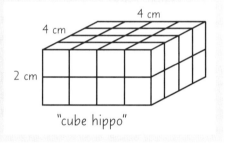

"cube hippo"

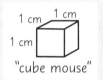

"cube mouse"

Compare this to a cube mouse measuring 1 cm × 1 cm × 1 cm.
Its **volume** is 1 × 1 × 1 = **1 cm³**
Its **surface area** is 6 × 1 × 1 = **6 cm²**
So the mouse has a **surface area:volume ratio** of **6:1**.

The cube mouse's surface area is six times its volume, but the cube hippo's surface area is only twice its volume. Smaller animals have a bigger surface area compared to their volume.

Multicellular Organisms Need *Exchange Organs* and *Mass Transport Systems*

An organism needs to supply **every one of its cells** with substances like **glucose** and **oxygen** (for respiration).
It also needs to **remove waste products** from every cell to avoid damaging itself.

1) In **single-celled** organisms, these substances can **diffuse directly** into (or out of) the cell across the cell-surface membrane. The diffusion rate is quick because of the small distances the substances have to travel (see p. 61).

2) In **multicellular** animals, diffusion across the outer membrane is **too slow**, for two reasons:

   • Some cells are **deep within the body** — there's a big distance between them and the **outside environment**.

   • Larger animals have a **low surface area to volume ratio** — it's difficult to exchange **enough** substances to supply a **large volume of animal** through a relatively **small outer surface**.

So rather than using straightforward diffusion to absorb and excrete substances, multicellular animals need specialised **exchange organs** (like lungs — see p. 73).

They also need an efficient system to carry substances to and from their individual cells — this is **mass transport**. In mammals, 'mass transport' normally refers to the **circulatory system** (see p. 82), which uses **blood** to carry glucose and oxygen around the body. It also carries **hormones**, **antibodies** (p. 123) and **waste** like CO_2.
Mass transport in **plants** involves the transport of **water** and **solutes** in the **xylem** and **phloem** (see pages 94 and 95).

Specialised Exchange Surfaces

Body Size and Shape Affect Heat Exchange

As well as creating **waste products** that need to be transported away, the metabolic activity inside cells creates **heat**. Staying at the right temperature is difficult, and it's pretty heavily influenced by your **size** and **shape**...

Size

The **rate of heat loss** from an organism depends on its **surface area**. If an organism has a large volume, e.g. a hippo, its surface area is relatively **small**. This makes it **harder** for it to lose heat from its body. If an organism is small, e.g. a mouse, its relative surface area is **large**, so heat is lost more **easily**. This means **smaller** organisms need a relatively **high metabolic rate**, in order to **generate** enough **heat** to stay warm.

Shape

1) Animals with a **compact** shape have a **small surface area** relative to their volume — **minimising heat loss** from their surface.

2) Animals with a **less compact** shape (those that are a bit **gangly** or have **sticky outy** bits) have a **larger surface area** relative to their volume — this **increases heat loss** from their surface.

3) Whether an animal is compact or not depends on the **temperature** of its **environment**. Here's an example:

Arctic fox
Body temperature 37 °C
Average outside temperature 0 °C

African bat-eared fox
Body temperature 37 °C
Average outside temperature 25 °C

European fox
Body temperature 37 °C
Average outside temperature 12 °C

The Arctic fox has **small ears** and a **round head** to **reduce** its SA : V ratio and heat loss.

The African bat-eared fox has **large ears** and a more **pointed nose** to **increase** its SA : V ratio and heat loss.

The European fox is **intermediate** between the two, matching the temperature of its environment.

Organisms have Behavioural and Physiological Adaptations to Aid Exchange

Not all organisms have a body size or shape to suit their climate — some have **other adaptations** instead...

1) Animals with a high SA : volume ratio tend to **lose more water** as it evaporates from their surface. Some **small desert mammals** have **kidney structure adaptations** so that they produce **less urine** to compensate.

2) To support their **high metabolic rates**, small mammals living in **cold regions** need to eat large amounts of **high energy foods** such as seeds and nuts.

3) Smaller mammals may have thick layers of **fur** or **hibernate** when the weather gets really cold.

4) **Larger organisms** living in **hot regions**, e.g. elephants and hippos, find it hard to keep cool as their heat loss is relatively slow. **Elephants** have developed **large flat ears** to **increase** their **surface area**, allowing them to lose more heat. **Hippos** spend much of the day in the **water** — a **behavioural adaptation** to help them lose heat.

Practice Questions

Q1 Give four things that organisms need to exchange with their environment.

Q2 Describe how body shape affects heat exchange.

Exam Question

Q1 Explain why a small mammal needs a relatively high metabolic rate compared to a large mammal. [3 marks]

Cube animals indeed — it's all gone a bit Picasso...

Surface area to volume ratios can be a bit mind-bending — larger organisms have smaller surface area to volume ratios than smaller organisms. But once you've gone over it all a few times, it should start to make sense.

Adaptations of Gas Exchange Surfaces

Lots of organisms have developed adaptations to improve their rate of gas exchange. It's a tricky business if you're an insect or a plant though — you've got to exchange enough gas but avoid losing all your water and drying to a crisp...

Gas Exchange Surfaces have **Two** Major **Adaptations**

Most gas exchange surfaces have two things in common:

1) They have a **large surface area**.

2) They're **thin** (often just one layer of epithelial cells)
   — this provides a **short diffusion pathway** across the gas exchange surface.

The organism also maintains a **steep concentration gradient** of gases across the exchange surface.

> All these features **increase** the **rate of diffusion** — see page 61.

Single-celled Organisms Exchange Gases across their **Body Surface**

1) Single-celled organisms absorb and release gases by **diffusion** through their **outer surface**.

2) They have a relatively **large surface area**, a **thin surface** and a **short diffusion pathway** (oxygen can take part in **biochemical reactions** as soon as it **diffuses** into the cell) — so there's **no need** for a gas exchange system.

Fish Use a **Counter-Current System** for Gas Exchange

There's a **lower concentration** of oxygen in water than in air. So **fish** have special **adaptations** to get enough of it.

1) Water, containing oxygen, enters the fish through its **mouth** and passes out through the **gills**.

2) Each gill is made of lots of **thin branches** called **gill filaments** or **primary lamellae**, which give a **big surface area** for **exchange of gases**.

3) The gill filaments are covered in lots of tiny structures called **gill plates** or **secondary lamellae**, which **increase** the **surface area** even more. Each gill is supported by a **gill arch**.

4) The gill plates have lots of **blood capillaries** and a **thin surface layer of cells** to speed up diffusion.

vessels (oxygenated blood from the gill)

gill plate / secondary lamella (plural = lamellae)

artery (deoxygenated blood to gill)

gill arch

gill filaments / primary lamellae

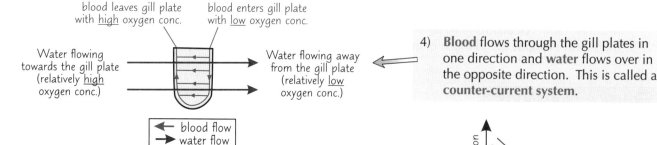

blood leaves gill plate with <u>high</u> oxygen conc.

blood enters gill plate with <u>low</u> oxygen conc.

Water flowing towards the gill plate (relatively <u>high</u> oxygen conc.)

Water flowing away from the gill plate (relatively <u>low</u> oxygen conc.)

← blood flow
→ water flow

4) **Blood** flows through the gill plates in one direction and **water** flows over in the opposite direction. This is called a **counter-current system**.

5) The counter-current system maintains a **large concentration gradient** between the water and the blood. The **concentration of oxygen** in the **water** is always **higher** than that in the **blood**, so as much oxygen as possible diffuses from the water into the blood.

oxygen concentration

water

blood

distance along gill plate

Adaptations of Gas Exchange Surfaces

Dicotyledonous Plants Exchange Gases at the Surface of the Mesophyll Cells

1) Plants need carbon dioxide (CO_2) for **photosynthesis**, which produces oxygen (O_2) as a waste gas. They need O_2 for **respiration**, which produces CO_2 as a waste gas.

2) The main gas exchange surface is the **surface of the mesophyll cells** in the leaf. They're well adapted for their function — they have a **large surface area**.

3) The mesophyll cells are inside the leaf. Gases move in and out through special pores in the **epidermis** called **stomata** (singular = stoma).

4) The stomata can **open** to allow exchange of gases, and **close** if the plant is losing too much water. **Guard cells** control the opening and closing of stomata.

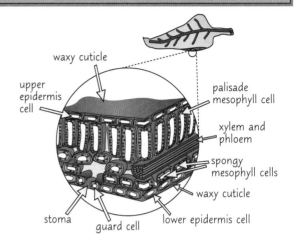

waxy cuticle
upper epidermis cell
palisade mesophyll cell
xylem and phloem
spongy mesophyll cells
waxy cuticle
stoma
guard cell
lower epidermis cell

Insects use Tracheae to Exchange Gases

1) Insects have microscopic air-filled pipes called **tracheae** which they use for gas exchange.

2) Air moves into the tracheae through pores on the insect's surface called **spiracles**.

3) **Oxygen** travels down the **concentration gradient** towards the **cells**. Carbon dioxide from the cells moves down its own concentration gradient towards the spiracles to be **released** into the atmosphere.

4) The tracheae branch off into smaller **tracheoles** which have **thin, permeable walls** and go to individual cells. The tracheoles also contain **fluid**, which oxygen **dissolves** in.

5) The oxygen then **diffuses** from this fluid **into body cells**. **Carbon dioxide** diffuses in the **opposite direction**.

6) Insects use **rhythmic abdominal movements** to **change** the **volume** of their bodies and **move air in** and **out** of the spiracles. When larger insects are **flying**, they use their **wing movements** to **pump** their **thoraxes** too.

7) You can examine insect tracheae under a **light microscope** using a **wet mount slide** (see page 48). You should be able to see **rings of chitin** in the walls of the tracheae — these are there for **support**.

'Tracheae' is the plural of 'trachea'.

tracheae and tracheoles give large surface area
spiracle
thorax
abdomen
trachea
tracheole lined with single layer of cells to minimise diffusion distance
CO_2 diffuses into tracheoles
O_2 diffuses into respiring cells

Insects and Plants can Control Water Loss

Exchanging gases tends to make you **lose water** — there's a sort of **trade-off** between the two. Luckily for plants and insects though, they've evolved **adaptations** to **minimise water loss** without reducing gas exchange too much.

1) If **insects** are losing too much water, they **close** their **spiracles** using muscles. They also have a **waterproof, waxy cuticle** all over their body and **tiny hairs** around their spiracles, both of which **reduce evaporation**.

2) Plants' stomata are usually kept **open** during the day to allow **gaseous exchange**. Water enters the guard cells, making them **turgid**, which **opens** the stomatal pore. If the plant starts to get **dehydrated**, the guard cells lose water and become **flaccid**, which **closes** the pore.

See p. 101 for more on water loss in plants.

Adaptations of Gas Exchange Surfaces

In Mammals *Gas Exchange* Happens in the *Alveoli*

Lungs contain millions of microscopic air sacs where gas exchange occurs — called **alveoli**. Each **alveolus** is made from a **single layer** of **thin, flat cells** called **alveolar epithelium**.

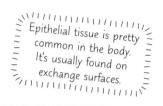

Epithelial tissue is pretty common in the body. It's usually found on exchange surfaces.

1) There's a huge number of alveoli in the lungs, which means there's a **big surface area** for exchanging O_2 and CO_2.

2) The alveoli are surrounded by a network of **capillaries**.

alveoli ('air sacs') covered in a network of capillaries

— bronchiole

— one alveolus

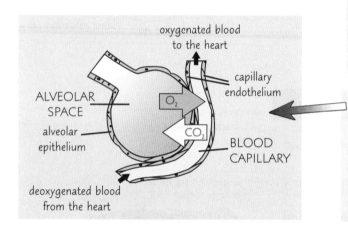

3) O_2 diffuses **out of** the alveoli, across the **alveolar epithelium** and the **capillary endothelium** (a type of epithelium that forms the capillary wall), and into **haemoglobin** (see p. 92) in the **blood**.

4) CO_2 diffuses **into** the alveoli from the blood, and is breathed out.

The *Alveoli* are *Adapted* for *Gas Exchange*

Alveoli have features that **speed up** the **rate of diffusion** so gases can be exchanged quickly:

1) The **alveolar epithelium** is only **one cell thick**. This means there's a **short diffusion pathway**.

2) The **large number** of alveoli means there's a large **surface area** for gas exchange.

There's also a **steep concentration gradient** of oxygen and carbon dioxide between the alveoli and the capillaries, which increases the rate of diffusion. This is constantly maintained by the **flow of blood** and **ventilation** (see page 75).

Practice Questions

Q1 How are single-celled organisms adapted for efficient gas exchange?

Q2 What is the advantage to fish of having a counter-current exchange system in their gills?

Q3 Through which pores are gases exchanged in plants?

Q3 Name the structures on an insect's surface that allow air to enter the tracheae.

Exam Questions

Q1 A student is examining grasshopper tracheae under the microscope. The tracheae are surrounded by rings of chitin. What is their function?

[1 mark]

Q2 Describe two ways in which lungs are adapted for efficient gas exchange.

[2 marks]

Keep revising and you'll be on the right trachea...

There's a pretty strong theme on these pages — whatever organism it is, to exchange gases efficiently it needs exchange organs with a large surface area, a thin exchange surface and a high concentration gradient. Just don't you forget that.

The Gas Exchange System — Mammals

The gas exchange system in mammals consists of the lungs, plus a few related tubes, muscles, etc., all enclosed in a protective ribcage. These pages show you the structure and function of the different parts.

In Mammals the **Lungs** are **Exchange Organs**

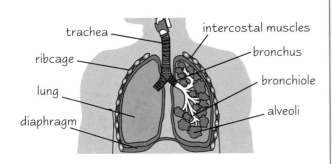

1) As you breathe in, air enters the trachea (windpipe).
2) The trachea splits into two bronchi — one bronchus leading to each lung.
3) Each bronchus then branches off into smaller tubes called bronchioles.
4) The bronchioles end in small 'air sacs' called alveoli (see previous page) where gases are exchanged.
5) The ribcage, intercostal muscles and diaphragm all work together to move air in and out (see page 75).

There are actually three layers of intercostal muscles — but you'll only come across two of them in this book (the internal and external intercostal muscles — see p. 75). We've only shown one layer here for simplicity.

Structures in the **Gas Exchange System** Have Different **Functions**

The gas exchange system is made up of different **cells** and **tissues**. These help it to exchange gases **efficiently**.

1) **Goblet cells** (lining the airways) secrete **mucus**. The mucus **traps** microorganisms and dust particles in the inhaled air, stopping them from reaching the alveoli.

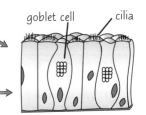

2) **Cilia** (on the surface of cells lining the airways) **beat** the **mucus**. This **moves** the mucus (plus the trapped microorganisms and dust) upward away from the alveoli towards the throat, where it's swallowed. This helps **prevent lung infections**.

3) **Elastic fibres** in the walls of the trachea, bronchi, bronchioles and alveoli help the process of **breathing out** (see p. 75). On breathing in, the lungs inflate and the elastic fibres are **stretched**. Then, the fibres **recoil** to help push the air out when exhaling.

4) **Smooth muscle** in the walls of the trachea, bronchi and bronchioles allows their **diameter to be controlled**. During exercise the smooth muscle **relaxes**, making the tubes **wider**. This means there's **less resistance** to airflow and air can move in and out of the lungs more easily.

Derek was quickly mastering efficient gas exchange.

5) **Rings of cartilage** in the walls of the trachea and bronchi **provide support**. It's strong but flexible — it stops the trachea and bronchi **collapsing** when you breathe in and the pressure drops (see p. 75).

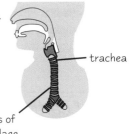

The Gas Exchange System — Mammals

The Different **Parts** are Found in **Different Places** in the System

Part of the lung	Cross section	Cartilage	Smooth muscle	Elastic fibres	Goblet cells	Epithelium
trachea	smooth muscle, elastic fibres, c-shaped cartilage, ciliated epithelium	large C-shaped pieces	✓	✓	✓	ciliated
bronchi	smooth muscle, small cartilage pieces, elastic fibres, ciliated epithelium	smaller pieces	✓	✓	✓	ciliated
larger bronchiole	smooth muscle and elastic fibres	none	✓	✓	✓	ciliated
smaller bronchiole		none	✓	✓	✗	ciliated
smallest bronchiole	ciliated epithelium	none	✗	✓	✗	no cilia
alveoli	blood capillary, elastic fibres, alveolar epithelium	none	✗	✓	✗	no cilia

Practice Questions

Q1 What is the function of goblet cells in the mammalian gas exchange system?

Q2 Describe the distribution of smooth muscle in the mammalian gas exchange system.

Q3 Describe the distribution of ciliated epithelium in the mammalian gas exchange system.

Exam Questions

Q1 A student is observing a dissection of a pig's lungs.

a) The student is given the pig's trachea, a bronchus and a larger bronchiole. Apart from the differences in size, explain how the student will be able to tell the trachea, bronchus and bronchiole apart. [3 marks]

b) The student is given two tissue samples. One was taken from one of the smallest bronchioles and one was taken from a larger bronchiole. The student looks at each sample under the microscope. Suggest one way in which the student will be able to tell the two samples apart. [1 mark]

Q2 a) Smoking destroys the elastic fibres in the walls of the alveoli. Suggest and explain what effect this will have on the process of breathing out. [2 marks]

b) Smoking also destroys cilia in the gaseous exchange system. Suggest two problems this could cause. [2 marks]

Rings of cartilage — I prefer mine in gold... with diamonds...

There's a fair bit on these two pages. Copying out my beautiful blue table will help you remember it — then you can write out what the function of each part is. You can breathe easily once you know this lot...

Ventilation

If you're in need of inspiration then there's plenty on this page... sadly I'm only talking about the kind of inspiration that gets air into your lungs — if you want the other sort head over to the Grand Canyon.

Ventilation in Mammals is Breathing In and Out

Ventilation can also mean 'changing air' in general. Fish gills are ventilated, but fish don't breathe in and out like we do.

Ventilation consists of **inspiration** (breathing in) and **expiration** (breathing out).
It's controlled by the movements of the **diaphragm**, **internal** and **external intercostal muscles** and **ribcage**.

Inspiration

1) The **external intercostal** and **diaphragm muscles contract**.
2) This causes the **ribcage** to move **upwards and outwards** and the **diaphragm** to **flatten**, **increasing the volume** of the thorax (the space where the lungs are).
3) As the volume of the thorax increases the **lung pressure decreases** (to below atmospheric pressure).
4) This causes air to flow **into the lungs**.
5) Inspiration is an **active process** — it requires **energy**.

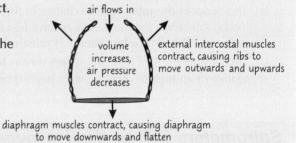

air flows in

volume increases, air pressure decreases

external intercostal muscles contract, causing ribs to move outwards and upwards

diaphragm muscles contract, causing diaphragm to move downwards and flatten

Expiration

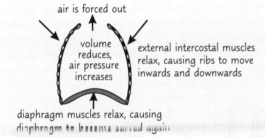

air is forced out

volume reduces, air pressure increases

external intercostal muscles relax, causing ribs to move inwards and downwards

diaphragm muscles relax, causing diaphragm to become curved again

1) The **external intercostal** and **diaphragm muscles relax**.
2) The **ribcage** moves **downwards and inwards** and the **diaphragm** becomes **curved** again.
3) The thorax volume **decreases**, causing the **air pressure** to **increase** (to above atmospheric pressure).
4) Air is forced **out of the lungs**.
5) Normal expiration is a passive process — it **doesn't** require energy.
6) Expiration can be **forced** though (e.g. if you want to blow out the candles on your birthday cake). During forced expiration, the **internal intercostal muscles contract**, to **pull the ribcage down** and **in**. During this time, the **movement** of the two sets of intercostal muscles is said to be **antagonistic** (opposing).

Tidal Volume is a Measure of Lung Function

Here are some terms about breathing and lung function:

dm^3 is short for decimetres cubed — it's the same as litres.

1) **Tidal volume (TV)** — the volume of air in **each breath** — usually about **0.4 dm^3**.
2) **Vital capacity** — the **maximum** volume of air that can be breathed **in** or **out**.
3) **Breathing rate** or **ventilation rate** — **how many** breaths are taken — usually in a minute.
4) **Oxygen consumption** or **oxygen uptake** — the rate at which an organism **uses up** oxygen (e.g. the number of dm^3 used per minute).

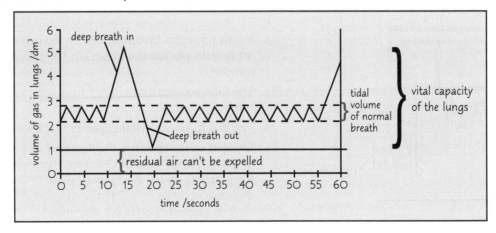

Ventilation

Measures of Lung Function Can Help to Diagnose Lung Diseases

Lung diseases affect both **ventilation** (breathing) and **gas exchange** in the lungs — in other words, how well the lungs **function**. For example:

Pulmonary Tuberculosis (TB)

1) When someone becomes infected with **tuberculosis bacteria**, immune system cells build a **wall** around the bacteria in the **lungs**. This forms small, hard lumps known as **tubercles**.

2) Infected tissue within the tubercles **dies** and the **gas exchange surface** is **damaged**.

3) This **reduces the rate of gas exchange** in the alveoli. Less oxygen is able to diffuse into the bloodstream, the body cells **receive less oxygen** and the rate of **aerobic respiration** is **reduced**. This means **less energy is released** and sufferers often feel **tired** and **weak**.

4) **Tidal volume** is also reduced, which means **less air** can be inhaled with each breath. In order to take in **enough oxygen**, patients have to breathe faster, i.e. **breathing rate** is **increased**.

Spirometers Can be Used to Investigate Breathing and Lung Function

A spirometer is a machine that can give readings of **tidal volume**, **vital capacity**, **breathing rate** and **oxygen uptake**.

1) A spirometer has an **oxygen-filled** chamber with a **movable lid**.

2) The person breathes through a **tube** connected to the oxygen chamber.

3) As the person breathes in and out, the lid of the chamber moves **up and down**.

4) These movements can be recorded by a **pen** attached to the lid of the chamber — this writes on a **rotating drum**, creating a **spirometer trace**. Or the spirometer can be hooked up to a **motion sensor** — this will use the movements to produce **electronic signals**, which are picked up by a **data logger**.

5) The **soda lime** in the tube the subject breathes into absorbs **carbon dioxide**.

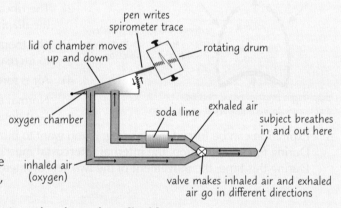

The **total volume of gas** in the chamber **decreases** over time. This is because the air that's breathed out is a **mixture** of oxygen and carbon dioxide. The carbon dioxide is absorbed by the **soda lime** — so there's **only oxygen** in the chamber which the subject inhales from. As this oxygen gets **used up** by respiration, the **total volume decreases**.

Here's How You Analyse Data from a Spirometer

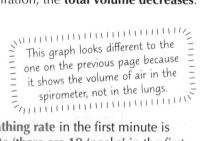
This graph looks different to the one on the previous page because it shows the volume of air in the spirometer, not in the lungs.

You can find the **breathing rate**, **tidal volume**, **vital capacity** and **oxygen consumption** from a spirometer trace. For example:

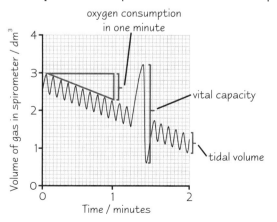

1) In this trace, the **breathing rate** in the first minute is **10 breaths per minute** (there are 10 'peaks' in the first minute).

2) The **tidal volume** may change from time to time, but in this trace it's about **0.5 dm³**.

3) The graph shows a **vital capacity** of **2.65 dm³**.

4) **Oxygen consumption** is the **decrease** in the **volume of gas** in the **spirometer chamber**. It can be read from the graph by taking the **average slope** of the trace. In this case, it drops by 0.7 dm³ in the first minute — so, oxygen consumption is **0.7 dm³ min⁻¹**.

Ventilation

Bony Fish **Gulp Water** to **Ventilate** Their **Gills**

It's not just mammals that need to ventilate their gas exchange organs. Here's how the **gills** are usually ventilated in **bony fish**:

Bony fish include salmon and cod. Unsurprisingly, they have a skeleton made of bone — not all fish do.

1) The fish **opens** its **mouth**, which **lowers** the **floor** of the **buccal cavity** (the space inside the mouth). The **volume** of the buccal cavity **increases**, **decreasing** the **pressure** inside the cavity. **Water** is then **sucked in** to the cavity.

2) When the fish **closes** its **mouth**, the **floor** of the **buccal cavity** is **raised again**. The **volume** inside the cavity **decreases**, the **pressure increases**, and **water** is **forced out** of the cavity **across the gill filaments**.

3) Each gill is covered by a **bony flap** called the **operculum** (which protects the gill). The **increase** in **pressure** forces the operculum on each side of the head to **open**, allowing **water** to **leave the gills**.

In some bony fish, the operculum bulges out (increasing the volume of the cavity behind the operculum) just after the floor of the buccal cavity lowers. This contributes to the decrease in pressure that causes water to enter the fish's mouth.

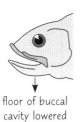

floor of buccal cavity lowered

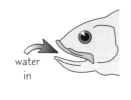

water in

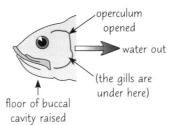

operculum opened

water out

(the gills are under here)

floor of buccal cavity raised

You Can **Dissect Fish Gills**

1) First up, fish dissection is messy so make sure you're wearing an **apron** or **lab coat**, and **gloves**.

2) Place your chosen fish (something like a perch or salmon works well) in a **dissection tray** or on a **cutting board**.

3) **Push back** the **operculum** and use **scissors** to carefully **remove the gills**. Cut each **gill arch** through the bone at the **top** and **bottom**. They should look a bit like this:

4) If you look closely, you should be able to see the **gill filaments**.

5) Finish off by **drawing** the gill and **labelling** it.

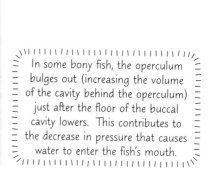

A single gill arch

gill filaments

HERVE CONGE ISM/ SCIENCE PHOTO LIBRARY

For more on the structure of the gills, flick back to page 70.

Practice Questions

Q1 What is meant by tidal volume and vital capacity?

Q2 What happens to the lung tissue of someone with TB?

Q3 Describe how a spirometer can be used to measure oxygen consumption.

Exam Questions

Q1 Describe the changes that take place in the human thorax during inspiration. [5 marks]

Q2 Salmon are bony fish. Explain how water is drawn into the salmon's mouth during ventilation. [4 marks]

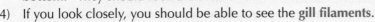

Investigate someone's breathing — make sure they've had a mint first...

Ventilation in fish is actually a lot like ventilation in mammals. In fish, when the volume of the buccal cavity is increased, the pressure drops and water rushes in. In mammals, it's the volume of the lungs that's increased, and they fill with air instead of water, but the principle is the same. Lucky for you really because it should make all this easier to learn.

Interpreting Lung Disease Data

Interpreting data can be quite tricky — so being my usual nice self, I've given you some examples to show you how to do it. I know it looks a bit dull but believe me, it'll really help.

Here's How to Interpret Data on Risk Factors and Lung Disease

1) All diseases have factors that will **increase** a person's **chance** of getting that disease. These are called **risk factors**. For example, it's widely known that if you **smoke** you're more likely to get **lung cancer** (smoking is a risk factor for lung cancer).

2) This is an example of a **correlation** — a link between two things (see page 8). However, a correlation doesn't always mean that one thing **causes** the other. Smokers have an **increased risk** of getting cancer but that doesn't necessarily mean smoking **causes** the disease — there are lots of other factors to take into consideration.

3) Here are some examples of how you might **describe** and **analyse** some data on risk factors:

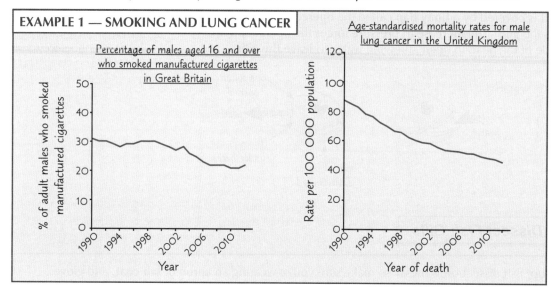

EXAMPLE 1 — SMOKING AND LUNG CANCER

Percentage of males aged 16 and over who smoked manufactured cigarettes in Great Britain

Age-standardised mortality rates for male lung cancer in the United Kingdom

1) **Describing the data** — The graph on the left shows that the **number** of adult males in Great Britain who **smoke decreased** between 1990 and 2012. The graph on the right shows that the male lung cancer **mortality (death) rate decreased** between 1990 and 2012 in the United Kingdom.

2) **Drawing conclusions** — You need to be careful what you say here. There's a **correlation** (link) between the **number** of males **who smoked** and the **mortality rate** for male lung cancer. But you **can't** say that one **caused** the other. There could be **other reasons** for the trend, e.g. deaths due to lung cancer may have decreased because less asbestos was being used in homes (not because fewer people were smoking).

3) **Other points to consider** — The graph on the right shows mortality (**death**) rates. The rate of **cases** of lung cancer **may have been increasing** but medical advances may mean more people were **surviving** (so only mortality was decreasing).

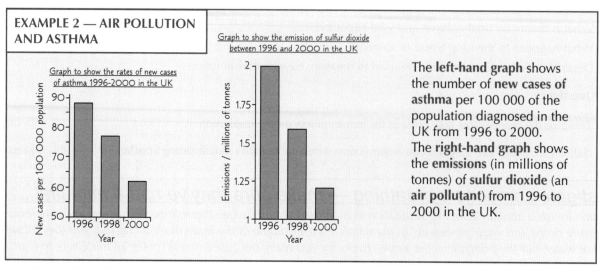

EXAMPLE 2 — AIR POLLUTION AND ASTHMA

Graph to show the rates of new cases of asthma 1996-2000 in the UK

Graph to show the emission of sulfur dioxide between 1996 and 2000 in the UK

The **left-hand graph** shows the number of **new cases of asthma** per 100 000 of the population diagnosed in the UK from 1996 to 2000. The **right-hand graph** shows the **emissions** (in millions of tonnes) of **sulfur dioxide** (an **air pollutant**) from 1996 to 2000 in the UK.

Interpreting Lung Disease Data

1) <u>Describing the data</u> — The **left-hand graph** on the previous page shows that the number of **new cases of asthma** in the UK **fell** between 1996 and 2000, from 87 to 62 per 100 000 people. The **right-hand graph** shows that the **emissions of sulfur dioxide** in the UK **fell** between 1996 and 2000, from 2 to 1.2 million tonnes.

2) <u>Drawing conclusions</u> — Be careful what you say when drawing conclusions. Here there's a **link** between the **number** of new cases of **asthma** and **emissions** of **sulfur dioxide** in the **UK** — the rate of new cases of asthma has **fallen** as sulfur dioxide emissions have **fallen**. You **can't** say that one **causes** the other though because there could be **other reasons** for the trend, e.g. the number of new cases of asthma could be falling due to the **decrease** in the number of people **smoking**. You can't say the **reduction** in asthma cases is **linked** to a **reduction in air pollution** (in general) either as **only** sulfur dioxide levels were studied.

3) <u>Other points to consider</u> — The left-hand graph shows **new cases** of asthma. The rate of new cases may be **decreasing** but existing cases may be becoming **more severe**. The emissions were for the whole of the UK but air pollution **varies from area to area**, e.g. **cities** tend to be **more polluted**. The asthma data doesn't take into account any **other factors** that may **increase** the risk of developing asthma, e.g. allergies, smoking, etc.

The **Government Restricts Sources** of **Risk Factors**

Scientific data has led to **government restrictions** on the **sources** of **risk factors** for lung disease. E.g.

Responses to data on smoking

Medical studies in 1950s and 1960s documented the **link** between **smoking** and various forms of **cancer**, particularly lung cancer. The evidence prompted the first **voluntary agreement** between the UK government and tobacco companies in 1971, which stated that tobacco products and adverts should carry a **health warning label**. As of October 2008, **picture health warnings** were made **compulsory** on all UK boxes of cigarettes after studies suggested they were more effective than written warnings alone.

Responses to data on air pollution

In response to **studies** connecting **air pollution** to various **diseases**, the EU adopted the **National Emissions Ceilings Directive**. This set **upper limits** on the total emissions of **four major pollutants** in the **atmosphere**, to be achieved by **2010**. **New limits** are being agreed on for **2020**. The EU also introduced the **Clean Power for Transport Package** to promote **cleaner fuels** for vehicles, and the UK **taxes car owners** according to their car's **emissions**.

Practice Question

Q1 Give an example of where scientific data has led to restrictions on the source of a risk factor in lung disease.

Exam Question

Q1 In early December 1952, a dense layer of cold air trapped pollutants close to ground level in London. The graph opposite shows daily deaths and levels of sulfur dioxide and smoke between 1st and 15th December.

a) Describe the changes in the daily death rate and the levels of pollutants over the days shown. [3 marks]

b) What conclusion can be drawn from this graph? [1 mark]

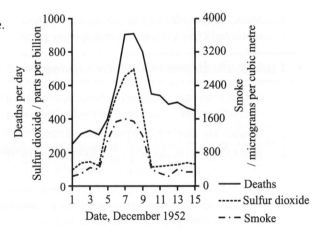

<u>Drawing conclusions — you'll need your wax crayons and some paper...</u>

You'll come across data analysis everywhere, on exciting programs like 'The News' — so it's good to get to grips with it. There's some important advice here (even if I say so myself) — it's easy to leap to a conclusion that isn't really there — stick to your guns about the difference between correlation and cause and you'll be just fine.

Digestion and Absorption

The whole point of digestion is to break down the food you eat into small molecules that your cells can absorb. As you might imagine, this involves loads of different chemical reactions and our old friends, enzymes.

Food is **Broken Down** into **Smaller Molecules** During **Digestion**

1) The **large biological molecules** (e.g. starch, proteins) in food are **too big** to cross **cell membranes**. This means they **can't** be **absorbed** from the gut into the blood.

2) During digestion, these large molecules are **broken down** into **smaller molecules** (e.g. glucose, amino acids), which **can** move across cell membranes. This means they can be **easily absorbed** from the gut into the blood, to be **transported** around the body for use by the body cells.

3) Most **large biological molecules** are **polymers**, which can be **broken down** into **smaller** molecules (**monomers**) using **hydrolysis reactions**. Hydrolysis reactions **break bonds** by **adding water**.

4) During hydrolysis, **carbohydrates** are broken down into **disaccharides** and then **monosaccharides**. **Fats** are broken down into **fatty acids** and **monoglycerides**. **Proteins** are broken down into **amino acids**.

Digestive Enzymes are Used to **Break Down Biological Molecules** in **Food**

1) A variety of different **digestive enzymes** are produced by **specialised cells** in the **digestive systems** of mammals. These enzymes are then released into the gut to mix with food.

2) Since enzymes only work with **specific substrates** (see page 25), **different enzymes** are needed to **catalyse** the breakdown of **different food molecules**.

Carbohydrates are Broken Down by **Amylase** and **Membrane-Bound Disaccharidases**

1) **Amylase** is a digestive enzyme that catalyses the conversion of **starch** (a polysaccharide) into the smaller sugar **maltose** (a disaccharide). This involves the **hydrolysis** of the **glycosidic bonds** in starch.

2) Amylase is produced by the **salivary glands** (which release amylase into the **mouth**) and also by the **pancreas** (which releases amylase into the **small intestine**).

3) **Membrane-bound disaccharidases** are enzymes that are attached to the **cell membranes** of **epithelial cells** lining the **ileum** (the final part of the small intestine). They help to break down **disaccharides** (e.g. maltose, sucrose and lactose) into **monosaccharides** (e.g. glucose, fructose and galactose). Again, this involves the hydrolysis of glycosidic bonds.

There's more on polysaccharides, disaccharides and monosaccharides on pages 12-13.

Disaccharide	Disaccharidase	Monosaccharide Products
maltose	maltase	glucose + glucose
sucrose	sucrase	glucose + fructose
lactose	lactase	glucose + galactose

4) **Monosaccharides** can be transported across the cell membranes of the ileum epithelial cells via specific **transporter proteins** (see next page).

Lipids are Broken Down by **Lipase** (with the Help of **Bile Salts**)

1) **Lipase** enzymes catalyse the breakdown of **lipids** into **monoglycerides** and **fatty acids**. This involves the **hydrolysis** of the **ester bonds** in lipids.

A monoglyceride is a glycerol molecule with one fatty acid attached.

2) Lipases are made in the **pancreas**. They work in the **small intestine**.

3) **Bile salts** are produced by the **liver** and **emulsify** lipids — this means they cause the lipids to form **small droplets**.

4) Bile salts are really important in the process of lipid digestion. **Several small lipid droplets** have a **bigger surface area** than a **single large droplet** (for the same volume of lipid). So the formation of small droplets greatly increases the surface area of lipid that's available for **lipases** to work on.

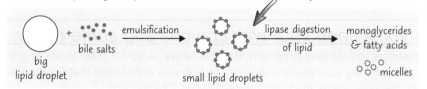

5) Once the lipid has been broken down, the **monoglycerides** and **fatty acids** stick with the **bile salts** to form tiny structures called **micelles**.

Digestion and Absorption

Proteins are Broken Down by *Endopeptidases* and *Exopeptidases*

Proteins are broken down by a combination of different **proteases** (or **peptidases**). These are enzymes that catalyse the conversion of **proteins** into **amino acids** by **hydrolysing** the **peptide bonds** between amino acids. **Endopeptidases** and **exopeptidases** (including **dipeptidases**) are types of protease enzymes:

Endopeptidases

- Endopeptidases act to hydrolyse peptide bonds **within** a protein.
- **Trypsin** and **chymotrypsin** are two examples of endopeptidases. They're synthesised in the **pancreas** and secreted into the **small intestine**.
- **Pepsin** is another endopeptidase. It's released into the **stomach** by cells in the **stomach lining**. Pepsin only works in **acidic conditions** — these are provided by **hydrochloric acid** in the **stomach**.

Remember: endopeptidases break bonds inside the protein.

Exopeptidases

- Exopeptidases act to hydrolyse peptide bonds **at the ends** of protein molecules. They remove **single amino acids** from proteins.
- **Dipeptidases** are exopeptidases that work specifically on **dipeptides**. They act to separate the two amino acids that make up a dipeptide by **hydrolysing** the **peptide bond** between them.
- Dipeptidases are often located in the **cell-surface membrane** of **epithelial cells** in the **small intestine**.

The *Products* of Digestion are *Absorbed Across Cell Membranes*

The products of digestion are absorbed across the **ileum epithelium** into the bloodstream.

Monosaccharides

- **Glucose** is absorbed by **active transport** with **sodium ions** via a **co-transporter protein** (see page 64). **Galactose** is absorbed in the same way using the same co-transporter protein.
- **Fructose** is absorbed via **facilitated diffusion** through a different transporter protein.

Monoglycerides and fatty acids

Micelles (see previous page) help to **move** monoglycerides and fatty acids **towards** the **epithelium**. Because micelles constantly break up and reform they can '**release**' monoglycerides and fatty acids, allowing them to be absorbed — whole micelles are **not** taken up across the epithelium. **Monoglycerides** and **fatty acids** are **lipid-soluble**, so can **diffuse** directly across the epithelial cell membrane.

Amino acids

Amino acids are absorbed in a similar way to glucose and galactose. **Sodium ions** are **actively transported** out of the epithelial cells into the ileum itself. They then **diffuse** back into the cells through **sodium-dependent transporter proteins** in the epithelial cell membranes, carrying the amino acids with them.

Practice Questions

Q1 What is the function of amylase in digestion?
Q2 Describe the role of bile salts in lipid digestion.

Exam Question

Q1 Some people suffer from lactose intolerance.
This can be caused by an inability to break down lactose in the upper small intestine.

a) Suggest which disaccharidase enzyme is deficient or missing in people who are lactose-intolerant. [1 mark]

b) How are the digestion products of lactose absorbed across the epithelial cells of the ileum? [2 marks]

Crikey, this all looks a bit tricky to digest... belch...

Don't panic. There's a lot to take in here but as long as you break it down a bit (ha, just like digestion) then it's not too bad. Helpfully, the names of each of the enzymes are usually linked to what they do — maltase breaks down maltose, lipase enzymes break down lipids and dipeptidases break down dipeptides. See, it's not as bad as it looks...

Circulatory Systems

Right then, these pages are all about pumping lots of blood around bodies, so if that's not up your street, then prepare to feel queasy. Whether you're a fish, a mammal or an insect you need a decent circulatory system to get by.

Multicellular Organisms need Transport Systems

1) As you saw on page 68, **single-celled** organisms can get substances that they need by **diffusion** across their outer membrane.

2) If you're **multicellular** though, it's a bit **harder** to supply all your cells with everything they need — multicellular organisms are relatively **big**, they have a **low surface area to volume ratio** and a **higher metabolic rate** (the speed at which chemical reactions take place in the body).

3) A lot of multicellular organisms (e.g. mammals) are also **very active**. This means that a **large number of cells** are all **respiring very quickly**, so they need a constant, rapid supply of glucose and oxygen.

4) To make sure that every cell has a good enough supply, multicellular organisms need a **transport system**.

5) In mammals, this is the **circulatory system**, which uses **blood** to carry glucose and oxygen around the body. It also carries hormones, antibodies (to fight disease) and waste (like CO_2).

Fish and Mammals have Different Circulatory Systems

Not all organisms have the same type of circulatory system
— **fish** have a **single circulatory system** and **mammals** have a **double circulatory system**.

1) In a **single** circulatory system, blood only passes through the heart **once** for each complete circuit of the body.

2) In a **double** circulatory system, the blood passes through the heart **twice** for each complete circuit of the body.

Fish

In **fish**, the **heart** pumps blood to the **gills** (to pick up oxygen) and then on through the **rest of the body** (to deliver the oxygen) in a single circuit.

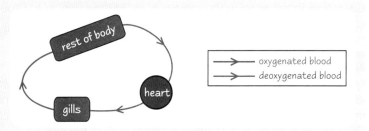

→ oxygenated blood
→ deoxygenated blood

Single you say? How interesting. Now pass us the tartare sauce...

Mammals

In **mammals**, the heart is **divided** down the middle, so it's really like **two** hearts joined together.

1) The **right side** of the heart pumps blood to the **lungs** (to pick up oxygen).

2) From the lungs it travels to the **left side** of the heart, which pumps it to the rest of the **body**.

3) When blood **returns** to the heart, it enters the right side again.

→ oxygenated blood
→ deoxygenated blood

So, our circulatory system is really two linked loops. One sends blood to the lungs — this is called the **pulmonary** system, and the other sends blood to the rest of the body — this is called the **systemic** system.

The right and left sides of the heart are reversed in the diagram because it's the right and left of the person the heart belongs to.

An **advantage** of the mammalian double circulatory system is that the heart can give the blood an **extra push** between the lungs and the rest of the body. This makes the blood travel **faster**, so oxygen is delivered to the tissues **more quickly**.

Circulatory Systems

Circulatory Systems can be Open or Closed

All vertebrates (e.g. fish and mammals) have **closed circulatory systems** — the blood is **enclosed** inside **blood vessels**.

1) The heart pumps blood into **arteries**. These **branch out** into millions of **capillaries** (see next page).
2) Substances like oxygen and glucose **diffuse** from the blood in the capillaries into the body cells, but the blood **stays inside** the blood vessels as it circulates.
3) **Veins** take the blood back to the heart.

Some invertebrates (e.g. insects) have an **open circulatory system** — blood **isn't enclosed** in blood vessels all the time. Instead, it flows freely through the **body cavity**.

1) The heart is **segmented**. It **contracts** in a **wave**, starting from the back, pumping the blood into a **single main artery**.
2) That artery **opens up** into the body cavity.
3) The blood flows around the insect's **organs**, gradually making its way back into the heart segments through a series of **valves**.

The circulatory system supplies the insect's cells with nutrients, and transports things like hormones around the body. It **doesn't supply** the insect's cells with **oxygen** though — this is done by a system of tubes called the **tracheal system** (see p. 71 for more).

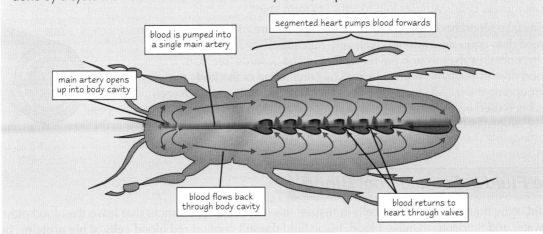

segmented heart pumps blood forwards

blood is pumped into a single main artery

main artery opens up into body cavity

blood flows back through body cavity

blood returns to heart through valves

Practice Questions

Q1 Give three reasons why multicellular organisms usually need a transport system, but unicellular organisms don't.

Q2 Explain why the mammalian circulatory system is described as a double circulatory system.

Q3 What is an open circulatory system?

Exam Questions

Q1 Explain why the circulatory system of a trout is described as being closed. [1 mark]

Q2 Briefly describe the circulatory system of a beetle. [2 marks]

Q3 The Atlantic salmon *(Salmo salar)* and the red fox *(Vulpes vulpes)* have circulatory systems. Describe one way in which the circulatory system of the Atlantic salmon is:

a) similar to that of the red fox. [1 mark]

b) different from that of the red fox. [1 mark]

OK, open circulatory systems are officially grim. Body cavities?! Bleurgh...

After reading this page, we can all finally put to rest the idea that the Earth will eventually be overrun by giant insects. Their circulatory system just isn't up to it you see... All the nutrients and stuff in their blood have to diffuse through the whole body cavity, so if they were giant they wouldn't be able to supply all their organs and bits and pieces properly...

Blood Vessels

Watch out — these pages are about all the bits and bobs that make up that useful circulatory system of yours...

Blood Vessels Transport Substances Round the Body

There are five major types of blood vessel: **arteries**, **arterioles**, **capillaries**, **venules** and **veins**:

1) **Arteries** carry blood **from** the heart **to** the rest of the body. Their walls are thick and **muscular** and have elastic tissue to **stretch** and **recoil** as the heart beats, which helps maintain the **high pressure**. The inner lining (**endothelium**) is **folded**, allowing the artery to expand — this also helps it to maintain the high pressure. All arteries carry **oxygenated** blood except for the **pulmonary arteries**, which take deoxygenated blood to the lungs.

2) Arteries branch into **arterioles**, which are **much smaller** than arteries. Like arteries, arterioles have a layer of **smooth muscle**, but they have less elastic tissue. The **smooth muscle** allows them to **expand** or **contract**, thus controlling the amount of blood flowing to tissues.

3) Arterioles branch into **capillaries**, which are the **smallest** of the blood vessels. Substances like glucose and oxygen are exchanged between cells and capillaries, so they're adapted for **efficient diffusion**, e.g. their walls are only **one cell thick**.

4) Capillaries connect to **venules**, which have very **thin walls** that can contain some muscle cells. Venules join together to form veins.

5) **Veins** take blood **back to the heart** under low pressure. They have a **wider lumen** than equivalent arteries, with very little elastic or muscle tissue. Veins contain **valves** to stop the blood flowing backwards (see p. 87). Blood flow through the veins is helped by contraction of the **body muscles** surrounding them. All veins carry **deoxygenated** blood (because oxygen has been used up by body cells), except for the **pulmonary veins**, which carry oxygenated blood to the heart from the lungs.

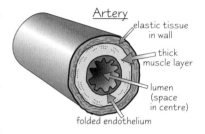

Artery
- elastic tissue in wall
- thick muscle layer
- lumen (space in centre)
- folded endothelium

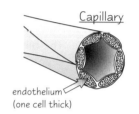

Capillary
- endothelium (one cell thick)

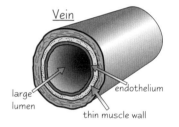

Vein
- large lumen
- endothelium
- thin muscle wall

Tissue Fluid is Formed from Blood

Tissue fluid is the fluid that **surrounds cells** in tissues. It's made from substances that leave the blood plasma, e.g. oxygen, water and nutrients. (Unlike blood, tissue fluid **doesn't** contain **red blood cells** or **big proteins**, because they're **too large** to be pushed out through the capillary walls.) Cells take in oxygen and nutrients from the tissue fluid, and release metabolic waste into it. In a **capillary bed** (the network of capillaries in an area of tissue), substances move out of the capillaries, into the tissue fluid, by **pressure filtration**:

1) At the **start** of the capillary bed, nearest the arteries, the **hydrostatic (liquid) pressure** inside the capillaries is **greater** than the hydrostatic pressure in the tissue fluid. This difference in hydrostatic pressure **forces fluid out** of the **capillaries** and into the **spaces** around the cells, forming tissue fluid.

2) As fluid leaves, the hydrostatic pressure reduces in the capillaries — so the hydrostatic pressure is much **lower** at the **end** of the capillary bed that's nearest to the venules.

3) There is another form of pressure at work here called **oncotic pressure** — this is generated by **plasma proteins** present in the capillaries which lower the water potential. At the venule end of the capillary bed, the water potential in the capillaries is **lower** than the water potential in the tissue fluid due to the **fluid loss** from the capillaries and the **high oncotic pressure**. This means some **water re-enters** the capillaries from the tissue fluid at the venule end by **osmosis**.

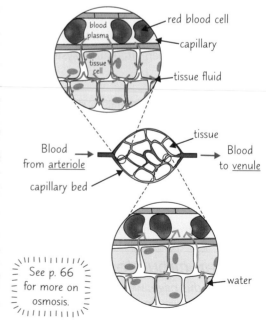

- blood plasma
- red blood cell
- capillary
- tissue cell
- tissue fluid

Blood from arteriole → capillary bed → tissue → Blood to venule

water

See p. 66 for more on osmosis.

Blood Vessels

Excess Tissue Fluid Drains into the Lymph Vessels

Not all of the tissue fluid **re-enters** the capillaries at the venule end of the capillary bed — some **excess tissue fluid** is left over. This extra fluid eventually gets returned to the blood through the **lymphatic system** — a kind of **drainage** system, made up of **lymph vessels**.

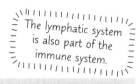
The lymphatic system is also part of the immune system.

1) The smallest lymph vessels are the **lymph capillaries**.

2) Excess tissue fluid passes into lymph vessels. Once inside, it's called **lymph**.

3) **Valves** in the lymph vessels stop the lymph going **backwards**.

4) Lymph gradually moves towards the main lymph vessels in the **thorax** (chest cavity). Here, it's returned to the **blood**, near the **heart**.

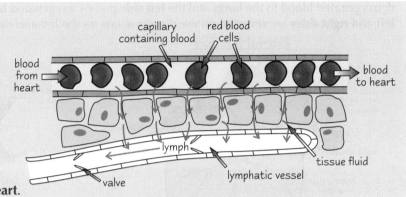

There are Key Differences Between Blood, Tissue Fluid and Lymph

Blood, tissue fluid and lymph are all quite **similar** — tissue fluid is formed from **blood**, and **lymph** is formed from **tissue fluid**. The main differences are shown in the table.

	blood	tissue fluid	lymph	comment
red blood cells	✓	✗	✗	Red blood cells are too big to get through capillary walls into tissue fluid.
white blood cells	✓	very few	✓	Most white blood cells are in the lymph system. They only enter tissue fluid when there's an infection.
platelets	✓	✗	✗	Only present in tissue fluid if the capillaries are damaged.
proteins	✓	very few	only antibodies	Most plasma proteins are too big to get through capillary walls.
water	✓	✓	✓	Tissue fluid and lymph have a higher water potential than blood.
dissolved solutes	✓	✓	✓	Solutes (e.g. salt) can move freely between blood, tissue fluid and lymph.

Practice Questions

Q1 Is the blood pressure highest in veins or arteries?

Q2 Explain the differences between blood, tissue fluid and lymph.

Exam Questions

Q1 The diameter of different types of blood vessel are shown on the right. Select the row that shows the most appropriate diameter for each type of blood vessel.

Type of blood vessel and its diameter				
	Artery	Arteriole	Capillary	Vein
A	13 mm	8 µm	2 cm	200 µm
B	8 µm	2 cm	200 µm	13 mm
C	200 µm	13 mm	2 cm	8 µm
D	2 cm	200 µm	8 µm	13 mm

[1 mark]

Q2 At the arteriole end of a capillary bed the hydrostatic pressure is 5.1 kPa in a capillary and 0.13 kPa in the space around the cells. Explain the effect this has on the movement of fluid between the capillary and cell space. [2 marks]

Tissue fluid... Imagine draining the fluid out of a used tissue. Urrrgh.

That table looks a bit terrifying, but a lot of it's pretty obvious when you think about it — there can't be any red blood cells floating around loose in your tissues, otherwise you'd be bright red. And platelets are the bits that cause blood clots, so they're going to be in your blood... In fact, proteins and white blood cells are the only tricky bits.

The Heart

As I'm sure you know already, your heart is the 'pump' that gets oxygenated blood to your cells. It's very important, so you should learn how it works. You'll find that these pages definitely get to the heart of it... groan...

The **Heart** Consists of **Two Muscular Pumps**

The diagrams below show the **internal** and **external structure** of the heart. The **right side** of the heart pumps **deoxygenated blood** to the **lungs** and the **left side** pumps **oxygenated blood** to the **rest of the body**. Note — the **left and right sides** are **reversed** on the diagrams, cos it's the left and right of the person that the heart belongs to.

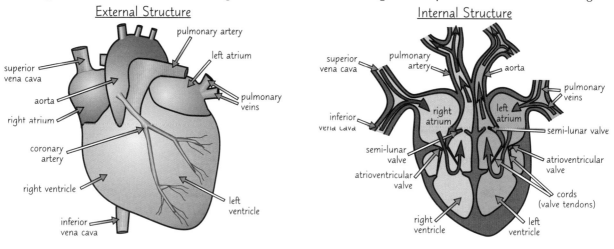

External Structure — Internal Structure

Heart Dissection Shows How the **Heart's Structure** Relates to its **Function**

You may get to carry out a heart dissection or you may get to watch one being carried out.

External examination: If you look at the outside of the heart you will see the **four main vessels** attached to it. The feel of the vessels can be used to help identify each one — arteries are thick and rubbery, whereas veins are much thinner.

You will also be able to see the right and left **atria**, the right and left **ventricles** and the **coronary arteries**.

Internal examination: The ventricles can be cut open using a scalpel so you can see inside each one. You should be able to see that the wall of the left ventricle is **thicker** than the wall of the right ventricle.

The **atria** can also be cut open. If you look at the atria walls, you should notice that they are **thinner** than the ventricle walls.

You can also look at the structures of the **atrioventricular valves** and **semi-lunar valves**.

Make sure you wash your hands and disinfect work surfaces once you're finished.

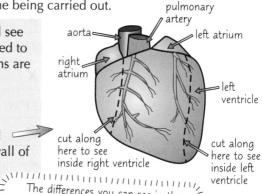

The differences you can see in the thicknesses of the walls of each ventricle, and between the ventricles and the atria are due to their different functions. See below for more.

The **Different Parts** of the **Heart** Have **Different Functions**

Each bit of the heart is adapted to do its job effectively.

1) The **left ventricle** of the heart has **thicker**, more muscular walls than the **right ventricle**, because it needs to contract powerfully to pump blood all the way round the body. The right side only needs to get blood to the lungs, which are nearby.

2) The **ventricles** have **thicker walls** than the **atria**, because they have to push blood out of the heart whereas the atria just need to push blood a short distance into the ventricles.

3) The **atrioventricular (AV) valves** link the atria to the ventricles and **stop blood flowing back** into the atria when the ventricles contract. **Cords** attach the atrioventricular valves to the ventricles to stop them being forced up into the atria when the ventricles contract.

4) The **semi-lunar (SL) valves** link the ventricles to the pulmonary artery and aorta, and **stop blood flowing back** into the heart after the ventricles contract.

The Heart

*Valves Help the **Blood** to Flow in **One Direction***

The **valves** only **open one way** — whether they're open or closed depends on the relative **pressure** of the heart chambers. If there's higher pressure **behind** a valve, it's forced **open**, but if pressure is higher **in front** of the valve it's forced **shut**. This means blood only flows in **one direction** through the heart.

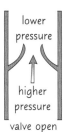 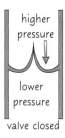

lower pressure / higher pressure
valve open / valve closed

*The **Cardiac Cycle** Pumps Blood Round the Body*

The cardiac cycle is an ongoing sequence of **contraction** (**systole**) and **relaxation** (**diastole**) of the atria and ventricles that keeps blood **continuously** circulating round the body. The **volume** of the atria and ventricles **changes** as they contract and relax. **Pressure** changes also occur, due to the changes in chamber volume (e.g. decreasing the volume of a chamber by contraction will increase the pressure in a chamber). The cardiac cycle can be simplified into three stages:

① Ventricular diastole, atrial systole

The **ventricles are relaxed**. The **atria contract**, decreasing the volume of the chambers and **increasing** the **pressure** inside the chambers. This **pushes** the blood into the **ventricles**. There's a slight **increase** in **ventricular pressure** and **chamber volume** as the **ventricles receive the ejected blood** from the contracting atria.

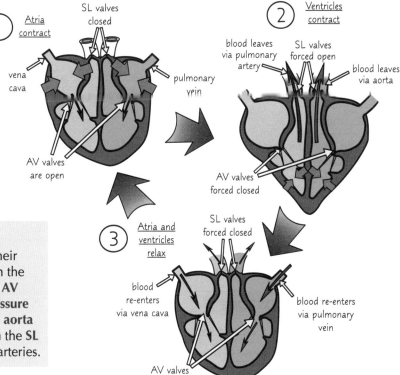

② Ventricular systole, atrial diastole

The **atria relax**. The **ventricles contract**, decreasing their volume and **increasing** their **pressure**. The pressure becomes **higher** in the ventricles than the atria, which forces the **AV valves shut** to prevent back-flow. The **pressure** in the **ventricles** is also **higher** than in the **aorta** and **pulmonary artery**, which forces **open** the **SL valves** and blood is forced out into these arteries.

③ Cardiac diastole

The **ventricles and the atria both relax**. The higher pressure in the pulmonary artery and aorta closes the SL valves to prevent back-flow into the ventricles. Blood returns to the heart and the **atria fill again** due to the higher pressure in the vena cava and pulmonary vein. In turn this starts to **increase the pressure** of the atria. As the ventricles continue to **relax**, their **pressure falls below the pressure of the atria** and so the **AV valves open**. This allows blood to flow **passively** (without being pushed by atrial contraction) into the ventricles from the atria. The atria contract, and the whole process begins again.

The Heart

You Might be Asked to Interpret Data on the Cardiac Cycle

The changes in **pressure** and **volume** during the cardiac cycle can be illustrated in a number of ways.

Example 1

❶ Ventricles relaxed Atria contract

❷ Ventricles contract Atria relax

❸ Ventricles relax Atria relaxed

KEY
— ventricles
— atria

pressure increase due to contraction

pressure increase due to contraction

slight increase due to passive filling

pressure decrease as atria relax

A

pressure increase due to contraction

pressure decrease as ventricles relax

pressure increase as atria fill

pressure decrease as some blood passively moves from atria into ventricle

pressure increase as atria continue to fill

C

pressure increase as ventricles fill

Pressure / mmHg

Volume / ml

volume decrease due to contraction

ventricles stretch while filling

atria expand as they relax and fill with blood

B

some blood passively moves from atria to ventricle as AV valves open

ventricles expand as they relax and fill with blood

Time / s

You can use a graph like this to find when **specific events** happen or what is happening at a **particular point** in time.

1) **When** does blood start flowing into the **aorta**? At **point A**, the ventricles are **contracting** (and the AV valves are shut), forcing blood into the aorta.

2) Why is **ventricular volume decreasing** at **point B**? The ventricles are **contracting**, **reducing** the volume of the chamber.

3) Are the **semi-lunar valves** open or closed at **point C**? **Closed**. The ventricles are **relaxed** and **refilling**, so the pressure is **higher** in the **pulmonary artery** and **aorta**, forcing the SL valves **closed**.

Example 2

You can infer from a diagram any **changes** in **pressure** and **volume** that occur. In this diagram the **AV valves** are **open**. So you know that the **pressure** in the **atria** is **higher** than in the **ventricles**. So you also know that the **atria are contracting** because that's what causes the **increase** in **pressure**.

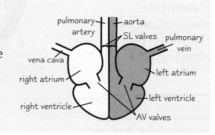

pulmonary artery

aorta

SL valves

pulmonary vein

vena cava

right atrium

left atrium

right ventricle

left ventricle

AV valves

The left ventricle has a thicker wall than the right ventricle and so it contracts more forcefully. This means the pressure is higher in the left ventricle (and in the aorta compared to the pulmonary artery).

Practice Questions

Q1 Which side of the heart carries oxygenated blood?

Q2 Explain the purpose of the semi-lunar valves.

Exam Question

Q1 The table opposite shows the blood pressure in two heart chambers at different times during part of the cardiac cycle. Use the data in the table to answer the following questions.

	Blood pressure / kPa	
Time / s	Left atrium	Left ventricle
0.0	0.6	0.5
0.1	1.3	0.8
0.2	0.4	6.9
0.3	0.5	16.5
0.4	0.9	7.0

a) Between what times are the AV valves shut? [1 mark]

b) Between what times do the ventricles start to relax? [1 mark]

c) Calculate the percentage increase in left ventricle blood pressure between 0.0 s and 0.3 s. [1 mark]

The cardiac cycle — a bewilderingly complicated pump-action bicycle...

Three whole pages full of important stuff. If you understand all the pressure and volume changes then you should be able to interpret a diagram, graph or something else, no probs.

Investigating Heart Rate

There are lots of things that affect heart rate, but when it comes to testing the effect of substances such as caffeine, we sometimes use animals rather than humans. A common choice of animal to use is Daphnia...

You Can **Investigate** the Effect of **Caffeine** on the **Heart Rate** of **Daphnia**

Daphnia are tiny aquatic **invertebrates**. They're **transparent**, so you can see their internal organs. This means it's pretty easy to monitor their **heart rate** (the **number of heartbeats** in a **minute**) by observing them through a **microscope**. Here's how you could investigate the effect of caffeine on their heart rate:

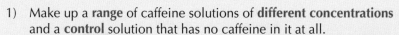
There's more on controls on page 4.

1) Make up a **range** of caffeine solutions of **different concentrations** and a **control** solution that has no caffeine in it at all.

2) Transfer **one** *Daphnia* into the dimple on a **cavity slide** (a microscope slide with a rounded dip).

3) Using a pipette, place a few drops of **caffeine solution** onto the *Daphnia*.
Wait for 5 minutes while the caffeine is absorbed.

4) Place the slide onto the stage of a **light microscope** and **focus** it on the beating heart of the *Daphnia*.

5) **Count** the number of **heartbeats** in **20 seconds** and multiply this by **three** to calculate beats per minute (**heart rate**).

6) **Repeat** this 10 times using the **same concentration** of caffeine but a **different** *Daphnia* individual each time.

7) Don't forget to keep **all other factors constant** (e.g. temperature and volume of caffeine solution).

8) Repeat the experiment using the **other concentrations** of caffeine solution.

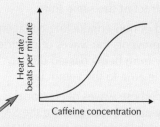

9) Calculate the **average reading** for each concentration and draw a graph of the results. The graph should show a **positive correlation** — as caffeine concentration **increases**, heart rate also **increases**.

There are Some **Ethical Issues** Involved in Using **Invertebrates**

Here are some points to think about:

1) Experimenting on **animals** allows scientists to study things that would be **unethical** to study using humans.

2) But many people believe that using animals is **also unethical** — they can't give **consent** and they may be subjected to **painful procedures**.

3) Some people believe it's **more acceptable** to perform experiments on **invertebrates** (like *Daphnia*, spiders and insects) than on **vertebrates** (like dogs and monkeys).

4) This is because they're considered to be **simpler organisms** than vertebrates. For example, they have a much **less sophisticated nervous system**, which could mean that they feel less pain (or no pain). Also, invertebrates are more **distantly related** to humans than other vertebrates.

5) But there are still ethical issues to consider when experimenting with invertebrates. For example, some people believe it's unethical to cause **distress** or **suffering** to **any living organism** — e.g. by subjecting them to **extremes of temperature** or depriving them of **food**.

Practice Questions

Q1 Describe the relationship between caffeine concentration and heart rate in *Daphnia*.

Exam Questions

Q1 Suggest two reasons why some people may feel it's more acceptable to carry out experiments on invertebrates, such as *Daphnia*, than on vertebrates.

[2 marks]

I reckon there are some ethical issues involved with sitting exams...

It's a tricky business this science lark. Researchers need to try to balance human needs with animal discomfort. In the case of invertebrates, it's not always clear exactly what will cause them distress or suffering.

Heart Activity

You don't have to think about making your heart beat — your body does it for you.
So you couldn't stop it beating even if for some strange reason you wanted to. Which is nice to know.

Cardiac Muscle Controls the Regular Beating of the Heart

Cardiac (heart) muscle is 'myogenic' — it can contract and relax without receiving signals from nerves.
This pattern of contractions controls the regular heartbeat.

1) The process starts in the sino-atrial node (SAN), which is in the wall of the right atrium.

2) The SAN is like a pacemaker — it sets the rhythm of the heartbeat by sending out regular waves of electrical activity to the atrial walls.

3) This causes the right and left atria to contract at the same time.

4) A band of non-conducting collagen tissue prevents the waves of electrical activity from being passed directly from the atria to the ventricles.

5) Instead, these waves of electrical activity are transferred from the SAN to the atrioventricular node (AVN).

6) The AVN is responsible for passing the waves of electrical activity on to the bundle of His. But, there's a slight delay before the AVN reacts, to make sure the ventricles contract after the atria have emptied.

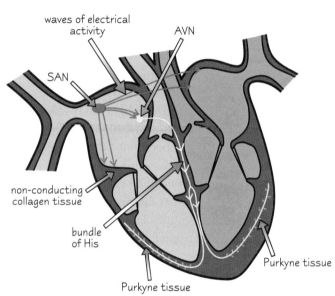

7) The bundle of His is a group of muscle fibres responsible for conducting the waves of electrical activity to the finer muscle fibres in the right and left ventricle walls, called the Purkyne tissue.

8) The Purkyne tissue carries the waves of electrical activity into the muscular walls of the right and left ventricles, causing them to contract simultaneously, from the bottom up.

An Electrocardiograph Records the Electrical Activity of the Heart

A doctor can check someone's **heart function** using an **electrocardiograph** — a machine that **records** the **electrical activity** of the heart. The heart muscle **depolarises** (loses electrical charge) when it **contracts**, and **repolarises** (regains charge) when it **relaxes**. An electrocardiograph records these changes in electrical charge using **electrodes** placed on the chest.

When Ed did that special thing to her beak, Polly's heart activity increased 10-fold.

The trace produced by an electrocardiograph is called an **electrocardiogram**, or **ECG**. A **normal** ECG looks like this:

1) The **P wave** is caused by **contraction** (depolarisation) of the **atria**.

2) The main peak of the heartbeat, together with the dips at either side, is called the **QRS complex** — it's caused by **contraction** (depolarisation) of the **ventricles**.

3) The **T wave** is due to **relaxation** (repolarisation) of the **ventricles**.

4) The **height** of the wave indicates how much electrical charge is passing through the heart — a **bigger wave** means more electrical charge, so (for the P and R waves) a bigger wave means a **stronger contraction**.

Heart Activity

Doctors use ECGs to Diagnose Heart Problems

Doctors **compare** their patients' ECGs with a **normal trace**. This helps them to diagnose any heart problems.

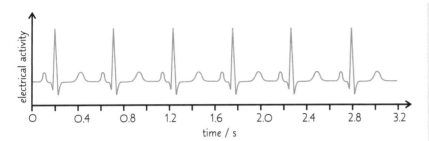

This heartbeat is **too fast** — around 120 beats per minute. It's called **tachycardia**. That might be OK during **exercise**, but at **rest** it shows that the heart **isn't pumping blood efficiently**. A heartbeat can also be **too slow** — below 60 beats per minute at rest. This is called **bradycardia**.

The 5th heartbeat on this ECG is an **ectopic heartbeat** — an 'extra' heartbeat. Here it's caused by an **earlier contraction of the atria** than in the previous heartbeats (you can see that the P wave is different and that it comes earlier than it should). However, it can be caused by **early contraction of the ventricles** too. Occasional ectopic heartbeats in a healthy person don't cause a problem.

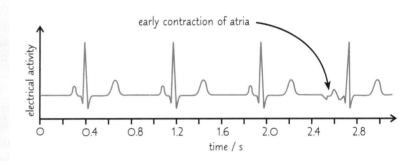

early contraction of atria

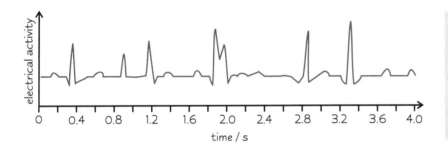

This is **fibrillation** — a really **irregular heartbeat**. The atria or ventricles completely **lose their rhythm** and **stop contracting properly**. It can result in anything from chest pain and fainting to lack of pulse and death.

Practice Questions

Q1 What prevents impulses from the atria travelling straight into the ventricles?

Q2 What is the name of the structure that picks up impulses from the atria and passes them on to the ventricles?

Q3 What causes the QRS part of an ECG trace?

Exam Questions

Q1 Describe the function of:

a) the sino-atrial node. [1 mark]

b) the Purkyne tissue. [1 mark]

Q2 Suggest the cause of an ECG which has a QRS complex that is not as high as normal. [2 marks]

Apparently an adult heart is the size of two fists. Two whole fists! Huge!

It's pretty incredible that your heart manages to go through all those stages in the right order, at exactly the right time, without getting it even slightly wrong. It does it perfectly, about 70 times every minute. That's about 100 800 times a day. If only my brain was that efficient. I'd have all this revision done in five minutes, then I could go and watch TV...

Haemoglobin

Haemoglobin's a protein that carries oxygen around the body. Different species have different versions of it depending on where each species lives. All of which adds up to two pages of no-holds-barred fun...

Oxygen is Carried Round the Body by Haemoglobin

1) **Red blood cells** contain **haemoglobin** (Hb).

2) Haemoglobin is a large **protein** with a **quaternary** structure (see p. 17 for more) — it's made up of **more than one** polypeptide chain (**four** of them in fact).

3) Each chain has a **haem group**, which contains an **iron ion** (see page 19) and gives haemoglobin its **red** colour.

4) Haemoglobin has a **high affinity for oxygen** — each molecule can carry **four oxygen molecules**.

5) In the lungs, oxygen **joins** to haemoglobin in red blood cells to form **oxyhaemoglobin**.

6) This is a **reversible reaction** — when oxygen leaves oxyhaemoglobin (**dissociates** from it) near the body cells, it turns back to haemoglobin.

> *'Affinity' for oxygen means 'tendency to combine with' oxygen.*

$$Hb + 4O_2 \rightleftharpoons HbO_8$$
$$\text{haemoglobin} + \text{oxygen} \rightleftharpoons \text{oxyhaemoglobin}$$

There are many **chemically similar** types of haemoglobin found in many different organisms, all of which carry out the **same function**. As well as being found in all vertebrates, haemoglobin is found in earthworms, starfish, some insects, some plants and even in some bacteria.

Haemoglobin Saturation Depends on the Partial Pressure of Oxygen

1) The **partial pressure** of oxygen (pO_2) is a measure of **oxygen concentration**. The **greater** the concentration of dissolved oxygen in cells, the **higher** the partial pressure.

2) Similarly, the **partial pressure** of **carbon dioxide** (pCO_2) is a measure of the concentration of CO_2 in a cell.

3) Haemoglobin's **affinity** for oxygen **varies** depending on the **partial pressure** of **oxygen**:

> Oxygen **loads onto** haemoglobin to form oxyhaemoglobin where there's a high pO_2. Oxyhaemoglobin **unloads** its oxygen where there's a **lower** pO_2.

4) Oxygen enters blood capillaries at the **alveoli** in the **lungs**. Alveoli have a high pO_2 so oxygen **loads onto** haemoglobin to form oxyhaemoglobin.

5) When **cells respire**, they use up oxygen — this **lowers the** pO_2. Red blood cells deliver oxyhaemoglobin to respiring tissues, where it unloads its oxygen.

6) The haemoglobin then returns to the lungs to pick up more oxygen.

There was no use pretending — the partial pressure of CH_4 had just increased, and Keith knew who was to blame.

Dissociation Curves Show How Affinity for Oxygen Varies

A **dissociation curve** shows how **saturated** the haemoglobin is with oxygen at any given partial pressure.

> *100% saturation means every haemoglobin molecule is carrying the maximum of 4 molecules of oxygen.*

> *0% saturation means none of the haemoglobin molecules are carrying any oxygen.*

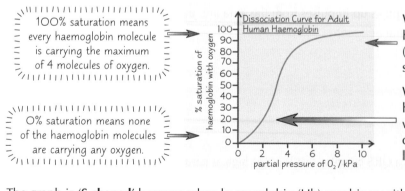

Where pO_2 is high (e.g. in the lungs), haemoglobin has a **high affinity** for oxygen (i.e. it will **readily combine** with oxygen), so it has a **high saturation** of oxygen.

Where pO_2 is low (e.g. in respiring tissues), haemoglobin has a **low affinity** for oxygen, which means it **releases oxygen** rather than combines with it. That's why it has a **low saturation** of oxygen.

The graph is 'S-shaped' because when haemoglobin (Hb) combines with the **first O_2 molecule**, its **shape alters** in a way that makes it **easier** for other molecules to join too. But as the Hb starts to become saturated, it gets **harder** for more oxygen molecules to join. As a result, the curve has a **steep** bit in the middle where it's really easy for oxygen molecules to join, and **shallow** bits at each end where it's harder. When the curve is steep, a **small change in** pO_2 causes a **big change** in the **amount of oxygen** carried by the Hb.

Haemoglobin

Carbon Dioxide Concentration Affects Oxygen Unloading

To complicate matters, haemoglobin gives up its oxygen **more readily** at **higher partial pressures of carbon dioxide** (pCO_2). It's a cunning way of getting more oxygen to cells during activity.

1) When cells respire they produce carbon dioxide, which **raises the** pCO_2.

2) This increases the rate of **oxygen unloading** (i.e. the rate at which oxyhaemoglobin **dissociates** to form haemoglobin and oxygen) — so the dissociation curve 'shifts' right. The saturation of blood with oxygen is **lower** for a given pO_2, meaning that **more oxygen** is being **released**.

3) This is called the **Bohr effect**.

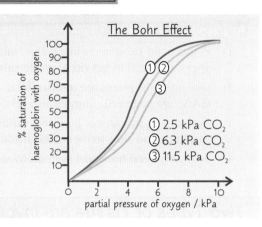

The Bohr Effect

① 2.5 kPa CO_2
② 6.3 kPa CO_2
③ 11.5 kPa CO_2

% saturation of haemoglobin with oxygen

partial pressure of oxygen / kPa

Haemoglobin is Different in Different Organisms

Different organisms have different **types** of haemoglobin with different **oxygen transporting capacities**. Having a particular type of haemoglobin is an **adaptation** that helps the organism to **survive** in a **particular environment**.

1) Organisms that live in environments with a **low concentration of oxygen** have haemoglobin with a **higher affinity** for oxygen than human haemoglobin — the dissociation curve is to the **left** of ours.

2) Organisms that are very **active** and have a **high oxygen demand** have haemoglobin with a **lower affinity** for oxygen than human haemoglobin — the curve is to the **right** of the human one.

A = animal living in depleted oxygen environment, e.g. a lugworm.
B = animal living at high altitude where the partial pressure of oxygen is lower, e.g. a llama in the Andes.
C = human dissociation curve.
D = active animal with a high respiratory rate living where there's plenty of available oxygen, e.g. a hawk.

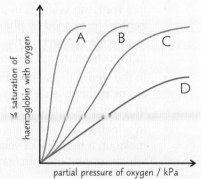

% saturation of haemoglobin with oxygen

A B C

D

partial pressure of oxygen / kPa

Some organisms have different affinities for O_2 at different stages of their life cycles too, e.g. human fetal haemoglobin has a higher affinity for O_2 than adult haemoglobin so that the fetus can absorb enough O_2 from its mother's blood.

Practice Questions

Q1 How many oxygen molecules can each haemoglobin molecule carry?

Q2 Where in the body would you find a low partial pressure of oxygen?

Q3 Why are oxygen dissociation curves S-shaped?

Exam Question

Q1 a) Haemoglobin is a protein with a quaternary structure. Explain what this means. [1 mark]

b) The graph shows the normal oxygen dissociation curve for human haemoglobin.
   i) On the graph, sketch the curve you would expect to see for a human in a high carbon dioxide environment. Explain the position of your sketched curve. [3 marks]
   ii) Earthworms live in a low oxygen environment. On the graph, sketch the curve you would expect to see for an earthworm. [1 mark]

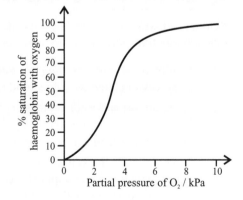

% saturation of haemoglobin with oxygen

Partial pressure of O_2 / kPa

The Bore effect — it's happening right now...

Well, I don't know about you but after these pages I need a sit down. Most people get their knickers in a twist over partial pressure — it's not the easiest thing to understand. Whenever you see it written down just pretend it says concentration instead (cross it out and write concentration if you like) and everything should become clearer. Honest.

Xylem and Phloem

A whole section on plants... just what I always dreamed of...

Multicellular Plants Need Transport Systems

Plants also need carbon dioxide, but this enters at the leaves (where it's needed).

1) Plants need substances like **water**, **minerals** and **sugars** to live.
They also need to **get rid of waste substances**.

2) Like animals, plants are **multicellular** — so they have a **small surface area : volume ratio**
(SA:V, see page 68). They're also relatively **big** with a relatively **high metabolic rate**.

3) Exchanging substances by **direct diffusion** (from the outer surface to the cells)
would be **too slow** to meet their metabolic needs.

4) So plants **need transport systems** to move substances to and from individual cells **quickly**.

Two Types of Tissue are Involved in Transport in Plants

1) **Xylem tissue** transports **water** and **mineral ions** in solution. These substances move **up** the plant from the roots
to the leaves. **Phloem tissue** mainly transports **sugars** (also in solution) both **up and down** the plant.

2) Xylem and phloem make up a plant's **vascular system**. They are found **throughout** a plant and **transport
materials** to all parts. **Where** they're found in each part is connected to the **xylem's** other function — **support**:

- In a **root**, the xylem is in the
  centre surrounded by phloem
  to **provide support** for the root
  as it **pushes** through the soil.
- In the **stems**, the xylem and phloem
  are **near the outside** to provide a sort
  of 'scaffolding' that reduces bending.
- In a **leaf**, xylem and phloem
  make up a **network of veins**
  which support the thin leaves.

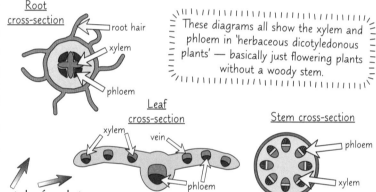

These diagrams all show the xylem and phloem in 'herbaceous dicotyledonous plants' — basically just flowering plants without a woody stem.

3) The position of the xylem and phloem in the root, leaf and stem
are shown in these **transverse cross-sections**. Transverse means the
sections cut through each structure at a **right angle** to its **length**.

4) You can also get **longitudinal** cross-sections. These are taken
along the length of a structure. For example, this cross-section
shows where the **xylem** and **phloem** are located in a **typical stem**.

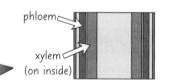

Xylem Vessels are Adapted for Transporting Water and Mineral Ions

Xylem is a **tissue** made from several **different cell types**. **Xylem vessels** are the part of xylem tissue
that actually transports the water and ions. Xylem vessels are adapted for their **function**:

1) Xylem vessels are very **long, tube-like** structures formed from
cells (**vessel elements**) joined end to end.

2) There are **no end walls** on these cells, making an **uninterrupted
tube** that allows water to pass up through the middle easily.

3) The cells are **dead**, so they contain **no cytoplasm**.

4) Their walls are **thickened** with a **woody** substance called
lignin, which helps to **support** the xylem vessels and stops
them **collapsing inwards**. Lignin can be deposited in xylem
walls in different ways, e.g. in a **spiral** or as **distinct rings**.

5) The amount of lignin **increases** as the cell gets **older**.

6) **Water** and **ions** move **into** and **out of** the vessels through
small pits in the walls where there's **no lignin**.

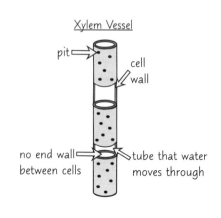

Xylem and Phloem

Phloem Tissue is Adapted for Transporting Solutes

1) Phloem tissue transports **solutes** (dissolved substances), mainly sugars like sucrose, round plants.
2) Like xylem, phloem is formed from cells arranged in **tubes**.
   But, unlike xylem, it's purely a **transport tissue** — it **isn't** used for support as well.
3) Phloem tissue contains **phloem fibres**, **phloem parenchyma**, **sieve tube elements** and **companion cells**.
4) **Sieve tube elements** and **companion cells** are the most important cell types in phloem for **transport**:

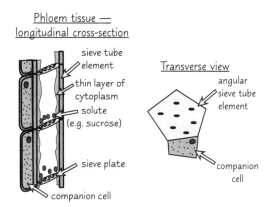

Phloem tissue —
longitudinal cross-section

sieve tube element

thin layer of cytoplasm

solute (e.g. sucrose)

sieve plate

companion cell

Transverse view

angular sieve tube element

companion cell

1) Sieve tube elements

1) These are **living cells** that form the tube for **transporting solutes** through the plant.
2) They are joined **end to end** to form **sieve tubes**.
3) The 'sieve' parts are the **end walls**, which have lots of **holes** in them to allow **solutes** to pass through.
4) Unusually for living cells, sieve tube elements have **no nucleus**, a **very thin** layer of **cytoplasm** and **few organelles**.
5) The cytoplasm of adjacent cells is **connected** through the holes in the sieve plates.

2) Companion cells

1) The **lack** of a **nucleus** and **other organelles** in sieve tube elements means that they **can't survive** on their own. So there's a **companion cell** for **every** sieve tube element.
2) Companion cells carry out the living functions for **both** themselves and their sieve cells. For example, they provide the **energy** for the **active transport** of solutes.

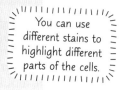

The active transport of solutes requires energy (see p. 63).

You Can Dissect Plant Stems

You can **look at plant tissue** (e.g. part of a plant stem) under a **microscope**, and then **draw** it. But first you need to **dissect** the plant and **prepare** a section of the tissue. You can do this using the following method:

1) Use a scalpel (or razor blade) to cut a **cross-section** of the stem (transverse or longitudinal). Cut the sections as thinly as possible — thin sections are better for viewing under a microscope.
2) Use tweezers to gently place the cut sections in water until you come to use them. This stops them from drying out.
3) Transfer each section to a dish containing a stain, e.g. toluidine blue O (TBO), and leave for one minute. TBO stains the lignin in the walls of the xylem vessels blue-green. This will let you see the position of the xylem vessels and examine their structure.
4) Rinse off the sections in water and mount each one onto a slide (see page 48).

You can use different stains to highlight different parts of the cells.

Practice Questions

Q1 Why do multicellular plants need transport systems?
Q2 What is the name of the substance that thickens the walls of xylem vessels?
Q3 What is the function of companion cells?

Exam Question

Q1 Explain two ways in which the structure of the xylem vessels makes them well-adapted to their function. [4 marks]

Sieve tube — WLTM like-minded cell for long-term companionship...

Sieve tube elements sound a bit feeble to me — not being able to survive on their own, and all that. Anyway, some of the structures and functions of the cell types covered here are quite similar, so don't get confused. You don't want to mix up your sieve tube elements with your vessel elements — you'd never forgive yourself...

Plant Fibres and Sustainability

You can use plants to make ropes, fabrics and other things. Making things from plants is sustainable, which is nice...

Sclerenchyma Fibres Support Plant Stems

As well as xylem and phloem, plant stems also contain **sclerenchyma fibres**.

1) The function of sclerenchyma fibres is to provide **support** — they are not involved in transport.
2) Like xylem vessels, they're also made of bundles of **dead cells** that run vertically up the stem.
3) The cells are **longer** than they are **wide**, and have a **hollow lumen** but, unlike xylem vessels (see page 94), they do have **end walls**.
4) Their cell walls are also **thickened** with **lignin** and they have **more cellulose** than other plant cells.

Plant Fibres are Useful to Humans Because They're Strong

1) Plant fibres are made up of **long tubes** of **plant cells**, e.g. sclerenchyma fibres and xylem vessels are made of tubes of dead cells.
2) They're **strong**, which makes them useful for loads of things, e.g. **ropes** or **fabrics** like hemp.
3) They're strong for a **number of reasons**. Here are **two** of them:

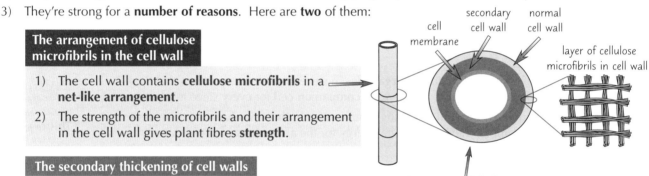

The arrangement of cellulose microfibrils in the cell wall

1) The cell wall contains **cellulose microfibrils** in a **net-like arrangement**.
2) The strength of the microfibrils and their arrangement in the cell wall gives plant fibres **strength**.

The secondary thickening of cell walls

1) When some structural plant cells (like sclerenchyma and xylem) have finished growing, they produce a **secondary cell wall** between the normal cell wall and the cell membrane.
2) The secondary cell wall is **thicker** than the normal cell wall and usually has **more lignin**.
3) The growth of a secondary cell wall is called **secondary thickening**.
4) Secondary thickening makes plant fibres even **stronger**.

You Can Measure the Tensile Strength of Plant Fibres

The **tensile strength** of a fibre is the **maximum load** it can take before it **breaks**. Knowing the tensile strength of plant fibres can be really important, especially if they're going to be used for things like ropes (e.g. a rock climber would want to know the rope they're using is going to hold their weight). Here's how you'd find out the tensile strength of a plant fibre:

I don't know Dave, we usually use weights to test tensile strength...

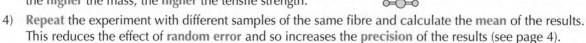

1) Attach the fibre to a **clamp stand** and **hang a weight** from the other end.
2) Keep **adding weights**, one at a time, until the **fibre breaks**.
3) Record the **mass needed** to break the fibre — the **higher** the mass, the **higher** the tensile strength.
4) **Repeat** the experiment with different samples of the same fibre and calculate the **mean** of the results. This reduces the effect of **random error** and so increases the **precision** of the results (see page 4).
5) The fibres being tested should always be the **same length**.
6) Throughout the experiment all **other variables**, like temperature and humidity, must be kept **constant**.
7) You also need to take **safety measures** when doing this experiment, e.g. wear goggles to protect your eyes, and leave the area where the weights will fall clear so they don't squish your toes.

Plant Fibres and Sustainability

Sustainable Practices Don't Deplete Resources

1) Sustainability is all about **using resources** in a way that meets the **needs** of the **present generation** without messing it up for **future generations** (i.e. not using something up so there's none left).

2) To **make products sustainably** you have to use **renewable resources**.

3) Renewable resources are resources that can be **used indefinitely** without **running out**, e.g. **plants** are a renewable resource because harvested plants can be **regrown** (so there'll be plenty for future generations). **Fossil fuels** (e.g. petrol) are **not** a renewable resource — once you've used it all there's no more.

4) An example of a **sustainable practice** is replacing trees after logging. Whenever a tree is cut down, a **new one** is planted in its place. When the tree is fully grown the process can **begin again** — the environment isn't **significantly damaged** in the long term.

5) **Unsustainable practices** can't continue indefinitely. The **resources** would eventually **run out**.

6) An example of an unsustainable practice is the use of **fossil fuels** to make oil-based plastics like polythene.

Using Plant Fibres and Starch can Contribute to Sustainability

Plant fibres

1) **Ropes** and **fabrics** can be made of **plastic**, which is made from **oil**. They can also be made from **plant fibres** (see previous page).

2) Making products from plant fibres is **more sustainable** than making them from oil — **less fossil fuel** is used up, and crops can be **regrown** to **maintain the supply** for future generations.

3) Products made from plant fibres are **biodegradable** — they can be broken down by **microbes**, unlike most oil-based plastics (which can't be broken down and remain in the environment for many years).

4) Plants are **easier to grow** and **process** (to extract the fibres) than extracting and processing oil. This makes them **cheaper** and it's easier to do in developing countries (as less technology and expertise is needed).

One disadvantage of making ropes from plant fibres is that they're generally not as strong as ropes made of plastic.

Starch

1) Starch is found in **all plants** — crops such as **potatoes** and **corn** are particularly rich in starch.

2) **Plastics** are usually made from **oil**, but some can be made from **plant-based** materials, like **starch**. These plastics are called **bioplastics**.

3) Making plastics from starch is **more sustainable** than making them from oil because less fossil fuel is used up and the **crops** from which the starch came from can be **regrown**.

4) **Vehicle fuel** is also usually made from **oil**, but you can make fuel from **starch**. E.g. **bioethanol** is a fuel that can be made from starch.

5) Making fuel from starch is **more sustainable** than making it from oil because, you guessed it, **less fossil fuel** is used up and the **crops** from which the starch came from can be **regrown**.

Practice Questions

Q1 What is the purpose of sclerenchyma fibres?

Q2 Give two advantages of using plant fibres rather than oil-based plastics to make rope.

Q3 Name two products, other than rope, that can be made from plants.

Exam Question

Q1 The physical properties of plant fibres can make them useful to humans. Describe the arrangement of cellulose microfibrils in a plant cell wall, and explain how this relates to the properties of plant fibres. [2 marks]

Potatoes, good for plastics and fuel — we'll be eating them next...

Renewable resources are great — they'll never run out (like my bad jokes — plenty more where they came from...). As you can see, some of the properties that make plant structures useful for plants are also useful for us — neat.

Water Transport in Plants

Water enters a plant through its roots and eventually, if it's not used, exits via the leaves. "Ah-ha", I hear you say, "but how does it flow upwards, against gravity?" Well that, my friends, is a mystery that's about to be explained...

Water Enters a Plant through its *Root Hair Cells*

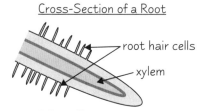

Cross-Section of a Root

root hair cells

xylem

1) Water has to get from the **soil**, through the **root** and into the **xylem** to be transported around the plant.

2) Water enters through **root hair cells** and then passes through **the root cortex**, including the **endodermis**, to reach the xylem (see below).

3) Water is drawn into the roots via **osmosis**. This means it travels down a **water potential gradient**:

- Water always moves from areas of **higher water potential** to areas of **lower water potential** — it goes down a **water potential gradient**.

- The **soil** around roots generally has a **high water potential** (i.e. there's lots of water there) and **leaves** have a **lower water potential** (because water constantly **evaporates** from them).

- This creates a water potential gradient that keeps water moving through the plant in the right direction, **from roots (high) to leaves (low)**.

> Remember: osmosis is the diffusion of water molecules across a partially permeable membrane, from an area of higher water potential to an area of lower water potential — see p. 66.

Water **Moves** Through the **Root** into the **Xylem**...

Water travels through the **roots** (via the **root cortex**) into the **xylem** by **two** different paths:

1) The **symplast pathway** — goes through the **living** parts of cells — the **cytoplasm**. The cytoplasms of neighbouring cells connect through **plasmodesmata** (small channels in the cell walls). Water moves through the symplast pathway via **osmosis**.

2) The **apoplast pathway** — goes through the **non-living** parts of the cells — the **cell walls**. The walls are very absorbent and water can simply **diffuse** through them, as well as pass through the spaces between them. The water can carry **solutes** and move from areas of **high hydrostatic pressure** to areas of **low hydrostatic pressure** (i.e. along a pressure gradient). This is an example of **mass flow** (see page 102).

The prison had been strangely quiet ever since plasmodesmata were installed.

- When water in the **apoplast pathway** gets to the **endodermis** cells in the root, its path is blocked by a **waxy strip** in the cell walls, called the **Casparian strip**. Now the water has to take the **symplast pathway**.

- This is useful, because it means the water has to go through a **cell membrane**. Cell membranes are **partially permeable** and are able to **control** whether or not substances in the water get through (see p. 56).

- Once past this barrier, the water moves into the **xylem**.

3) Both pathways are used, but the main one is the **apoplast pathway** because it provides the **least resistance**.

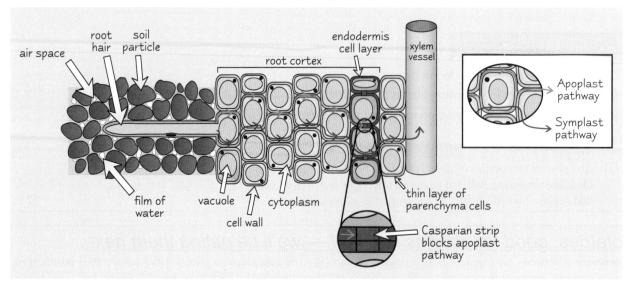

Water Transport in Plants

...then *Up* the *Xylem* and *Out* at the *Leaves*

1) **Xylem vessels** transport the water **all around** the plant.

2) At the **leaves**, water leaves the xylem and moves into the cells mainly by the **apoplast pathway**.

3) Water **evaporates** from the cell walls into the **spaces** between cells in the leaf.

4) When the **stomata** (tiny pores in the surface of the leaf) open, the water **diffuses** out of the leaf (down the **water potential gradient**) into the **surrounding air**.

5) The loss of water from a plant's surface is called **transpiration** (see next page).

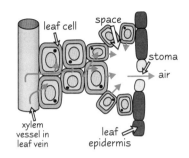

Water Moves *Up* a Plant *Against* the Force of *Gravity*

The movement of water from **roots to leaves** is called the **transpiration stream**. The **mechanisms** that **move** the water include **cohesion**, **tension** and **adhesion**.

Cohesion and **tension** help water move up plants, from roots to leaves, **against** the force of gravity.

1) Water **evaporates** from the **leaves** at the 'top' of the xylem (**transpiration**).

2) This creates a **tension** (**suction**), which pulls more water into the leaf.

3) Water molecules are **cohesive** (they **stick together**) so when some are pulled into the leaf others follow. This means the whole **column** of water in the **xylem**, from the leaves down to the roots, **moves upwards**.

4) **Water** enters the stem through the **root cortex cells**.

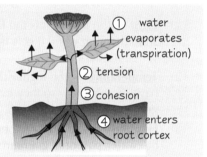

Adhesion is also partly responsible for the **movement of water**.

1) As well as being attracted to each other, water molecules are **attracted to the walls** of the xylem vessels.

2) This helps water to **rise up** through the xylem vessels.

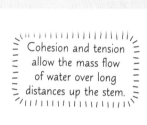

Cohesion and tension allow the mass flow of water over long distances up the stem.

Practice Questions

Q1 In terms of water potential, why does water move into the roots from the soil?

Q2 Describe how water moves through a plant root via the symplast pathway.

Q3 What is the Casparian strip?

Q4 How does adhesion help to move water through a plant?

Exam Questions

Q1 Explain the role of cohesion and tension in the loss of water from the leaves of plants. [4 marks]

Q2 Plants that are infected by a pathogen are able to block their plasmodesmata. This is thought to be an attempt to reduce the spread of the pathogen. Suggest how this would affect the way that water travels through a plant. [2 marks]

So many routes through the roots...

As you've probably noticed, there are lots of impressive biological words on these pages that you can amaze your friends with. Go over the pages again, and whenever you see a word like plasmodesmata, stop and check you know exactly what it means. (Personally I think they should just call them cell wall channels, but nobody ever listens to me.)

Transpiration

Plants can't sing, juggle or tap dance (as you will hopefully be aware). But they can exchange gases — how exciting. What makes it all the more thrilling though is that they lose water vapour as they do it. Gripping stuff.

Transpiration is a Consequence of Gas Exchange

So you know that **transpiration** is the evaporation of **water** from a plant's surface, especially the **leaves**. But I bet you didn't know it happens as a result of **gas exchange**. Read on...

1) A plant needs to **open** its **stomata** to let in **carbon dioxide** so that it can produce **glucose** (by **photosynthesis**).

2) But this **also lets water out** — there's a **higher concentration** of water **inside** the leaf than in the air **outside**, so water moves **out** of the leaf down the **water potential gradient** when the stomata open.

3) So transpiration's really a **side effect** of the gas exchange needed for photosynthesis.

Four Main Factors Affect Transpiration Rate

Temperature, humidity and wind all alter the **water potential gradient**, but **light** is a bit different:

1) <u>Light</u> — the **lighter** it is the **faster** the **transpiration rate**. This is because the **stomata open** when it gets **light**, so CO_2 can diffuse into the leaf for photosynthesis. When it's **dark** the stomata are usually **closed**, so there's little transpiration.

2) <u>Temperature</u> — the **higher the temperature** the **faster** the **transpiration rate**. Warmer water molecules have more energy so they **evaporate** from the cells inside the leaf **faster**. This **increases** the **water potential gradient** between the inside and outside of the leaf, making water **diffuse** out of the leaf **faster**.

3) <u>Humidity</u> — the **lower** the **humidity**, the **faster** the **transpiration rate**. If the air around the plant is **dry**, the **water potential gradient** between the leaf and the air is **increased**, which increases transpiration.

4) <u>Wind</u> — the **windier** it is, the **faster** the **transpiration rate**. Lots of air movement **blows away** water molecules from around the stomata. This **increases** the water potential gradient, which increases the rate of transpiration.

A Potometer can be Used to Estimate Transpiration Rate

A **potometer** is a special piece of apparatus used to **estimate transpiration rates**. It actually measures **water uptake** by a plant, but it's **assumed** that water uptake by the plant is **directly related** to **water loss** by the **leaves**. You can use it to estimate how different factors **affect** the transpiration rate.

A potometer

Reservoir of water used to return bubble to start for repeats.

As the plant takes up water, the air bubble moves along the scale.

Tap is shut off during experiment.

capillary tube with a scale

water moves this way

bubble moves this way

beaker of water

The air bubble is sometimes called the air-water meniscus.

Here's what you'd do:

1) **Cut** a **shoot underwater** to prevent air from entering the xylem. Cut it at a **slant** to increase the surface area available for water uptake.

2) Assemble the potometer **in water** and insert the shoot **underwater**, so no air can enter.

3) Remove the apparatus from the water but keep the **end of the capillary tube submerged** in a beaker of water.

4) Check that the apparatus is **watertight** and **airtight**.

5) **Dry** the leaves, allow time for the shoot to **acclimatise**, and then **shut the tap**.

6) Remove the end of the capillary tube from the beaker of water until **one air bubble** has formed, then put the end of the tube back into the water.

7) Record the **starting position** of the **air bubble**.

8) Start a **stopwatch** and record the **distance** moved by the bubble **per unit time**, e.g. per hour. The **rate of air bubble movement** is an estimate of the **transpiration rate**.

9) Remember, only change **one variable** (e.g. temperature) at a time. All other **conditions** (e.g. light, humidity) must be kept **constant**.

Transpiration

Xerophytic Plants are Adapted to Reduce Water Loss

Xerophytes are plants like **cacti** and **marram grass** (which grows on sand dunes). They're **adapted** to live in **dry climates**. Their adaptations prevent them **losing too much water** by **transpiration**...

1) Marram grass has stomata that are sunk in pits, so they're **sheltered from the wind**. This helps to slow transpiration down.

2) It also has a layer of 'hairs' on the epidermis — this **traps moist air** round the stomata, which **reduces** the water potential gradient between the leaf and the air, **slowing** transpiration down.

3) In hot or windy conditions marram grass plants roll their leaves — again this **traps moist air**, slowing down transpiration. It also reduces the **exposed surface area** for losing water and protects the stomata from wind.

4) Both marram grass and cacti have a **thick, waxy layer** on the epidermis — this **reduces** water loss by evaporation because the layer is **waterproof** (water can't move through it).

5) Cacti have **spines** instead of leaves — this reduces the **surface area** for water loss.

6) Cacti also **close** their **stomata** at the hottest times of the day when transpiration rates are the **highest**.

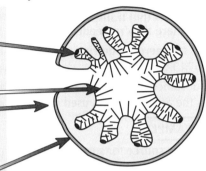

Cross-section through a marram grass leaf.

Cacti spines   Marram grass

Hydrophilic Plants are Adapted to Survive in Water

Hydrophytes are plants like **water lilies**, which live in **aquatic habitats**. As they **grow in water**, they **don't need** adaptations **to reduce water loss** (like xerophytes), but they do need adaptations to help them cope with a **low oxygen level**. Here are some adaptations of hydrophytes...

1) **Air spaces** in the tissues help the plants to **float** and can act as a **store of oxygen** for use in respiration. For example, **water lilies** have **large air spaces** in their **leaves**. This allows the leaves to **float on the surface** of the water, **increasing** the amount of **light** they receive. Air spaces in the **roots** and **stems** allow **oxygen** to move from the floating leaves down to parts of the plant that are **underwater**.

2) **Stomata** are usually only present on the **upper surface** of **floating leaves**. This helps **maximise gas exchange**.

3) Hydrophytes often have **flexible leaves and stems** — these plants are **supported** by the **water** around them, so they don't need rigid stems for support. Flexibility helps to **prevent damage** by water currents.

Practice Questions

Q1 Explain why transpiration is a consequence of gaseous exchange.

Q2 Name a piece of apparatus used to measure transpiration.

Q3 What is a hydrophyte?

Exam Question

Q1 The diagram shows a section of a leaf of a xerophytic plant. Describe and explain two ways, visible in the picture, in which this leaf is adapted to reduce water loss.   [4 marks]

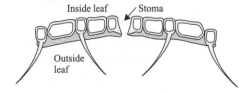

Xerophytes — an exciting word for a boring subject...

Actually, that's unfair. It's taken millions of years for plants to evolve those adaptations, and here I am slagging them off. When I've managed to develop a thick waxy cuticle on my leaves and stems, then I can comment, and not before.

Translocation

Translocation is the movement of dissolved solutes through a plant. Annoyingly, translocation sounds a lot like transpiration. Or is that just me? Make sure you don't get them confused.

Translocation is the Movement of Dissolved Substances

1) **Translocation** is the **movement** of dissolved substances (e.g. sugars like sucrose, and amino acids) to **where they're needed** in a plant. Dissolved substances are sometimes called **assimilates**.

2) It's an **energy-requiring** process that happens in the **phloem** (see p. 95 for more on the phloem).

3) Translocation moves substances from '**sources**' to '**sinks**'. The **source** of a substance is **where it's made** (so it's at a **high concentration** there). The **sink** is the area where it's **used up** (so it's at a **lower concentration** there).

> *Sugars are transported as sucrose because sucrose is both soluble and metabolically inactive — so it doesn't get used up during transport.*

> **EXAMPLE**
>
> The **source** for **sucrose** is usually the **leaves** (where it's made), and the **sinks** are the **other parts** of the plant, especially the **food storage organs** and the **meristems** (areas of growth) in the roots, stems and leaves.

4) Some parts of a plant can be both a **sink** and a **source**.

> **EXAMPLE**
>
> Sucrose can be **stored** in the **roots**. During the **growing season**, sucrose is transported from the roots to the **leaves** to provide the leaves with **energy** for **growth**. In this case, the **roots** are the **source** and the **leaves** are a **sink**.

Howard liked a bit of translocation in his spare time.

5) **Enzymes** maintain a **concentration gradient** from the source to the sink by **changing** the dissolved substances at the **sink** (e.g. by breaking them down or making them into something else). This makes sure there's always a **lower concentration** at the sink than at the source.

> **EXAMPLES**
>
> In **potatoes**, **sucrose** is converted to **starch** in the **sink** areas, so there's always a **lower concentration** of sucrose **at the sink** than inside the phloem. This makes sure a **constant supply** of new sucrose reaches the sink from the phloem. In other sinks, enzymes such as invertase **break down sucrose** into **glucose** (and fructose) for use by the plant — again this makes sure there's a **lower concentration** of sucrose **at the sink**.

The Mass Flow Hypothesis Best Explains Phloem Transport

Scientists still aren't certain **exactly how** the dissolved substances (solutes) are transported from source to sink by **translocation**. The best supported theory is the **mass flow hypothesis**:

①
1) Active transport is used to **actively load** the solutes (e.g. sucrose from photosynthesis) into the **sieve tubes** of the phloem at the **source** (e.g. the **leaves**).

2) This **lowers** the **water potential** inside the **sieve tubes**, so water enters the tubes by **osmosis** from the **xylem** and **companion cells**.

3) This creates a **high pressure** inside the sieve tubes at the **source end** of the phloem.

②
1) At the **sink** end, **solutes** are removed from the phloem to be used up.

2) This **increases** the **water potential** inside the sieve tubes, so water also leaves the tubes by **osmosis**.

3) This **lowers the pressure** inside the sieve tubes.

③
1) The result is a **pressure gradient** from the **source** end to the **sink** end.

2) This gradient pushes solutes along the sieve tubes to where they're needed.

① SOURCE
low water potential, high pressure

Water enters from xylem

water flow
solute flow

companion cell

HIGH
Pressure gradient forces sap down.
LOW

sieve plate

plasmodesma

solute (e.g. sucrose)

Water flows to xylem

② SINK
high water potential, low pressure

Translocation

There is **Evidence For** and **Against** The **Mass Flow Hypothesis**

Supporting evidence

1) If a **ring** of **bark** (which includes the phloem, but not the xylem) is removed from a woody stem, a **bulge forms above** the ring. The fluid from the bulge has a **higher concentration** of **sugars** than the fluid from below the ring — this is evidence that there's a **downward flow** of sugars.

2) A **radioactive tracer** such as radioactive carbon (^{14}C) can be used to **track** the movement of organic substances in a plant (see below).

3) Pressure in the phloem can be investigated using **aphids** (they pierce the phloem, then their bodies are removed leaving the mouthparts behind, which allows the sap to flow out... gruesome). The sap flows out **quicker nearer the leaves** than further down the stem — this is evidence that there's a **pressure gradient**.

4) If a **metabolic inhibitor** (which stops ATP production) is put into the **phloem**, then **translocation stops** — this is evidence that **active transport** is involved.

Objections

1) Sugar travels to **many different sinks**, not just to the one with the **highest water potential**, as the model would suggest.

2) The **sieve plates** would create a **barrier** to mass flow. A **lot** of **pressure** would be needed for the solutes to get through at a reasonable rate.

The **Translocation** of **Solutes** Can be **Demonstrated Experimentally**

Translocation of solutes in plants can be modelled in an experiment using **radioactive tracers**.

1) This can be done by supplying part of a plant (often a **leaf**) with an **organic substance** that has a **radioactive label**. One example is **carbon dioxide** containing the radioactive isotope ^{14}C. This radioactively-labelled CO_2 can be supplied to a single leaf by being pumped into a container which completely surrounds the leaf.

2) The radioactive carbon will then be **incorporated** into organic substances produced by the leaf (e.g. sugars produced by **photosynthesis**), which will be moved around the plant by **translocation**.

Photosynthesis produces glucose. This is converted to sucrose for transport around the plant.

3) The movement of these substances can be tracked using a technique called **autoradiography**. To reveal where the radioactive tracer has **spread to** in a plant, the plant is killed (e.g. by freezing it using liquid nitrogen) and then the whole plant (or sections of it) is placed on **photographic film** — the radioactive substance is present wherever the film turns **black**.

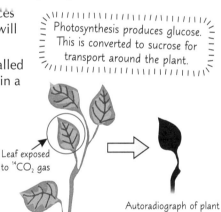

Leaf exposed to $^{14}CO_2$ gas

4) The results demonstrate the translocation of substances from **source** to **sink** over time — for example, autoradiographs of plants **killed** at **different times** show an overall movement of solutes (e.g. products of photosynthesis) from the leaves **towards the roots**.

Autoradiograph of plant showing how radioactivity has spread from the leaf.

Practice Questions

Q1 According to the mass flow hypothesis, how is a pressure gradient set up in the phloem?

Exam Question

Q1 A scientist is investigating where the products of photosynthesis are translocated to in a plant. To do this several upper leaves of a plant were exposed to a radioactive tracer in the form of radioactively-labelled CO_2. The plant was then left for 24 hours before an autoradiograph of the whole plant was taken.

   a) Explain how the leaves of the plant can act as a source in translocation. [1 mark]

   b) The autoradiograph showed radioactivity in the roots and fruits. Explain why radioactivity was seen in the fruits. [1 mark]

Human mass flow — running out of the hall at the end of an exam...

The mass flow hypothesis is just the best theory that scientists have come up with so far. If other evidence came along, a different theory could be developed based on the new findings. It could happen tomorrow, you never know...

Plant Minerals

If plants don't get enough of the right nutrients, they get sick just like us — the poor dears...

Plants Need Water and Inorganic Ions

Plants need **water** and **inorganic ions** (**minerals**) for a number of different functions. They're absorbed through the **roots** and travel through the plant in the xylem. If there isn't enough water or inorganic ions in the soil, the plant will show **deficiency symptoms**, like stunted growth. Here are some reasons why plants need water and certain ions:

- **Water** is needed for **photosynthesis**, to **transport minerals**, to maintain **structural rigidity** (water exerts pressure in cell vacuoles — see page 41) and to **regulate temperature** (water evaporating from leaves helps cool plants down).
- **Magnesium ions** are needed for the production of **chlorophyll** — the **pigment** needed for **photosynthesis**.
- **Nitrate ions** are needed for the production of **DNA**, **proteins** (including enzymes) and **chlorophyll**. They're required for **plant growth**, **fruit production** and **seed production**.
- **Calcium ions** are important components in plant **cell walls**. They're required for **plant growth**.

You Can Investigate Plant Mineral Deficiencies in the Lab

Here's how to **investigate mineral deficiency** in a plant using calcium ions as an example (you could do the same experiment with any of the minerals mentioned above):

1) Make up three **nutrient broths** containing all the essential minerals, but vary the concentration of **calcium ions**. Make up one broth with a **high** concentration, one with a **medium** concentration and one with a **low** concentration of calcium ions.

2) Split 9 test tubes into **three groups** and fill the tubes of each group with one of the three broths.

3) Take 9 seedlings of the **same plant**, e.g. germinated mung beans (they should be the **same age**). For each seedling, measure its **mass** using a balance and record it. Then put it gently into the top of one of the test tubes so that the **root is suspended** in the nutrient broth. You will have to **support** the seedling to stop it from falling into the test tube, e.g. by putting cotton wool inside the opening of the tube.

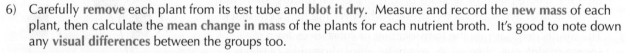
Don't forget to label each of your tubes with the preparation of nutrient broth it contains and the starting mass of the seedling.

4) **Cover the outside** of each test tube in aluminium foil so that **no light** can get to the nutrient broth and cause other organisms, such as algae, to grow.

5) Place all the tubes near a **light source**, e.g. on a windowsill, and leave them for the same amount of time, e.g. **2 weeks**. You may have to **top up** the nutrient broth in each tube during this time to ensure the roots stay suspended in the liquid.

6) Carefully **remove** each plant from its test tube and **blot it dry**. Measure and record the **new mass** of each plant, then calculate the **mean change in mass** of the plants for each nutrient broth. It's good to note down any **visual differences** between the groups too.

7) During the experiment it's important to keep all other **variables the same**, e.g. the amount of light the plants receive.

You could use a similar method to investigate the effect on **plant growth** when plants are **completely deficient** in one mineral — instead of varying the concentration of one mineral in each broth, you would use broths containing **all the nutrients** apart from **the nutrient you were testing**. In this experiment you would also need two **control broths** — one **containing all** the nutrients and one **lacking all** the nutrients.

Practice Questions

Q1 List four reasons why plants need to have an adequate supply of water.

Q2 Why do plants need magnesium ions?

Exam Question

Q1 A student wants to investigate both the effects of magnesium ion deficiency and nitrate ion deficiency on plant growth. Describe four different broths she would need to prepare for her investigation to produce valid results. [2 marks]

Starving those little seedlings — how could you..?

It's pretty amazing that plants are able to take the right ingredients out of all that mucky soil and make leaves or flowers. Different plants need different conditions — but they all need water and the minerals on this page.

Drugs from Plants and Drug Testing

As you might have already gathered from this section, plants are dead useful. We even use them to make medicines.

Testing Drugs Used to be Trial and Error

Before **new drugs** become available to the general public they need to be **tested** — to make sure they **work** and don't have any horrible **side effects**. In the past, drug testing was a lot **less scientific** than modern clinical trials (see below) and a bit more dangerous for the participants...

1) **William Withering** was a scientist in the 1700s. He discovered that an extract of **foxgloves** could be used to treat **dropsy** (swelling brought about by heart failure). This extract contained the drug **digitalis**.

2) Withering made a **chance observation** — a patient suffering from dropsy made a good recovery after being treated with a **traditional remedy** containing foxgloves. Withering knew foxgloves were **poisonous**, so he started testing **different versions** of the remedy with **different concentrations** of digitalis — this became known as his **digitalis soup**.

3) **Too much** digitalis **poisoned** his patients, while **too little** had **no effect**.

4) It was through this crude method of **trial and error** that he discovered the right amount to give to a patient.

Modern Drug Testing is More Rigorous

Nowadays **drug testing protocols** are much more **controlled**. Before a drug is tried on any live subjects, computers are used to **model** the **potential effects**. Tests are also carried out on **human tissues** in a **lab**, then they're tested on **live animals** before **clinical trials** are carried out on **humans**. During clinical trials new drugs undergo **three phases of testing**. This involves three different stages, with more people at each stage:

<u>Phase 1</u> — This involves testing a new drug on a **small group** of **healthy individuals**. It's done to find out things like **safe dosage**, if there are any **side effects**, and how the body **reacts** to the drug.

<u>Phase 2</u> — If a drug passes Phase 1 it will then be tested on a **larger group** of people (this time **patients**) to see **how well** the drug actually **works**.

Drugs that pass all three phases are considered for clinical use.

<u>Phase 3</u> — During this phase the drug is **compared** to **existing treatments**. It involves testing the drug on **hundreds**, or even **thousands**, of patients. Using a large sample size makes the results of the test more **reliable**. Patients are randomly split into two groups — one group receives the **new treatment** and the other group receives the **existing treatment**. This allows scientists to tell if the new drug is **any better** than existing drugs.

Using **placebos** and a **double blind study design** make the results of clinical trials **more valid**.

Placebos

In Phase 2 clinical trials the patients are split into **two groups**. One group is given the drug and the other is given a **placebo** — an **inactive substance** that looks exactly like the drug but doesn't actually do anything. Patients often show a **placebo effect** — where they show some improvement because they **believe** that they're receiving treatment. Giving half the patients a placebo allows researchers to see if the **drug actually works** (if it improves patients more than the placebo does).

Double blind study design

Phase 2 and 3 clinical trials are usually **double blind** — **neither** the **patients** nor the **doctors** know who's been given the new drug and who's been given the placebo (or old drug). This **reduces bias** in the results because the **attitudes** of the patients and doctors **can't affect the results**. E.g. if a doctor knows someone has received the real drug, they may think they've improved more than they actually have — but if they don't know this can't happen.

Practice Questions

Q1 Describe how modern drug testing differs from historic drug testing.

Exam Question

Q1 Describe how William Withering discovered and tested the drug digitalis. [5 marks]

Digitalis soup — like Alphabetti Spaghetti with numbers...

Drug testing these days is really quite complicated, what with all this three phase testing and placebos. Though if you ask me, anything that's double blind just sounds like a recipe for disaster...

Cardiovascular Disease

Diseases associated with your heart and blood vessels are called cardiovascular diseases (cardio = heart, vascular = blood vessels — geddit?).

Most **Cardiovascular Disease** Starts With **Atheroma** Formation

1) The wall of an **artery** is made up of **several layers** (see page 84).

2) The **endothelium** (inner lining) is usually smooth and unbroken.

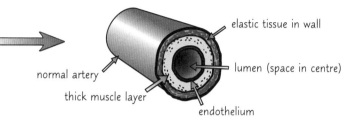

elastic tissue in wall

lumen (space in centre)

normal artery

thick muscle layer

endothelium

3) If **damage** occurs to the endothelium (e.g. by high blood pressure) there will be an **inflammatory response** — this is where white blood cells (mostly phagocytes — see page 122) move into the area.

4) These white blood cells and **lipids** (fats) from the blood, clump together under the endothelium to form **fatty streaks**.

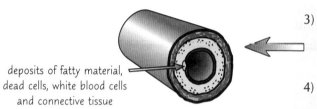

deposits of fatty material, dead cells, white blood cells and connective tissue

> Damage to the endothelium means the endothelium can't function normally — this is called endothelial dysfunction.

5) Over time, **more white blood cells, lipids** and **connective tissue** build up and harden to form a **fibrous plaque** called an **atheroma**.

6) This plaque **partially blocks** the lumen of the **artery** and **restricts blood flow**, which causes **blood pressure** to increase.

deposits of fatty material etc. build up and push out endothelium

lumen shrinks as artery wall swells, so it's more difficult for blood to pass through

7) The **hardening** of arteries, caused by atheromas, is called **atherosclerosis**.

Atheromas Increase the **Risk** of Thrombosis in Arteries

1) As you know, **atheromas** develop within the **walls** of **arteries** (see above).

2) An atheroma can **rupture** (burst through) the **endothelium** of an artery, **damaging** the artery wall and leaving a **rough** surface.

3) This triggers **thrombosis** (blood clotting) — a **blood clot** forms at the **site** of the rupture (see next page).

4) This blood clot can cause a complete **blockage** of the artery, or it can become **dislodged** and block a blood vessel elsewhere in the body.

5) The **blood flow** to **tissues** supplied by the blocked blood vessel will be severely **restricted**, so **less oxygen** will reach those tissues, resulting in damage.

6) **Heart attack, stroke** and **deep vein thrombosis** are three forms of **cardiovascular disease** that can be caused by blood clots — these are explained in more detail on the next page.

Cardiovascular Disease

Thrombosis Involves a Series of Reactions

Thrombosis is used by the body to **prevent** lots of blood being **lost** when a **blood vessel** is **damaged**.
A **series** of **reactions** occurs that leads to the formation of a **blood clot** (**thrombus**):

1) A **protein** called **thromboplastin** is **released** from the **damaged** blood vessel.

2) Thromboplastin, along with calcium ions from the plasma, triggers the **conversion** of **prothrombin** (a **soluble protein**) into **thrombin** (an **enzyme**).

3) Thrombin then catalyses the **conversion** of **fibrinogen** (a **soluble protein**) to **fibrin** (solid **insoluble fibres**).

4) The fibrin fibres **tangle together** and form a **mesh** in which **platelets** (**small fragments of cells** in the blood) and **red blood cells** get **trapped** — this forms the **blood clot**.

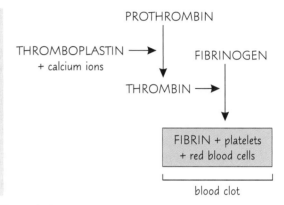

The **cardiovascular diseases** below can result from the formation of blood clots.

Blood Clots can Cause Heart Attacks...

(1) The **heart muscle** is supplied with **blood** by the **coronary arteries**.

(2) This blood contains the **oxygen** needed by heart muscle cells to carry out **respiration**.

(3) If a coronary artery becomes **completely blocked** by a **blood clot** an area of the heart muscle will be totally **cut off** from its blood supply, so it **won't** receive any **oxygen**.

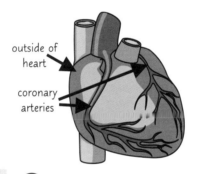

outside of heart

coronary arteries

(4) This causes a **myocardial infarction** — more commonly known as a **heart attack**.

(7) If **large areas** of the heart are affected complete **heart failure** can occur, which is often **fatal**.

(6) **Symptoms** include **pain** in the chest and upper body, **shortness of breath** and **sweating**.

(5) A heart attack can cause **damage** and **death** of the **heart muscle**.

Coronary heart disease (CHD) is when the **coronary arteries** have lots of **atheromas** in them, which restricts blood flow to the heart. The atheromas also increase the risk of **blood clots** forming, leading to an increased risk of heart attack.

...Stroke...

1) A **stroke** is a **rapid loss** of **brain function**, due to a **disruption** in the **blood supply** to the **brain**.

2) This can be caused by a **blood clot** in an **artery** leading to the brain, which **reduces** the amount of blood, and therefore **oxygen**, that can reach the brain.

...and Deep Vein Thrombosis

1) **Deep vein thrombosis** (DVT) is the formation of a **blood clot** in a **vein** deep inside the body — it usually happens in **leg veins**.

2) It can be caused by **prolonged inactivity**, e.g. during **long-haul flights**, and the risk **increases** with **age**.

Cardiovascular Disease

Many Factors Can Increase the Risk of Cardiovascular Disease (CVD)

Lifestyle Factors:

Diet

A diet **high** in **saturated fat** increases the risk of CVD. This is because it **increases blood cholesterol level**, which **increases atheroma formation**. Atheromas can lead to the formation of **blood clots**, which can cause a **heart attack, stroke** or **DVT**. A diet **high in salt** also increases the risk of CVD because it increases the risk of **high blood pressure** (see below).

See page 110 for more on blood cholesterol.

High blood pressure

High blood pressure **increases** the **risk of damage** to the **artery walls**, which **increases** the **risk** of **atheroma formation**, which can lead to CVD. **Excessive alcohol consumption, stress** and **diet** can **all** increase blood pressure.

Smoking

- **Carbon monoxide** in cigarette smoke combines with **haemoglobin** (the protein that carries oxygen in the blood) and **reduces** the amount of **oxygen** transported in the **blood**. This **reduces** the amount of **oxygen available to tissues**. If the heart muscle doesn't receive enough oxygen it can lead to a **heart attack** and if the brain doesn't receive enough oxygen it can lead to a **stroke**.

- **Nicotine** in cigarette smoke makes **platelets sticky**, increasing the chance of **blood clots forming**, which increases the risk of CVD.

- Smoking also **decreases** the **amount** of **antioxidants** in the blood — these are important for **protecting cells** from damage. Fewer antioxidants means **cell damage** in the **artery walls** is more likely, and this can lead to **atheroma formation**, which increases the risk of CVD.

Inactivity

A **lack** of **exercise** increases the risk of CVD because it **increases** the risk of **high blood pressure** (see above).

Factors Beyond Your Control:

Genetics

Some people inherit particular **alleles** (different versions of genes, see page 137) that make them **more likely** to have **high blood pressure** or **high blood cholesterol**, so they are **more likely** to suffer from CVD (see above).

Age

The risk of developing CVD **increases with age**. This is partly because **plaque** can **build up** very slowly over time, which can eventually lead to CVD.

Gender

Men are **three times more likely** to suffer from CVD than pre-menopausal women. This may be due to their different levels of **hormones** — for example, the hormone **oestrogen**, which is typically higher in females, increases levels of 'good' cholesterol (HDL) — see p. 110. The relatively low level of this hormone in men can lead to **higher levels** of total **blood cholesterol** and **increase** the **risk** of CVD.

Cardiovascular Disease

Perception of Risk Can be Different from Actual Risk

1) **Risk** can be defined as the **chance** of something **unfavourable** happening.
   E.g. if you **smoke** you **increase** your chance of developing CVD.

2) The **statistical chance** of something unfavourable happening is supported by **scientific research**.
   E.g. the actual risk of **dying** from **CVD** is **60%** higher for smokers than for non-smokers.

3) People's **perception** of risk may be very **different** from the actual risk:

   - People may **overestimate** the risk — they may believe things to be a **greater risk** than they actually are. E.g. they may have **known someone** who **smoked** and **died** from CVD, and therefore think that if you smoke you **will** die of CVD. Also, there are often **articles** in the **media** about health issues, e.g. articles that highlight the link between smoking and CVD or the link between having a high BMI (see p. 111) and CVD. **Constant exposure** to information like this can make people **constantly worry** that they'll get CVD.

   Melvin underestimated the risk of letting his mum dress him...

   - Some people may **underestimate** the risk — they may believe things to be a **lower risk** than they actually are. This could be due to a **lack of information** making them **unaware** of the **factors** that contribute to diseases like CVD.

Practice Questions

Q1 Describe how an atheroma forms.

Q2 What is the role of fibrin in the blood clotting process?

Q3 Describe why high blood pressure increases the risk of CVD.

Q4 Give three factors that increase the risk of CVD but can't be controlled.

Q5 Give one reason why a person may underestimate the risk of developing CVD.

Exam Questions

Q1 Explain why people might overestimate the risk of developing CVD. [2 marks]

Q2 On the right is a diagram showing the process of blood clotting.

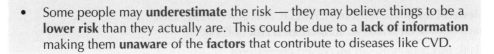

   a) Give the name of enzyme X. [1 mark]

   b) Name three things which make up a blood clot. [1 mark]

   c) What type of ions are involved in the conversion of prothrombin to enzyme X? [1 mark]

   d) People with the disorder called hypoprothrombinaemia have a reduced amount of prothrombin in their blood.
      Explain the likely effect this will have on their blood clotting mechanism. [2 marks]

PROTHROMBIN

THROMBOPLASTIN →   FIBRINOGEN

ENZYME X →

blood clot

Q3 Describe how atheromas can increase the risk that a person will suffer from a heart attack. [4 marks]

Q4* Explain how smoking can increase the risk of developing CVD. [6 marks]

* You will be assessed on the quality of your written response in this question.

Atherosclerosis, thrombosis — more like a spelling test than biology...

There's a lot to take in here, I know, but the basic process is — an atheroma forms in an artery, which can cause thrombosis (blood clotting), which can lead to CVD. Many factors increase the risk of developing CVD.

Lipids, CVD and Reducing Risk

Just when you thought it was safe... There's some more on risk factors for CVD coming up and some data analysis. Does the fun never end/start [delete as appropriate]?

High Blood Cholesterol Increases the Risk of CVD

1) **Cholesterol** is a type of **lipid** (see page 15) that is made in the body.

2) Some is **needed** for the body to **function normally**.

3) Cholesterol needs to be attached to **protein** to be moved around, so the body forms **lipoproteins** — substances composed of both **protein** and **lipid**. There are **two types** of lipoprotein:

HIGH DENSITY LIPOPROTEINS (HDLs)	LOW DENSITY LIPOPROTEINS (LDLs)
1) They are **mainly protein**.	1) They are **mainly lipid**.
2) They transport **cholesterol** from **body tissues** to the **liver** where it's **recycled** or **excreted**.	2) They transport cholesterol from the **liver** to the **blood**, where it circulates until needed by cells.
3) Their function is to **reduce total blood cholesterol** when the level is **too high**.	3) Their function is to **increase total blood cholesterol** when the level is **too low**.

4) **High total blood cholesterol level** (the level of HDL, LDL and other cholesterol) and **high LDL level** have both been linked to an **increased risk** of **CVD**.

5) As you saw on page 108, this is because an **increased cholesterol level** is thought to increase **atheroma formation**.

Here's How to Analyse Data on the Link Between Cholesterol and CVD

Studies are carried out by scientists to see if there are **links** between various **risk factors** and **CVD**. You can **analyse data** from these studies to determine whether there's **enough evidence** to suggest a link.

EXAMPLE:

There's more on interpreting data on risk factors on pages 116-117.

The graph shows the results of a study involving **27 939 American women**. The **LDL cholesterol level** was **measured** for each woman. These women were then **followed** for an average of **8 years** and the **occurrence** of **cardiovascular events** (e.g. heart attack, surgery on coronary arteries) or **death** from cardiovascular diseases was **recorded**. The **relative risk** of a cardiovascular event, **adjusted** for **other factors** that can affect cardiovascular disease, was then calculated.

Analysing this data might involve:

1) <u>Describing the data</u> — The **relative risk** of a cardiovascular event **increases** as the level of **LDL cholesterol** in the blood **increases**.

2) <u>Drawing conclusions</u> — The graph shows a **positive correlation** between the **relative risk** of a cardiovascular event and the level of **LDL cholesterol** in the blood.

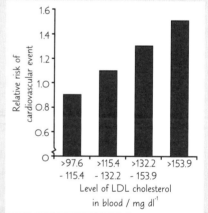

3) <u>Checking any conclusions are valid</u> — Make sure any conclusions **match** the data, e.g.

- This data only looked at **women** — no males were involved, so you can't say that this trend is true for **everyone**.

- You can't say that a high LDL cholesterol level is **correlated with** an increased risk of **heart attacks**, because the data shows **all** first cardiovascular events, including surgery on coronary arteries.

- Also, you can't conclude that a high LDL cholesterol level **caused** the increased relative risk of a cardiovascular event — there may be other reasons for the trend.

There's more on correlation and cause on page 8.

<u>Other things to think about</u> — A **large sample size** was used (27 939). Data based on large samples is **better** than data based on small samples. This is because a large sample is **more representative** of the whole population (i.e. it shares more of the various **characteristics** of the population).

Lipids, CVD and Reducing Risk

Lifestyle Advice to Reduce the Risk of CVD is Based on Scientific Research

The **results** from **scientific studies** into the risk factors for CVD are published in **scientific journals**. **Government organisations** (like the **NHS**) and the **media** report the findings to the **general public**. People can use this information to **make choices** about their **lifestyle**, so they can **reduce** their chance of developing CVD.

EXAMPLE: DIET

1) Scientific research has linked a **diet high in saturated fat** to an **increased risk** of CVD (see page 108).

   - This information can be used to **educate people** about the risk of **certain diets** and to encourage them to **reduce** their saturated fat intake.

   - The **Food Standards Agency** encourages **food manufacturers** to label their products to show the amount of **saturated fat** in them, so people can make an **informed choice** about what they eat.

2) Scientific studies have also shown that **obese** people are **more likely** to develop CVD. **Obesity indicators** such as **waist-to-hip ratio** or **BMI (body mass index)** can be used to assess if people are **overweight** or **obese**.

   Waist-to-hip ratio is calculated using this formula:

   $$\text{Waist-to-hip ratio} = \frac{\text{waist (cm)}}{\text{hips (cm)}}$$

   BMI is calculated using this formula:

   $$\text{BMI} = \frac{\text{body mass (kg)}}{\text{height}^2 \text{ (m}^2\text{)}}$$

   A 'normal' BMI for adults is between 18 and 25.

   Example:
   Calculate the BMI of a person who weighs 63 kg and is 1.7 m tall.

   $$\text{BMI} = \frac{\text{body mass (kg)}}{\text{height}^2 \text{ (m}^2\text{)}}$$

   $$= 63 \div 1.7^2 = \textbf{21.8 kg m}^{-2}$$

   The results of these obesity indicators are compared to 'normal' values in a **published data table**. For example, if a male has a waist-to-hip ratio of more than 1.0, he is carrying too much weight around his abdomen. If someone is overweight or obese, then that person can make **choices** to **reduce** their **weight** and reduce their **risk** of CVD — e.g. they may go on a low-calorie **diet** or **increase** their activity level. These obesity indicators can then be used to **monitor** the **effects** any **changes** in lifestyle have on the person's weight.

EXAMPLE: SMOKING

1) Scientific research has linked **smoking** to an **increased risk** of CVD.
2) This research has led to **TV adverts** and **warnings** on **cigarette packets** about the risks of smoking. The NHS encourages people to give up by giving **free advice** and **prescribing nicotine patches**.
3) All of this encourages people to **stop** smoking and so reduce their risk of CVD.

EXAMPLE: EXERCISE

1) Scientific research has linked **inactivity** to an **increased risk** of CVD.
2) This research has led to campaigns that encourage people to **exercise more frequently** to reduce their risk of CVD.

Practice Questions

Q1 What is a lipoprotein?
Q2 Why are obesity indicators useful?
Q3 Give two examples of how people can be encouraged to stop smoking.

Exam Questions

$$\text{Waist-to-hip ratio} = \frac{\text{waist (cm)}}{\text{hips (cm)}}$$

$$\text{BMI} = \frac{\text{body mass (kg)}}{\text{height}^2 \text{ (m}^2\text{)}}$$

Q1 A person's hip measurement is 95 cm and their waist measurement is 76 cm. They are 1.68 m tall and they have a BMI of 18.9 kg m^{-2}.

   a) Use the formula shown above to calculate the person's waist-to-hip ratio. [1 mark]
   b) Use the BMI formula shown above to calculate the person's body mass. [2 marks]

Q2 a) Describe the differences in structure and function between high density lipoproteins and low density lipoproteins. [3 marks]
   b) Low density lipoproteins are sometimes referred to as 'bad cholesterol'. Explain why low density lipoproteins are sometimes referred to in this way. [1 mark]

Revise more to decrease the risk of exam failure...

There you go — some free lifestyle advice for you. In fact, I'd pay attention to all the lifestyle advice on this page. Taking it on board could be good for your health and good for your grades... It doesn't get much better than that.

Treatment of CVD

It's not all doom and gloom with CVD — there are some different treatments available.

Drugs Can be Used to Treat CVD

Although **prevention** is **better** than **cure**, there are some **treatments** for CVD.
Here's **how** four of them work, plus their **benefits and risks**:

1) Antihypertensives Reduce High Blood Pressure

These drugs include **beta-blockers** (which **reduce** the **strength** of the **heartbeat**) and **vasodilators** (which **widen** the **blood vessels**). They also include **diuretics**, most of which work by **reducing** the amount of **sodium** that's **reabsorbed** by the **blood** in the kidneys. This results in **less water** being reabsorbed (due to **osmosis**), which **reduces blood volume**.

See pages 66-67 for more on osmosis.

All of these drugs **reduce blood pressure**, so there's **less chance** of **damage** occurring to the walls of the arteries. This **reduces** the risk of **atheromas** forming and **blood clots** developing (see pages 106-107).

BENEFITS:	RISKS:
The **different types** of antihypertensives work in **different ways**, so they can be given in **combination** to reduce blood pressure. Also, blood pressure can be **monitored at home**, so the patient can see if the drugs are **working**.	**Palpitations** (rapid beating of the heart), **abnormal heart rhythms, fainting, headaches** and **drowsiness** are all side effects of these drugs caused by the **blood pressure** becoming **too low**. Other side effects include **allergic reactions** and **depression**.

2) Statins Reduce Cholesterol in the Blood

Statins **reduce blood cholesterol** in humans by **reducing** the amount of 'bad' LDL cholesterol (see page 110) **produced** inside the **liver**. A lower blood cholesterol level **reduces atheroma formation**, which reduces the risk of CVD.

BENEFITS:	RISKS:
Statins reduce the risk of **developing** CVD.	Side effects include **muscle** and **joint pain**, **digestive system problems** and an **increased risk of diabetes**. **Nosebleeds, headaches** and **nausea** are also common side effects.

3) Anticoagulants Reduce the Formation of Blood Clots

Anticoagulants (e.g. warfarin and heparin) **reduce blood clotting**. This means blood clots are **less likely** to form at sites of **damage** in artery walls. So there's **less chance** of a **blood vessel** becoming **blocked** by a blood clot (see pages 106-107), reducing the risk of CVD.

BENEFITS:	RISKS:
Anticoagulants can be used to treat people who **already have blood clots** or **CVD** — they **prevent** any existing blood clots from **growing any larger** and prevent any **new blood clots** from **forming**. However, anticoagulants **can't get rid** of **existing** blood clots.	If a person taking these drugs is badly **injured**, the reduction in blood clotting can cause **excessive bleeding**, which can lead to **fainting** (and in serious cases **death**). Other side effects include **allergic reactions, osteoporosis** (weakened bones) and **swelling** of the tissues. These drugs can also **damage the fetus** if they're taken during pregnancy.

Treatment of CVD

4) Platelet Inhibitory Drugs Also Reduce the Formation of Blood Clots

Platelet inhibitory drugs (e.g. **aspirin**) are a type of **anticoagulant** (see previous page). They work by **preventing platelets clumping together** to form a blood clot. So, they **reduce** the formation of **blood clots**, reducing the chance of a blood vessel becoming **blocked** by a clot.

BENEFITS:

As with anticoagulants, these can be used to treat people who **already have blood clots** or **CVD**.

RISKS:

Side effects include **rashes, diarrhoea, nausea, liver function problems** and **excessive bleeding**, especially after a serious injury (see previous page).

These plate inhibitory drugs were doing a good job of preventing the plates from clumping together.

Practice Questions

Q1 State two benefits of treating CVD with antihypertensives.

Q2 How do anticoagulants work to reduce the risk of CVD?

Exam Questions

Q1 The graph below shows the numbers of prescriptions used in the prevention and treatment of CVD in England between 2006 and 2013.

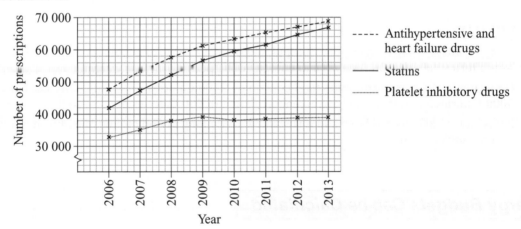

a) Describe the general trend in the number of prescriptions of each treatment of CVD shown by the graph above. [2 marks]

b) State the least commonly prescribed treatment and give one benefit and one risk of that type of treatment. [2 marks]

c) Using values rounded to 2 significant figures, calculate the percentage increase in statin prescriptions between 2006 and 2011. Give your answer as a whole number. [1 mark]

d) Explain how statins reduce the risk of developing CVD. [2 marks]

Q2 A patient who is at risk of developing coronary heart disease (CHD) goes to see his doctor. The patient is obese and suffers from high blood pressure.

a) State one type of drug the doctor could prescribe to treat the patient's high blood pressure and explain how it reduces the risk of CHD. [2 marks]

b) Give one disadvantage of taking this drug. [1 mark]

I'd need several spoonfuls of sugar to help all these medicines go down...

These drugs don't cure the problem — they don't get rid of existing atheromas or blood clots, they just prevent them from getting any worse. Still, it's good to know that there are treatments out there.

Diet and Energy

Obesity is a risk factor for cardiovascular disease (CVD) and other diseases too, so it's important to maintain a healthy weight. Weight is affected by your diet as well as how much energy you use doing things like playing video games and stealing traffic cones*...

Organisms Take In and Use Up Energy

1) Organisms need a **supply** of **energy**, so that they can **grow**, **move**, **reproduce** etc. — in animals this energy is provided in the form of **food**.

2) **Energy budget** is a term used to describe the **amount of energy taken in** by an organism (in food) **and** the amount of energy **used up** by an organism (e.g. by moving).

Henri knew the cheese would push him over budget — but what harm could it do?

Energy Imbalance Causes Changes in Weight

Ideally, a person should **take in** the **same amount** of energy as **they use up** — their energy budget should be **balanced**. If there's an **imbalance** in the energy budget, it will **affect** the **person's weight**:

WEIGHT GAIN

1) If energy **intake** is **higher** than energy **output**, the **excess energy** will be turned into **fat reserves** by the body, so the person will **gain weight**.

2) For example, if a person **consumes** food containing **4000 Calories** a day and carries out **activities** that burn **3000 Calories** a day, there'll be an **excess** of **1000 Calories** per day, so they'll put on weight.

3) If the energy difference is **a lot** and it's **sustained** over a **long period** of time, the person could become **obese**.

WEIGHT LOSS

1) If energy **intake** is **lower** than energy **output**, the body will have to **get** more energy from somewhere — it'll **turn** some of its **fat reserves** into energy, so the person will **lose weight**.

2) For example, if a person **consumes** food containing **2500 Calories** a day but carries out **activities** that burn **3000 Calories** a day, they will have an energy **deficit** of **500 Calories** per day, so they'll lose weight.

3) If this energy difference is **large** and is **sustained** over a **long period** of time, the person is likely to become **underweight**.

Energy Budgets Can be Calculated

1) The **recommended daily intake** of Calories is **2000** for **women** and **2500** for **men**.

2) **Different activities** use up **different amounts of Calories**, as shown in the table.

3) You can use this information to **calculate** people's **energy budgets** — you'll need to use this formula: **energy input – energy output = energy budget**

Activity	Number of Calories used per hour
Cooking	159
Dog walking	224
Gardening	328
Swimming	513

You need to multiply these figures by the number of hours the activity lasts.

- Ranjit takes in the recommended daily intake of Calories a day (**2500**). He swims for **one hour** and does **one hour** of **gardening** each day. He also **cooks** for **an hour** each day. His **bodily functions** (e.g. breathing) use up **1500** Calories per day. So his energy budget is:
  Energy input – energy output = energy budget
  $2500 – (1500 + 513 + 328 + 159) = 0$
  Ranjit's energy budget is **balanced** — he takes in as much as he uses up.

- Christina takes in **2000** Calories a day. She **walks the dog** for **an hour** every **morning** and every **night**. Her **bodily functions** use up **1200** Calories per day. So her energy budget is:
  Energy input – energy output = energy budget
  $2000 – (1200 + 224 + 224) = 352$ Calories
  Christina has an **excess** of **352 Calories** per day.

* CGP does not condone the stealing of traffic cones.

Diet and Energy

You Can **Measure** the **Amount** of **Vitamin C** in Your **Food**

1) Along with balancing their energy budget, people need to take in the right **vitamins** and **minerals** to remain **healthy**. You can carry out an **experiment** to find out **how much vitamin C** is in a **food sample**.

2) This can be done using a chemical called **DCPIP** — a **blue** dye that turns **colourless** in the presence of vitamin C. Here's how you do it:

First you need to make a calibration curve. To do this you need to:

1) Make up several **vitamin C solutions** of **different, known concentrations**. Ideally, you need about **six** different solutions.

2) Use a measuring cylinder to measure out a **set volume** of **DCPIP** (at a **set concentration**) into a test tube.

3) **Add** one of the **vitamin C solutions** to the DCPIP, **drop by drop**, using a pipette.

4) Gently **shake** the test tube for a **set length of time**, timed using a stopwatch, after each drop of vitamin C solution is added.

5) When the solution turns **colourless**, **record** the **volume** (no. of drops) of vitamin C solution that has been added.

6) **Repeat** the experiment **twice more**, with the **same** solution, and take an **average** of the three readings.

7) Make sure you keep **all** the other **variables** constant during the experiment, e.g. temperature.

8) **Repeat** the above procedure with **each solution**.

9) Use the results to draw a **curve of best fit**, showing volume of vitamin C solution against its concentration — this is the **calibration curve**.

> You could make up the different concentrations using a serial dilution technique — see page 21.

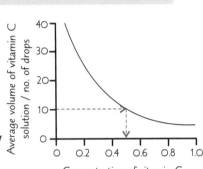

Then you can test the **unknown solution** in the same way as the known concentrations and use the calibration curve to find its concentration. E.g. 10 drops of an **unknown solution** is needed to turn DCPIP colourless. Reading **across** the calibration curve from a volume of **10 drops** shows that the concentration of vitamin C in the unknown solution is **0.5 mg cm⁻³**.

Practice Questions

Q1 What is an energy budget?

Q2 Explain how an energy imbalance causes weight gain.

Exam Questions

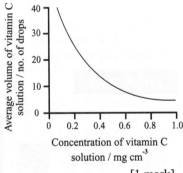

Q1 The graph on the right shows a calibration curve for vitamin C concentration.

    a) 25 drops of a food sample of unknown vitamin C concentration were needed to turn DCPIP colourless. Use the calibration curve to work out the concentration of the solution. [1 mark]

    b) State three variables that should be kept constant when making a calibration curve to test an unknown solution for vitamin C concentration. [3 marks]

Q2 A woman takes in 2000 Calories a day in food. She needs 1200 Calories each day to maintain her basic bodily functions. She also swims for two hours and does two hours of gardening each day.

    a) i) Use the table on page 114 to calculate her energy budget. [1 mark]

       ii) Explain what short-term effect this energy budget will have on her weight. [1 mark]

    b) If the woman sustained this energy budget over a long period of time, what effect would it have on her weight? [1 mark]

Eat beans to increase the amount of Calories used for bodily functions...

If you've done an hour's revision you've used up around 120 Calories (which is 90 more than you'd use just sat on your bum watching telly)... well done you — go and have a biscuit to celebrate (and even up your energy balance).

Interpreting Data on Risk Factors

Being able to interpret data on the risk factors for a variety of diseases is a really useful skill — for Biology, and for life.

Here's How to **Analyse** and **Interpret Data** About **Illness** or **Mortality**

Analysing illness or mortality data (for any disease) allows you to determine if something is a **risk factor**. Remember to watch out for mixing up **correlation** and **causation** in any data you're given — just because results are correlated **doesn't prove** that a change in one causes a change in the other (see page 8).

STUDY ONE

A study was carried out to analyse data, gathered from **53 studies worldwide**, about the **link** between **smoking** and **breast cancer**. The study looked at **22 255** women **with** breast cancer and **40 832** women **without** breast cancer, all of whom reported **drinking no alcohol**. The results below show the **relative risk** of breast cancer for women with **different smoking histories**.

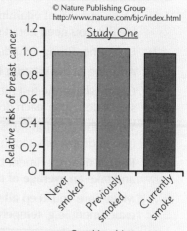

© Nature Publishing Group
http://www.nature.com/bjc/index.html

Analysing this data might involve:

1) <u>Describing the data</u> — The results show that the **relative risk** of breast cancer for women who don't drink alcohol is **similar regardless of smoking history**.

2) <u>Drawing conclusions</u> — The results show that for women who don't drink alcohol, smoking is **not associated** with an **increased risk** of breast cancer.

3) <u>Checking conclusions are valid</u> — This data appears to show **no link** between smoking history and the relative risk of breast cancer in women who don't drink, but you **can't** say that smoking **doesn't affect** breast cancer risk at all. The data **doesn't** take into account women who drink. Smoking and alcohol **together** could **affect the risk** of breast cancer. Also, the study doesn't take into account **other factors** that could affect risk of breast cancer such as the use of **hormone replacement treatment**, **physical activity**, etc.

Sometimes The **Evidence** is **Conflicting**

1) The **evidence** from **one study** alone **wouldn't usually be enough** to conclude that a factor is a **health risk**.

2) **Similar studies** would be carried out to investigate the link. If these studies came to the **same conclusion**, the conclusion would become **increasingly accepted**.

3) Sometimes studies come up with **conflicting evidence** though — evidence that leads to a **different conclusion** than other studies. For example, one study may conclude that a factor <u>isn't</u> **a health risk**, whereas another study may conclude that the **same** factor <u>is</u> **a health risk**:

STUDY TWO

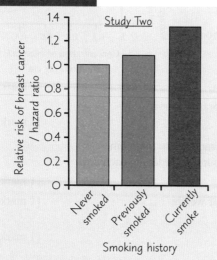

A study was carried out to determine if smoking is linked to an increased risk of breast cancer. **116 544** women without breast cancer in **California** were sent **questionnaires** to establish their **smoking history** and other personal information. The women were then followed for **5 years**. The results on the left show the **relative risk of breast cancer**, **adjusted** for **other factors** such as age and alcohol consumption, for women with **different smoking histories**.

1) <u>Describing the data</u> — The results show that the **relative risk** of breast cancer for women in California is **higher** for women who **previously smoked** or **still smoke** compared to those who have never smoked.

2) <u>Drawing conclusions</u> — The results show that for women in California, smoking **is associated** with an **increased risk** of breast cancer.

3) <u>Commenting on the conflicting evidence</u> — This second study shows that smoking **is linked** to an increased risk of breast cancer, which **conflicts** with the evidence from **study one** (see above). Because the two studies have produced conflicting evidence, **more results** would be needed in order to **fully assess** if smoking is an **important health risk** for the development of **breast cancer**.

Interpreting Data on Risk Factors

The Design of Studies is Important

A **well-designed study** will give you **valid** and **reliable** (repeatable and reproducible) results.
Here are some things to look out for when evaluating study design:

1) **Sample size** — the **greater** the number of people used in a study, the **more reliable** the results.

   Selecting the sample should also be done carefully. The sample should be <u>representative</u> (i.e. it should reflect the variety of characteristics that are found in the population you're interested in studying) so that the results can be <u>generalised</u> to the whole population. A sample that is <u>unrepresentative</u> is <u>biased</u> and can't <u>reliably</u> be generalised to the whole population.

2) **Variables** — the **more variables** (other factors that could affect the results) that have been **controlled** in a study, the **more reliable** the results. This also makes the results more **valid** — by controlling the variables, you're making sure that you're only testing the thing you want to.

3) **Data collection** — the **less bias** involved in collecting the data, the **more reliable** the results.

4) **Controls** — the presence of controls **increases** the validity of the results.

5) **Repetition** by other scientists — if other scientists produce the **same results**, then the results are **more reliable**.

EXAMPLE: STUDY ONE

1) **Sample size** — The study had a **large** sample size of **63 087 women** in total, which makes the results more reliable.

2) **Variables** — The study didn't take into account **some variables** that can affect the risk of breast cancer, like **hormone replacement therapy** and **physical activity**. This could have affected the results (decreasing their reliability and validity).

3) **Data collection** — The data was collected from **53 other studies** but we don't know how those other studies were designed.

4) **Controls** — There were a large number of controls, **40 832 women**. This increases the validity of the results.

5) **Repetition by other scientists** — Study two **doesn't agree** with the conclusion of study one.

EXAMPLE: STUDY TWO

1) **Sample size** — This study had a **really large** sample size of **116 544 women**, which makes the results more reliable.

2) **Variables** — This study took into account **other variables** like **hormone replacement therapy**, **physical activity**, alcohol consumption, etc. This **increases** the **reliability** and **validity** of the results.

3) **Data collection** — The data was collected from **questionnaires**, which can be biased. This **decreases** the **reliability** of the results.

4) **Repetition by other scientists** — Study one **doesn't agree** with the conclusion of study two.

Practice Questions

Q1 What is meant by conflicting evidence?

Q2 Why is it important to look at the data collection method when evaluating study design?

Exam Question

Q1 The results of a study involving 168 000 people in 63 countries have shown a strong correlation between waist measurement and risk of cardiovascular disease. Analysis of the results has shown that waist circumference is independently associated with cardiovascular disease.

    a) Give two reasons why the study provides strong evidence for a link between waist measurement and risk of cardiovascular disease.   [2 marks]

    b) Give two ways that the results of this study could be made more reliable.   [2 marks]

Exams — definitely a health risk...

There's more on controlling the variables, validity, the importance of repeating results and much, much more in the Development of Practical Skills section at the front of this book. If you've not read it yet, you should. It's a hoot.

Pathogens and Communicable Diseases

Coughs and sneezes spread diseases, as they say. Well now it's time to find out why...

Pathogens Can Cause Communicable Diseases

1) **Disease** is a **condition** that **impairs** the **normal functioning** of an **organism**. Both **plants** and **animals** can get diseases.

2) A **pathogen** is an organism that causes **disease**. Types of pathogen include **bacteria, viruses, fungi** and **protoctista** (a type of single-celled eukaryotic organism).

3) A **communicable disease** is a disease that can **spread between organisms**.

4) Here are some examples of **communicable diseases**, as well as the **pathogens** that cause them:

You might have heard communicable diseases referred to as infectious diseases.

Disease:	Affects:	Pathogen Responsible:			
		Bacterium	Virus	Fungus	Protoctist
Tuberculosis (TB)	Animals, typically humans and cattle	✔			
Bacterial meningitis	Humans	✔			
Ring rot	Potatoes, tomatoes	✔			
HIV/AIDS	Humans		✔		
Influenza	Animals, including humans		✔		
Tobacco mosaic virus	Plants		✔		
Black sigatoka	Banana plants			✔	
Ringworm	Cattle			✔	
Athlete's foot	Humans			✔	
Potato/tomato late blight	Potatoes/tomatoes				✔
Malaria	Animals, including humans				✔

Communicable Diseases Can be Transmitted Directly or Indirectly

1) **Direct transmission** is when a disease is transmitted **directly** from one organism to another. Direct transmission can happen in several ways, including: **droplet infection** (**coughing** or **sneezing** tiny droplets of mucus or saliva directly onto someone), **sexual intercourse**, or **touching** an infected organism.

Examples:
- **HIV** can be transmitted directly between humans via **sexual intercourse**.
- **Athlete's foot** can be spread via **touch**.

2) **Indirect transmission** is when a disease is transmitted from one organism to another **via an intermediate**. Intermediates include **air, water, food** or **another organism** (known as a **vector**).

Spores are the cells that some organisms use to reproduce asexually, including some protoctista and all fungi.

Examples:
- **Potato/tomato late blight** is spread when **spores** are carried between plants — first in the **air**, then in **water**.
- **Malaria** is spread between humans (and other animals) via **mosquitoes** — insects that feed on blood. The mosquitoes act as **vectors** — they don't cause malaria themselves, they just spread the protoctista that cause it.

Pathogens and Communicable Diseases

Living Conditions, Climate and Social Factors Affect Disease Transmission

1) **Overcrowded** living conditions **increase** the **transmission** of many communicable diseases.

> **Example:**
>
> **TB** is spread **directly** via **droplet infection** (see previous page). It's also spread **indirectly** because the bacteria can **remain** in the **air** for **long periods** of time and infect new people. The risk of TB infection is **increased** when **lots of people** live **crowded together** in a small space.

2) **Climate** can also affect the spread of communicable diseases.

> **Examples:**
>
> - **Potato/tomato late blight** is especially common during **wet summers** because the **spores** need **water** to **spread** (see previous page).
> - **Malaria** is most common in **tropical countries**, which are **humid** and **hot**. This is because these are the **ideal conditions** for **mosquitoes** (the malaria **vectors**) to **breed**.

3) In **humans**, **social factors** can increase the transmission of communicable diseases.

> **Example:**
>
> The risk of **HIV** infection is high in places where there's **limited access** to:
> - **good healthcare** — people are **less likely** to be **diagnosed** and **treated** for HIV, and the **most effective anti-HIV drugs** are **less likely** to be **available**, so the virus is **more likely** to be **passed on** to others.
> - **good health education** — to **inform people** about how HIV is **transmitted** and how it can be **avoided**, e.g. through **safe-sex practices** like using condoms.

Practice Questions

Q1 What is a communicable disease?
Q2 Name a virus that affects plants.
Q3 What type of pathogen causes malaria?
Q4 Give one way in which a disease can be transferred directly.
Q5 Give one example of how climate can affect the spread of a disease.

Exam Questions

Q1 Which of the following pathogens is responsible for causing black sigatoka?
  A bacterium   B virus   C fungus   D protoctista   [1 mark]

Q2 The most common way for the tobacco mosaic virus to be transferred between garden plants is via gardeners' hands and tools.
  a) Is this an example of direct or indirect disease transmission? Explain your answer.   [1 mark]
  b) Suggest one thing that gardeners could do to try to prevent transmission of the tobacco mosaic virus between plants.   [1 mark]

Q3 There are more deaths from tuberculosis in low-income countries than in high-income countries.
  a) What type of pathogen causes tuberculosis?   [1 mark]
  b) Suggest two reasons why more deaths from tuberculosis occur in low-income countries compared to wealthier countries.   [2 marks]

My computer has a virus — I knew I shouldn't have sneezed on it...

Different communicable diseases are caused by different types of pathogens. Make sure you understand how these pesky pathogens pass from organism to another, cos next up is how organisms put up their primary line of defence...

Defence Against Pathogens

Well, all that stuff about disease is making me feel a bit on edge. Luckily both animals and plants have a few tricks up their sleeves to defend themselves against pathogen invasion...

Animals Have Several Barriers to Prevent Infection

1) **Pathogens** need to **enter** an **organism** in order to **cause disease**.
2) So most **animals**, including **humans**, have a range of **primary**, **non-specific defences** to help **prevent** this from happening. These include:

> Non-specific means they work in the same way for all pathogens. There's more on non-specific and specific responses on page 122.

Skin — this acts as a **physical barrier**, **blocking pathogens** from **entering** the body. It also acts as a **chemical barrier** by producing **chemicals** that are **antimicrobial** and can **lower pH**, **inhibiting** the **growth** of pathogens.

Mucous membranes — these **protect body openings** that are **exposed** to the **environment** (such as the mouth, nostrils, ears, genitals and anus). Some membranes **secrete mucus** — a sticky substance that **traps pathogens** and contains **antimicrobial enzymes**.

Blood clotting — a blood clot is a mesh of **protein (fibrin) fibres**. Blood clots **plug wounds** to **prevent pathogen entry** and **blood loss**. They're formed by a series of **chemical reactions** that take place when **platelets** (fragments of cells in the blood) are exposed to **damaged blood vessels**.

Inflammation — the signs of inflammation include **swelling, pain, heat** and **redness**. It can be triggered by **tissue damage** — the damaged tissue releases **molecules**, which **increase** the **permeability** of the **blood vessels**, so they start to **leak fluid** into the surrounding area. This causes **swelling** and helps to **isolate any pathogens** that may have entered the damaged tissue. The molecules also cause **vasodilation** (widening of the blood vessels), which **increases blood flow** to the affected area. This makes the area **hot** and brings **white blood cells** to the area to fight off any pathogens that may be present.

Wound repair — the **skin** is able to repair itself in the event of **injury** and **re-form** a barrier against pathogen entry. The surface is repaired by the **outer layer of skin cells dividing** and **migrating** to the edges of the wound. The **tissue below the wound** then **contracts** to bring the edges of the wound closer together. It is repaired using **collagen fibres** — too many collagen fibres and you'll end up with a **scar**.

Expulsive reflexes — e.g. **coughing** and **sneezing**. A **sneeze** happens when the **mucous membranes** in the **nostrils** are **irritated** by things such as **dust** or **dirt**. A **cough** stems from **irritation** in the **respiratory tract**. Both coughing and sneezing are an attempt to **expel foreign objects**, including **pathogens**, from the body. They happen **automatically**.

It was all going so beautifully 'til Josie felt an expulsive reflex coming on.

If pathogens make it past these defences, they'll have the animal's **immune system** to deal with — see pages 122-125.

Defence Against Pathogens

Plants Have Physical Defences Against Pathogens...

Like animals, **plants** have **physical defences** against infection by **pathogens**.

1) Most plant leaves and stems have a **waxy cuticle**, which provides a **physical barrier** against pathogen entry. It may also **stop water** collecting on the leaf, which could reduce the risk of infection by pathogens that are transferred between plants in water.

2) Plant cells themselves are surrounded by **cell walls**. These form a **physical barrier** against pathogens that make it past the waxy cuticle.

3) Plants produce a **polysaccharide** called **callose**. Callose gets **deposited** between **plant cell walls** and **plasma membranes** during times of **stress**, e.g. **pathogen invasion**. Callose deposition may make it **harder** for **pathogens** to **enter cells**. Callose deposition at the **plasmodesmata** (small channels in the cell walls) may **limit the spread** of **viruses** between cells.

...as Well as Chemical Ones

1) Plants don't just rely on physical defences. They also produce **antimicrobial chemicals** (including **antibiotics**, see page 128) which **kill pathogens** or **inhibit** their **growth**.

Examples:

• Some plants produce chemicals called **saponins**. These are thought to **destroy** the **cell membranes** of **fungi** and other pathogens.

• Plants also produce chemicals called **phytoalexins**, which **inhibit** the **growth** of **fungi** and other pathogens.

2) Other chemicals secreted by plants are **toxic** to **insects** — this reduces the amount of **insect-feeding** on plants and therefore reduces the risk of infection by **plant viruses** carried by **insect vectors**.

Practice Questions

Q1 Give two ways in which skin helps defend animals against infection by pathogens.

Q2 What is the function of the mucous membranes?

Q3 What are expulsive reflexes?

Q4 Give one example of a plant chemical defence against pathogens.

Exam Question

Q1 The tobacco mosaic virus is a virus that affects plants.

a) The virus usually infects plants that have been damaged by feeding insects. Suggest why damaged plant cells are more susceptible to infection by the virus than normal cells. [2 marks]

b) Suggest one way a plant may respond to limit the spread of infection once the tobacco mosaic virus enters a plant. [1 mark]

Hiding under the duvet — a student's primary defence against revision...
Plant defences against pathogens are the "absolute bomb", or so says a colleague of mine. He's very excited by them. You don't need to be excited by them (although it's fine if you are), but it might help to learn them. And all those animal primary defences too. You've got your immune system to learn about next. What an absolute treat...

The Immune System

If a pathogen enters the body, the immune system will respond. Bad luck pathogens...

Foreign Antigens Trigger an Immune Response

1) **Antigens** are **molecules** (usually proteins or polysaccharides) found on the **surface** of **cells**.

2) When a pathogen (like a bacterium) **invades** the body, the antigens on its cell surface are **identified as foreign**, which **activates cells** in the **immune system**.

3) The immune response involves **specific** and **non-specific** stages. The **non-specific** response happens in the **same way** for **all microorganisms** — whatever foreign antigens they have. The **specific** response is **antigen-specific** — it is aimed at **specific pathogens**. It involves **white blood cells** called **T** and **B lymphocytes**.

There are Four Main Stages in the Immune Response

1) Phagocytes Engulf Pathogens

A **phagocyte** is a type of **white blood cell** that carries out **phagocytosis** (engulfment of pathogens).
They're found in the **blood** and in **tissues** and carry out a **non-specific** immune response. Here's how they work:

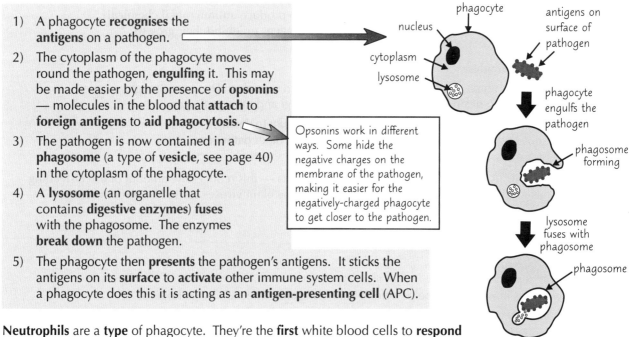

1) A phagocyte **recognises** the **antigens** on a pathogen.

2) The cytoplasm of the phagocyte moves round the pathogen, **engulfing** it. This may be made easier by the presence of **opsonins** — molecules in the blood that **attach** to **foreign antigens** to **aid phagocytosis**.

> Opsonins work in different ways. Some hide the negative charges on the membrane of the pathogen, making it easier for the negatively-charged phagocyte to get closer to the pathogen.

3) The pathogen is now contained in a **phagosome** (a type of **vesicle**, see page 40) in the cytoplasm of the phagocyte.

4) A **lysosome** (an organelle that contains **digestive enzymes**) **fuses** with the phagosome. The enzymes **break down** the pathogen.

5) The phagocyte then **presents** the pathogen's antigens. It sticks the antigens on its **surface** to **activate** other immune system cells. When a phagocyte does this it is acting as an **antigen-presenting cell** (APC).

Neutrophils are a **type** of phagocyte. They're the **first** white blood cells to **respond** to a pathogen inside the body. Neutrophils **move towards** a **wound** in response to signals from **cytokines** (proteins that act as messenger molecules — see page 58). The cytokines are released by cells at the site of the wound.

2) Phagocytes Activate T lymphocytes

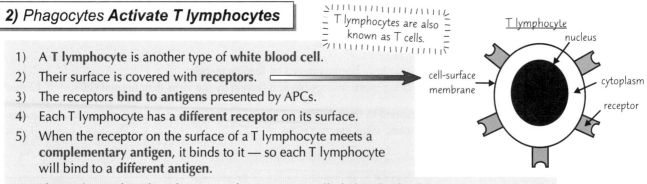

> T lymphocytes are also known as T cells.

1) A **T lymphocyte** is another type of **white blood cell**.

2) Their surface is covered with **receptors**.

3) The receptors **bind to antigens** presented by APCs.

4) Each T lymphocyte has a **different receptor** on its surface.

5) When the receptor on the surface of a T lymphocyte meets a **complementary antigen**, it binds to it — so each T lymphocyte will bind to a **different antigen**.

6) This **activates** the T lymphocyte — the process is called **clonal selection**.

7) The T lymphocyte then undergoes **clonal expansion** — it **divides** to produce **clones** of itself. **Different types** of T lymphocytes carry out **different functions** — see next page.

The Immune System

Different types of activated T lymphocytes include:

1) **T helper cells (TH cells)** — these **release substances** to **activate B lymphocytes** (see below) and **T killer cells**.

2) **T killer cells** (also known as **cytotoxic T cells** or **TC cells**) — these **attach** to and **kill cells** that are infected with a **virus**.

3) **T regulatory cells** — these **suppress** the **immune response** from **other white blood cells**. This helps to stop immune system cells from mistakenly attacking the host's body cells.

T cells, and the other immune system cells they interact with, form the cellular response.

Some activated T lymphocytes become **memory cells** (see next page).

3) T lymphocytes **Activate B lymphocytes**, Which Divide Into **Plasma Cells**

1) **B lymphocytes** are another type of **white blood cell**.

B lymphocytes are also known as B cells.

2) They're covered with proteins called **antibodies**.

3) Antibodies **bind to antigens** to form an **antigen-antibody complex**.

4) Each B lymphocyte has a **different shaped antibody** on its surface.

5) When the antibody on the surface of a B lymphocyte meets a **complementary shaped antigen**, it binds to it — so each B lymphocyte will bind to a **different antigen**.

6) This, together with substances **released from T helper cells, activates** the B lymphocyte. This process is another example of **clonal selection**.

7) The activated B lymphocyte **divides**, by mitosis, into **plasma cells** and **memory cells** (see next page). This is another example of **clonal expansion**.

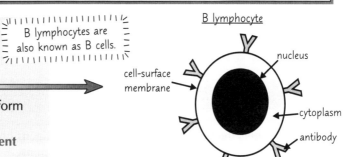

B lymphocyte

- nucleus
- cell-surface membrane
- cytoplasm
- antibody

Cell Signalling

1) Cell signalling is basically how **cells communicate**.

2) A cell may **release** (or present) a **substance** that **binds to the receptors on another cell** — this causes a response of some kind in the other cell.

3) Cell signalling is really important in the **immune response** because it helps to **activate** all the **different types** of **white blood cells** that are needed.

4) For example, **T helper cells** release **interleukins** (a type of **cytokine**) that bind to receptors on **B lymphocytes**. This **activates** the B lymphocytes — the T helper cells are signalling to the B lymphocytes that there's a pathogen in the body.

4) Plasma Cells Make More **Antibodies** to a Specific **Antigen**

1) Plasma cells are **clones** of the B lymphocyte (they're **identical** to the B lymphocyte).

2) They secrete **loads** of the **antibody**, specific to the antigen, into the blood.

3) These antibodies will bind to the antigens on the surface of the pathogen to form **lots** of **antigen-antibody complexes**.

B lymphocytes are part of the humoral response.

4) The **structure** of antibodies is important for their **function**:

- The **variable regions** of the antibody form the **antigen binding sites**. Each antibody has a variable region with a **unique tertiary structure** (due to different amino acid sequences) that's **complementary** to one **specific antigen**. Variable regions differ between antibodies.

- The **hinge region** allows **flexibility** when the antibody binds to the antigen.

- The **constant regions** allow binding to **receptors** on **immune system cells**, e.g. phagocytes. The constant region is the **same** (i.e. it has the same sequence of amino acids) **in all** antibodies.

- **Disulfide bridges** (a type of bond) hold the polypeptide chains of the protein together.

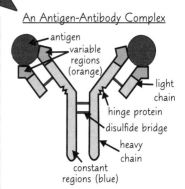

An Antigen-Antibody Complex

- antigen
- variable regions (orange)
- light chain
- hinge protein
- disulfide bridge
- heavy chain
- constant regions (blue)

The Immune System

Antibodies **help** to **clear** an **infection** by:

1) <u>Agglutinating pathogens</u> — each antibody has **two binding sites**, so an antibody can **bind** to **two pathogens** at the **same time** — the pathogens become **clumped together**. Phagocytes then bind to the antibodies and phagocytose a lot of pathogens **all at once**. Antibodies that behave in this way are known as **agglutinins**.

2) <u>Neutralising toxins</u> — like antigens, toxins have **different shapes**. Antibodies called **anti-toxins** can **bind** to the **toxins** produced by pathogens. This **prevents** the toxins from **affecting human cells**, so the toxins are **neutralised** (inactivated). The toxin-antibody complexes are also phagocytosed.

3) <u>Preventing the pathogen binding to human cells</u> — when antibodies bind to the antigens on pathogens, they may **block** the cell surface **receptors** that the pathogens need to **bind to the host cells**. This means the pathogen **can't attach to** or **infect** the host cells.

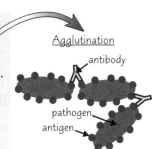
<u>Agglutination</u>
antibody
pathogen
antigen

The **Primary Response** is **Slow**...

1) When a **pathogen** enters the body for the **first time**, the **antigens** on its surface **activate** the **immune system**. This is called the **primary response**.

2) The primary response is **slow** because there **aren't many B lymphocytes** that can make the antibody needed to bind to it.

3) Eventually the body will produce **enough** of the right antibody to overcome the infection. Meanwhile the infected person will show **symptoms** of the disease.

4) After being exposed to an antigen, both T and B lymphocytes produce **memory cells**. These memory cells **remain in the body** for a **long** time.

5) **Memory T lymphocytes** remember the **specific antigen** and will recognise it a second time round. **Memory B lymphocytes** record the specific **antibodies** needed to bind to the antigen.

6) The person is now **immune** — their immune system has the **ability** to respond **quickly** to a second infection.

Don't get the primary response mixed up with primary defences (see p. 120).

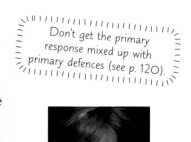
Neil's primary response — to his parents.

...the **Secondary Response** is **Faster**

1) If the **same pathogen** enters the body again, the immune system will produce a **quicker, stronger** immune response — the **secondary response**.

2) **Clonal selection** happens **faster**. Memory B lymphocytes are activated and divide into **plasma cells** that produce the right antibody to the antigen. **Memory T lymphocytes** are activated and divide into the **correct type** of **T lymphocytes** to kill the cell carrying the antigen.

3) The secondary response often gets rid of the pathogen **before** you begin to show any **symptoms**.

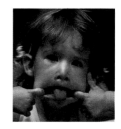
Concentration of the right antibody in the blood.
1st exposure to antigen
primary response
secondary response
2nd exposure to antigen
long interval
10   20   30
Time / days

The **similarities** and **differences** between the primary and secondary responses are summarised in the table:

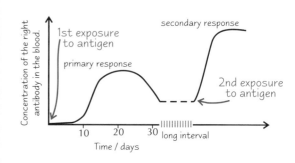

	Primary response	Secondary response
Pathogen	Enters for 1st time	Enters for 2nd time
Speed of response	Slow	Fast
Cells activated	B and T lymphocytes	Memory cells
Symptoms	Yes	No

The Immune System

(see page 48 for more on staining microscope samples).

Here's How to Examine and Draw Blood Smears

1) As the name suggests, a **blood smear** is a sample of blood smeared over a **microscope slide**.

2) **Stains** are added to the sample to make the **different cells** easy to see (see page 48 for more on staining microscope samples).

3) When looking at a blood smear you're likely to see **red blood cells**, **white blood cells** and **platelets** (tiny fragments of cells involved in blood clotting). Some types of white blood cells have **granules** in their cytoplasm (so they look **grainy**) and other types don't.

4) Here's an **example** of what a blood smear looks like:

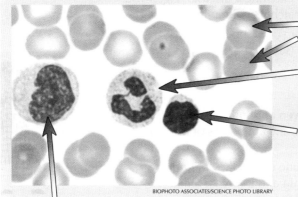

Most of the cells are red blood cells (see page 54). They're easy to spot because they don't have a nucleus.

This is a neutrophil. Its nucleus looks like three interconnected blobs — the posh way of saying this is that the nucleus is 'multi-lobed'. The cytoplasm of a neutrophil is grainy.

This is a lymphocyte. It's much smaller than the neutrophil. The nucleus takes up most of the cell and there's very little cytoplasm to be seen (it's not grainy either). You can't tell whether this is a T lymphocyte or a B lymphocyte under a light microscope.

BIOPHOTO ASSOCIATES/SCIENCE PHOTO LIBRARY

This is a monocyte. It's the biggest white blood cell and a type of phagocyte. It has a kidney-bean shaped nucleus and a non-grainy cytoplasm.

Practice Questions

Q1 What are antigens?

Q2 What structures are found on the surface of T lymphocytes?

Q3 Draw and label the structure of a B lymphocyte.

Q4 Draw and label the structure of an antibody.

Q5 Give two differences between the primary and secondary response.

Exam Questions

Q1 Three types of white blood cell are shown in the table.
Select the row in the table that correctly describes the function of each type of cell.
[1 mark]

		Neutrophil	T helper cell	B lymphocyte
A		Releases interleukins to activate other cells	Divides to form plasma cells	Engulfs pathogens
B		Engulfs pathogens	Divides to form plasma cells	Releases interleukins to activate other cells
C		Releases interleukins to activate other cells	Engulfs pathogens	Divides to form plasma cells
D		Engulfs pathogens	Releases interleukins to activate other cells	Divides to form plasma cells

Q2 IgG is a type of antibody, as well as an agglutinin and opsonin. Suggest how IgG works. [2 marks]

Q3 A scientist is looking at a blood smear under the microscope.
Explain how she will be able to tell the difference between a neutrophil and a B lymphocyte. [3 marks]

Q4 A person had chickenpox as a child. She was exposed to the virus that causes it again as a teenager, but did not experience any symptoms. Explain why. [5 marks]

The student-revision complex — only present the night before an exam...

Memory cells are still B and T lymphocytes, but they're the ones that stick around for a long time. So if a pathogen is stupid enough to invade the body again, these cells can immediately divide into more of themselves, and release antibodies specifically against the pathogen or bind to the pathogen and destroy it. Ha ha (evil laugh).

Immunity and Vaccinations

Immunity is the ability to respond quickly to an infection — because your immune system recognises the foreign antigens. There are different types of immunity though and different ways of developing it. And sometimes your immune system gets a bit mixed up, leading to autoimmunity...

Immunity can be Active or Passive

ACTIVE IMMUNITY

This is the type of immunity you get when **your immune system makes its own antibodies** after being **stimulated** by an **antigen**. There are **two** different types of active immunity:

1) **Natural** — this is when you become immune after **catching a disease**. E.g. if you have measles as a child, you shouldn't be able to catch it again in later life.

2) **Artificial** — this is when you become immune after you've been given a **vaccination** containing a harmless dose of antigen (see next page).

PASSIVE IMMUNITY

This is the type of immunity you get from being **given antibodies made by a different organism** — your immune system **doesn't** produce any antibodies of its own. Again, there are **two** types:

1) **Natural** — this is when a **baby** becomes immune due to the antibodies it receives from its **mother**, through the **placenta** and in **breast milk**.

2) **Artificial** — this is when you become immune after being **injected** with **antibodies** from **someone else**. E.g. if you contract tetanus you can be injected with antibodies against the tetanus toxin, collected from blood donations.

Claire was grateful for her mum's antibodies. She was less grateful for the dress.

There are Similarities and Differences Between Active and Passive Immunity

This handy summary table should help you understand them:

Active immunity	Passive immunity
Requires exposure to antigen	No exposure to antigen
It takes a while for protection to develop	Protection is immediate
Protection is long-term	Protection is short-term
Memory cells are produced	Memory cells aren't produced

Autoimmune Diseases Involve an Abnormal Immune Response

1) Sometimes, an organism's immune system **isn't able** to **recognise self-antigens** — the antigens present on the organism's **own cells**.

2) When this happens, the immune system treats the self-antigens as **foreign antigens** and launches an **immune response** against the organism's **own tissues**.

3) A disease resulting from this abnormal immune response is known as an **autoimmune disease**.

Examples of autoimmune diseases:

- **Lupus** — caused by the immune system attacking cells in the **connective tissues**. This **damages** the tissues and causes painful **inflammation** (see page 120). Lupus can affect the **skin** and **joints**, as well as **organs** such as the **heart** and **lungs**.

- **Rheumatoid arthritis** — caused by the immune system attacking cells in the **joints**. Again this causes **pain** and **inflammation**.

4) Autoimmune diseases are usually **chronic** (long-term). They can often be **treated**, but **not cured**.

Immunity and Vaccinations

Vaccines Help to Control Disease and Prevent Epidemics

1) While your B lymphocytes are busy **dividing** to build up their numbers to deal with a pathogen (i.e. the **primary response** — see p. 124), you **suffer** from the disease. **Vaccination** can help avoid this.

2) Vaccines **contain antigens** that cause your body to **produce memory cells** against a particular pathogen, **without** the pathogen **causing disease**. This means you become **immune** without getting any **symptoms**.

3) If most people in a **community** are **vaccinated**, the disease becomes extremely **rare**. This means that even people who haven't been vaccinated are **unlikely** to get the disease, because there's no one to catch it from. This is called **herd immunity**. It helps to **prevent epidemics** — **mass outbreaks** of **disease**.

4) Vaccines always contain antigens — these may be **free** or attached to a **dead** or **attenuated** (weakened) **pathogen**.

5) Sometimes **booster** vaccines are given later on (e.g. after several years) to **make sure** memory cells are produced.

6) **Vaccination** is **not the same** as **immunisation**. Vaccination is the **administration** of **antigens** (in a vaccine) into the body. **Immunisation** is the **process** by which you **develop immunity**. Vaccination **causes** immunisation.

Vaccines may be injected, or taken orally or in an aerosol.

Routine vaccines are offered to everybody. They include:

- the **MMR** — protects against **measles**, **mumps** and **rubella**. The MMR is usually given to **children** as an **injection** at around a year old, and again before they start school. It contains **attenuated measles**, **mumps** and **rubella viruses**.

- the **Meningitis C vaccine** — protects against the **bacteria** that cause **Meningitis C**. It is first given as an **injection** to babies at **3 months**. **Boosters** are then given to **1-year-olds** and **teenagers**.

Vaccines and Vaccination Programmes Change — EXAMPLE: the Influenza Vaccine

1) The **influenza (flu) vaccine** changes every year. That's because the **antigens** on the surface of the influenza virus **change regularly**, forming **new strains** of the virus.

This is known as antigenic variation.

2) **Memory cells** produced from **vaccination** with **one strain** of the flu will **not recognise** other strains with **different antigens**. The strains are **immunologically distinct**.

3) Every year there are **different strains** of the influenza virus **circulating** in the **population**, so a **different vaccine** has to be made.

4) **Laboratories** collect **samples** of these different strains, and organisations, such as the **WHO** (World Health Organisation) and **CDC** (Centre for Disease Control), **test** the **effectiveness** of different influenza **vaccines** against them.

5) **New vaccines** are **developed** and one is chosen **every year** that is the **most effective** against the **recently** circulating influenza viruses.

6) Governments and health authorities then implement a **programme** of **vaccination** using the most **suitable** vaccine. Sometimes people are given a vaccine that protects them from a strain causing an epidemic in **another country** — this helps to stop the strain spreading **globally**.

1st infection
influenza virus — antigens
new strain forms
2nd infection
influenza virus — different antigens

Practice Questions

Q1 What is the difference between active and passive immunity?

Q2 What are autoimmune diseases? Give an example.

Q3 Explain how vaccines help prevent epidemics.

Exam Question

Q1 Influenza is caused by a virus that constantly changes its antigens.
Explain why a new influenza vaccine is made every year.

[2 marks]

An injection of dead bugs — roll on my next vaccine...

The influenza virus is so clever that it would almost make you think it had a mind of its own. I mean, as soon as we catch up with it and develop a vaccine, off it goes and changes its surface antigens again. Influenza virus 1: humans 0.

Antibiotics and Other Medicines

Our immune systems aren't always enough to fight off an infection by pathogens.
Sometimes we need a bit of extra help from medicines like antibiotics.

Antibiotics are Extremely Useful

1) **Antibiotics** are **chemicals** that **kill** or **inhibit** the **growth** of **bacteria**.

2) They're **used** by humans as **drugs** to **treat bacterial infections**. They're useful because they can usually **target** bacterial cells **without damaging** human body cells.

3) **Penicillin** was the **first antibiotic** to be **isolated** (by Alexander Fleming, in 1928).

4) Antibiotic use became **widespread** from the **mid-twentieth century** — partly thanks to the successful treatment of soldiers with penicillin in the Second World War.

5) For the **past few decades**, we've been able to deal with bacterial infections **pretty easily** using **antibiotics**. As a result of this, the **death rate** from **infectious bacterial disease** has **fallen dramatically**.

6) Despite their usefulness, there are **risks** to using antibiotics. For example, they can cause **side effects** and even **severe allergic reactions** in some people. Perhaps the **biggest risk** though, is from **antibiotic resistance**...

Antibiotics are used to treat bacterial infections in animals too.

Antibiotic Resistance is a Big Problem

1) There is **genetic variation** in a population of bacteria. Genetic **mutations** make some bacteria **naturally resistant** to an **antibiotic**.

2) For the bacterium, this ability to **resist an antibiotic** is a big **advantage**. It's better able to **survive**, even in a host who's being treated with antibiotics to get rid of the infection, and so it lives for longer and **reproduces** many more times.

3) This leads to the **allele** for **antibiotic resistance** being **passed on** to lots of **offspring**. It's an example of **natural selection** — see page 172. This is how antibiotic resistance **spreads** and becomes **more common** in a population of bacteria over time.

An allele is a version of a gene — see page 137.

4) This is a **problem** for people who become **infected** with these bacteria, because you **can't easily get rid of them** with antibiotics.

5) **Increased use** of antibiotics means that **antibiotic resistance** is **increasing**. **'Superbugs'** that are resistant to **most known antibiotics** are becoming **more common**. This means we are **less able to treat** some **potentially life-threatening** bacterial **infections**.

Here are Some Examples of Antibiotic-Resistant Bacteria:

- **MRSA** (meticillin-resistant *Staphylococcus aureus*) causes **serious wound infections** and is **resistant** to **several antibiotics**, including **meticillin** (which used to be called methicillin).

- *Clostridium difficile* infects the **digestive system**, usually causing problems in people who have **already been treated** with **antibiotics**. It is thought that the **harmless bacteria** that are **normally present** in the digestive system are **killed** by the antibiotics, which *C. difficile* is **resistant** to. This allows *C. difficile* to **flourish**. *C. difficile* produces a **toxin**, which causes severe **diarrhoea**, **fever** and **cramps**.

MRSA and Clostridium difficile infections are most common in hospitals, where many antibiotics are used and patients who are already ill have weakened immune systems.

Developing new antibiotics and **modifying** existing ones are two ways of **overcoming** the current problem of antibiotic resistance. This isn't easy though.

To reduce the likelihood of antibiotic resistance developing in the first place, **doctors** are being encouraged to **reduce** their **use of antibiotics**, e.g. **not** to prescribe them for **minor infections** and **not** to prescribe them to **prevent infections** (except in patients with already weak immune systems, e.g. the elderly or people with HIV). **Patients** are advised to take **all** of the antibiotics they're **prescribed** to make sure the infection is fully cleared and all the bacteria have been killed (which reduces the likelihood of a population of antibiotic-resistant bacteria developing).

Antibiotics and Other Medicines

Possible Sources of Medicines Need to be Protected

1) Many **medicinal drugs** are manufactured **using natural compounds** found in **plants**, **animals** or **microorganisms**. E.g. **penicillin** is obtained from a **fungus**, some **cancer drugs** are made using **soil bacteria**, and **daffodils** are now grown to produce a drug used to treat **Alzheimer's disease**.

2) Only a **small proportion** of organisms have been **investigated** so far, so it's possible that plants or microorganisms **exist** that contain compounds that could be used to treat **currently incurable** diseases, such as AIDS. Others may produce **new antibiotics**.

3) Possible **sources of drugs** need to be **protected** by **maintaining** the **biodiversity** (the variety of different species) on Earth. If we **don't** protect them, some species could **die** out before we get a **chance** to study them.

4) Even organisms that have **already** been studied could still prove to be **useful** sources of medicines as **new techniques** are developed for identifying, purifying and testing compounds.

The Future of Medicine Looks Pretty High-Tech

Personalised Medicines

1) Your **genes** determine how your body **responds** to certain **drugs**. **Different people** respond to the **same drug** in **different ways** — which makes certain drugs **more effective** for **some people** than others. This is where **personalised medicines** come in.

2) Personalised medicines are medicines that are **tailored** to an **individual's DNA**. The theory is that if doctors have your **genetic information**, they can use it to **predict** how you will respond to different drugs and only prescribe the ones that will be **most effective** for you.

3) Scientists hope that by studying the **relationship** between someone's genetic make up and their responsiveness to drugs, **more effective drugs** can be produced in the future.

Synthetic biology

1) Synthetic biology involves using **technology** to **design** and **make** things like **artificial proteins**, **cells** and even **microorganisms**.

2) It has applications in lots of different areas, including **medicine**. For example, scientists are looking at engineering **bacteria** to **destroy cancer cells**, while leaving **healthy body cells intact**.

Not an example of synthetic biology.

Practice Questions

Q1 What are antibiotics?

Q2 Name two strains of antibiotic-resistant bacteria.

Q3 Why is protecting biodiversity important for the development of new medicines?

Exam Question

Q1 MRSA bacteria are resistant to several antibiotics, including meticillin.
Suggest how *Staphylococcus aureus* bacteria developed resistance to the antibiotic meticillin. [4 marks]

The Market Research Society of Australia — not a deadly bacterium...

In 2014, the World Health Organisation (WHO) released a report on the worldwide threat posed by antibiotic resistance — and it's not good news. Unless we take action now, relatively minor bacterial infections (that we've been able to treat successfully with antibiotics for decades) will once again become life-threatening illnesses. So we need to work on stopping the spread of antibiotic resistance and developing new antibiotics as soon as possible.

Antibodies in Medicine

Antibodies aren't only great for fighting off infection, they're also excellent tools for use in medical diagnosis and drug development. Let's all give three cheers for antibodies. Without them, we'd all probably be dead by now.

Monoclonal Antibodies can be used to Target Specific Substances or Cells

1) **Monoclonal antibodies** are antibodies **produced** from a **single group of genetically identical B lymphocytes** (plasma cells). This means that they're all **identical** in **structure**.

2) As you know, antibodies are **very specific** because their binding sites have a **unique tertiary structure** (see p.17) that only one particular antigen will fit into (one with a **complementary shape**).

3) You can make monoclonal antibodies **that bind to anything** you want, e.g. a cell antigen or other substance, and they will only bind to (target) this molecule.

Designing and making monoclonal antibodies is part of synthetic biology — see previous page.

EXAMPLE: Targeting drugs to a particular cell type — cancer cells

1) **Different cells** in the body have **different** surface **antigens**.

2) Cancer cells have antigens called **tumour markers** that are **not** found on normal body cells.

3) **Monoclonal antibodies** can be made that will bind to the tumour markers.

4) You can also attach **anti-cancer drugs** to the antibodies.

5) When the antibodies come into **contact** with the cancer cells they will **bind** to the tumour markers.

6) This means the drug will **only accumulate** in the body where there are **cancer cells**.

7) So, the **side effects** of an antibody-based drug are lower than other drugs because they accumulate near **specific cells**.

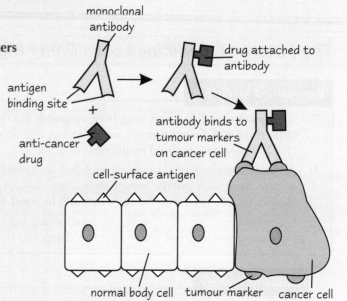

EXAMPLE: Targeting a particular substance for medical diagnosis — pregnancy testing

Pregnancy tests detect the hormone **human chorionic gonadotropin (hCG)** that's found in the **urine** of pregnant women:

1) The application area contains **antibodies for hCG** bound to a **coloured bead** (**blue**).

2) When urine is applied to the application area any hCG will **bind** to the antibody on the beads, forming an **antigen-antibody complex**.

3) The urine **moves** up the stick to the **test strip, carrying** any **beads** with it.

4) The test strip contains **antibodies to hCG** that are stuck in place (**immobilised**).

5) If there **is hCG present** the test strip turns **blue** because the **immobilised** antibody binds to any **hCG** — concentrating the hCG-antibody complex with the **blue beads** attached. If **no hCG** is present, the beads will **pass through** the test area **without** binding to anything, and so it **won't go blue**.

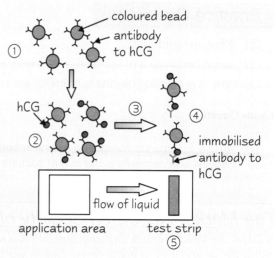

Antibodies in Medicine

The ELISA Test is a Medical Diagnostic Test that Uses Antibodies

1) The **enzyme-linked immunosorbent assay** (ELISA) allows you to see if a patient has any **antibodies** to a certain **antigen** (see example below) or any **antigen** to a certain **antibody**.

2) It can be used to test for **pathogenic infections**, for **allergies** (e.g. to nuts or lactose) and for just about **anything** you can make an **antibody** for.

3) In an ELISA test, an antibody is used which has an **enzyme attached** to it. This enzyme can **react** with a substrate to produce a **coloured product**. This causes the solution in the reaction vessel to **change colour**.

4) If there's a **colour change**, it demonstrates that the **antigen** or **antibody** of interest is **present** in the sample being tested (e.g. blood plasma). In some types of ELISA, the **quantity** of this antigen/antibody can be worked out from the **intensity** of the colour change.

5) There are several **different types** of ELISA. **Direct ELISA** uses a **single** antibody that is complementary to the antigen you're testing for. **Indirect ELISA** is different because it uses **two** different antibodies. This method is outlined below:

EXAMPLE: Using an ELISA as a HIV (Human Immunodeficiency Virus) Test

An **indirect ELISA test** can be used to see if a patient possesses **antibodies** to the HIV virus:

① **HIV antigen** is **bound** to the bottom of a **well** in a **well plate** (a plastic tray with loads of little circular pits in it).

② A sample of the **patient's blood plasma**, which might contain several different antibodies, is **added** to the **well**. If there are any **HIV-specific antibodies** (i.e. antibodies against HIV) these will **bind** to the **HIV antigen** stuck to the bottom of the **well**. The well is then **washed out** to remove any **unbound antibodies**.

③ A **secondary antibody**, that has a specific **enzyme** attached to it, is added to the **well**. This secondary antibody can bind to the **HIV-specific antibody** (which is also called the **primary antibody**). The well is **washed out** again to remove any **unbound secondary antibody**. If there's no primary antibody in the sample, all of the secondary antibody will be **washed away**.

④ A **solution** is added to the **well**. This solution contains a **substrate**, which is able to react with the **enzyme** attached to the secondary antibody and produce a coloured product. If the solution **changes colour**, it indicates that the patient has **HIV-specific antibodies** in their blood and is **infected** with HIV.

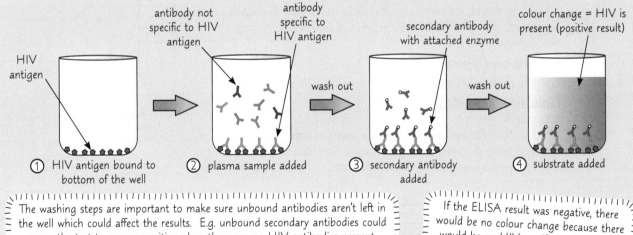

① HIV antigen bound to bottom of the well   ② plasma sample added   ③ secondary antibody added   ④ substrate added

The washing steps are important to make sure unbound antibodies aren't left in the well which could affect the results. E.g. unbound secondary antibodies could cause the test to appear positive when there are no HIV antibodies present.

If the ELISA result was negative, there would be no colour change because there would be no HIV-specific antibodies for the secondary antibodies to bind to.

Practice Questions

Q1 What are monoclonal antibodies?

Exam Question

Q1 Describe how monoclonal antibodies can be used to target a drug to cancer cells. [4 marks]

Antibodies — the multi-tool of the immune system...

Monoclonal antibodies are really useful — they can even be made against other antibodies. For example, people with asthma produce too many of a type of antibody that causes inflammation in the lungs. Monoclonal antibodies can be made to bind this type of antibody, so it can no longer cause inflammation, which can reduce the asthma symptoms.

Interpreting Vaccine and Antibody Data

If someone claims anything about a vaccine or antibody, the claim has to be validated (confirmed) before it's accepted. To do this, you need to evaluate the data used to support the claim and the methodology behind it.

New Knowledge About Vaccines and Antibodies is Validated by Scientists

When a **study** presents evidence for a **new theory** (e.g. a vaccine has a dangerous side effect) it's important that other scientists come up with **more evidence** to **validate** (confirm) the theory. Other scientists may **repeat** the study and try to **reproduce** the results, or **conduct other studies** to try to prove the same theory.

EXAMPLE 1: The MMR Vaccine

1) In 1998, a study was published about the **safety** of the **measles, mumps** and **rubella (MMR) vaccine**. The study was based on **12 children** with **autism** (a life-long developmental disability) and concluded that there may be a **link** between the MMR vaccine and autism.

2) Not everyone was convinced by this study because it had a **very small sample size** of 12 children, which increased the likelihood of the results being due to **chance**. The study may have been **biased** because one of the scientists was helping to gain evidence for a **lawsuit** against the MMR vaccine manufacturer. Also, studies carried out by different scientists found no link between autism and the MMR vaccine.

3) There have been **further scientific studies** to sort out the **conflicting** evidence. In **2005**, a **Japanese** study was published about the incidence of autism in Yokohama (an area of Japan). They looked at the medical records of **30 000 children** born between **1988 and 1996** and counted the number of children that developed **autism** before the age of seven. The **MMR jab** was first **introduced in Japan in 1989** and was **stopped in 1993**. During this time the MMR vaccine was administered to children at **12 months old**. The graph shows the results of the study.

4) **Evaluating evidence** like this tends to involve:

   - <u>Describing the data</u>
     The graph shows that the number of children diagnosed with autism continued to **rise** after the MMR vaccine was **stopped**. For example, from all the children born in 1992, who did receive the MMR jab, about 60 out of 10 000 were diagnosed with autism before the age of seven. However, from all the children born in 1994, who did not receive the MMR jab, about 160 out of 10 000 of them were diagnosed with autism before the age of seven.

   - <u>Drawing conclusions</u>
     There is **no link** between the MMR vaccine and autism.

   - <u>Evaluating the methodology</u>
     You can be much more confident in this study, compared to the 1998 study, because the **sample size** was so **large** — 30 000 children were studied. A larger sample size means that the results are less likely to be due to **chance**.

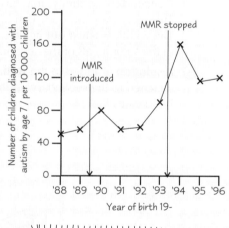

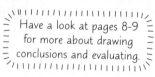

Have a look at pages 8-9 for more about drawing conclusions and evaluating.

EXAMPLE 2: Herceptin® — Monoclonal Antibodies

About **20%** of **women with breast cancer** have tumours that produce more than the usual amount of a **receptor** called **HER2**. **Herceptin®** is a **drug** used to treat this type of breast cancer — it contains **monoclonal antibodies** that **bind the HER2 receptor** on a **tumour cell** and **prevent** the cells from growing and dividing.

In **2005**, a study **tested** Herceptin® on women who had already undergone **chemotherapy** for HER2-type **breast cancer**. **1694** women took the **drug** for a **year** after chemotherapy and another **1694** women were **observed** for the **same time** (the control group). The results are shown in the graph on the right.

Describe the data: Almost **twice as many** women in the **control group** developed breast cancer again or died **compared** to the group taking Herceptin®.

Draw conclusions: A **one-year treatment** with Herceptin®, after chemotherapy, **increases** the disease-free survival rate for women with HER2-type breast cancer.

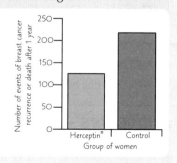

Interpreting Vaccine and Antibody Data

Use of Vaccines and Antibodies Raises Ethical Issues

Ethical issues surrounding vaccines include:

1) All vaccines are **tested on animals** before being tested on humans — some people **disagree** with animal testing. Also, **animal based substances** may be used to **produce** a vaccine, which some people disagree with.

2) **Testing** vaccines on **humans** can be **tricky**, e.g. volunteers may put themselves at **unnecessary risk** of contracting the disease because they think they're fully protected (e.g. they might have unprotected sex because they have had a new HIV vaccine and think they're protected — and the vaccine might not work).

3) Some people **don't** want to take the vaccine due to the **risk** of **side effects**, but they are **still protected** because of **herd immunity** (see p. 127) — other people think this is **unfair**.

4) If there was an **epidemic** of a **new disease** (e.g. a new influenza virus) there would be a rush to **receive** a vaccine and **difficult decisions** would have to be made about **who** would be the **first** to receive it.

Ethical issues surrounding monoclonal antibody therapy often involve animal rights issues. **Animals** are used to **produce the cells** from which the monoclonal antibodies are produced. Some people **disagree** with the use of animals in this way.

Practice Questions

Q1 Suggest one ethical issue surrounding vaccines.

Q2 Suggest one ethical issue surrounding monoclonal antibodies.

Exam Question

Q1 The graph below shows the number of laboratory reports of *Haemophilus influenzae* type b (Hib), in England and Wales, from 1990 to 2004. Hib affects children and can lead to meningitis and pneumonia.

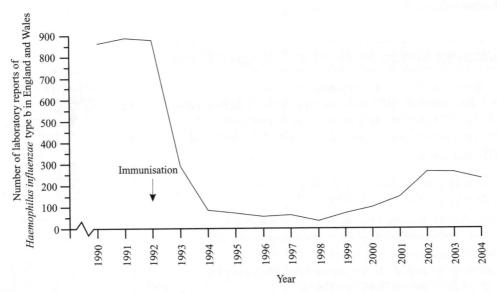

a) Explain how immunisation could have caused the sharp decrease in Hib cases after 1992. [2 marks]

b) Suggest a possible explanation for the increase in Hib cases after 1998. [1 mark]

Some scientists must have to validate the taste of chocolate — nice job...

After the 1998 study, some parents were worried about giving their kids the MMR vaccine, so the number of children given the vaccine fell. With fewer children in each community protected by the vaccine, herd immunity decreased. This meant that more people were vulnerable to measles, mumps and rubella, so the number of cases of went up.

HIV and Viruses

Viruses aren't cells like bacteria. They're not even living things — they can only reproduce inside the cells of another organism (called the host). All viruses cause disease, but these pages are about one particularly nasty blighter...

HIV is the Virus That Causes AIDS

1) **HIV (Human Immunodeficiency Virus)** is a virus that affects the **immune system**. It eventually leads to **acquired immune deficiency syndrome (AIDS)**.

2) **AIDS** is a condition where the immune system **deteriorates** and eventually **fails**. This makes someone with AIDS more **vulnerable** to **other infections**, like pneumonia (see next page).

3) **HIV** infects (and eventually kills) **T helper cells**, which act as the **host cells** (see p. 44) for the virus. Remember, T helper cells send chemical signals that **activate phagocytes**, **T killer cells** and **B lymphocytes** (see p. 123) so they're **hugely important cells** in the **immune response**. Without enough T helper cells, the immune system is **unable** to mount an **effective** response to **infections** because other immune system cells **don't behave** how they **should**.

4) People infected with HIV develop **AIDS** when the **T helper cell numbers** in their body reach a critically **low** level.

HIV has a Spherical Structure

HIV has the following **structure**:

Attachment proteins can also be called envelope proteins.

1) A **core** that contains the **genetic material** (RNA) and some **proteins** (including the enzyme **reverse transcriptase**, which is needed for virus replication).

2) An **outer coating** of protein called a **capsid**.

3) An **extra outer layer** called an **envelope**. This is made of **membrane** stolen from the cell membrane of a previous host cell.

4) Sticking out from the envelope are **loads of copies** of an **attachment protein** that help HIV **attach** to the host T helper cell.

Attachment protein

Capsid

Envelope

Genetic material

Reverse transcriptase

HIV Replicates Inside its Host's T Helper Cells

HIV (and all other viruses) can only **reproduce** inside the cells of the organism it has infected. HIV replicates inside the **T helper cells** of the host. It doesn't have the equipment (such as **enzymes** and **ribosomes**) to replicate on its own, so it uses those of the **host cell**.

Here's how **HIV** replicates:

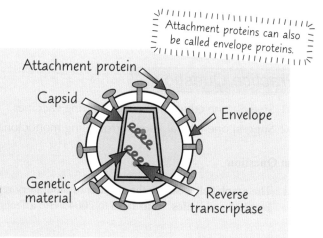

HIV

T helper cell

RNA

DNA

1) The attachment protein **attaches** to a **receptor molecule** on the cell membrane of the host T helper cell.

2) The capsid is released into the cell, where it **uncoats** and releases the **genetic material** (RNA) into the cell's cytoplasm.

3) Inside the cell, reverse transcriptase is used to make a **complementary strand** of DNA from the **viral RNA template** (see p. 32-33 for more on DNA and RNA).

4) From this, **double-stranded DNA** is made and **inserted** into the human DNA.

5) Host cell enzymes are used to make **viral proteins** from the **viral DNA** found within the human DNA.

6) The viral proteins are **assembled** into **new viruses**, which **bud** from the cell and go on to infect other cells.

During the initial infection period, HIV replicates rapidly and the infected person may experience severe flu-like symptoms. After this period, HIV replication drops to a lower level. This is the **latency period**. During the latency period (which can last for years), the infected person **won't experience** any **symptoms**.

HIV and Viruses

People with AIDS are Susceptible to a Range of Illnesses

People with HIV are classed as having AIDS when **symptoms** of their **failing immune system** start to **appear** or their **T helper cell count drops** below a certain level. People with AIDS generally develop diseases that **wouldn't** cause serious problems in people with a **healthy** immune system. The length of time between **infection** with HIV and the **development** of AIDS **varies** between individuals but without treatment it's usually around **10 years**.

1) The **initial symptoms** of AIDS include **minor infections** of mucous membranes (e.g. the inside of the nose, ears and genitals), and recurring respiratory infections.

2) As AIDS **progresses** the number of **immune system cells decreases** further. Patients become susceptible to **more serious infections** including chronic diarrhoea, severe bacterial infections and tuberculosis.

3) During the **late stages** of AIDS patients have a very **low number** of immune system cells and can develop a **range of serious infections** such as toxoplasmosis of the brain (a parasite infection) and candidiasis of the respiratory system (fungal infection). It's these serious infections that kill AIDS patients, not HIV itself.

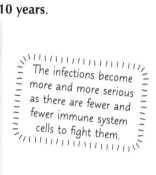
The infections become more and more serious as there are fewer and fewer immune system cells to fight them.

The length of time that people survive with AIDS varies a lot. Factors that affect progression of HIV to AIDS and survival time with AIDS include **existing infections**, the **strain of HIV** they're infected with, **age** and access to **healthcare**.

Antibiotics Don't Work Against Viruses

1) Antibiotics kill **bacteria** by **interfering** with their metabolic reactions. They target the **bacterial enzymes** and **ribosomes** used in these reactions.

2) Bacterial enzymes and ribosomes are **different** from **human** enzymes and ribosomes. Antibiotics are designed to **only target** the bacterial ones so they don't damage human cells. Makes sense.

3) Viruses **don't have their own** enzymes and ribosomes — they use the ones in the host's cells. So because human viruses use human enzymes and ribosomes to replicate, antibiotics **can't** inhibit them because they **don't** target human processes.

4) Most **antiviral drugs** are designed to target the few **virus-specific enzymes** (enzymes that only the virus uses) that exist. For example, HIV uses **reverse transcriptase** to replicate (see previous page). Human cells **don't** use this enzyme so drugs can be designed to inhibit it **without affecting** the host cell. These drugs are called reverse-transcriptase inhibitors.

There's No Cure for HIV

1) There's currently **no cure** or **vaccine** for HIV but **antiviral** drugs can be used to **slow down** the **progression** of HIV infection and AIDS in an infected person.

2) The best way to control HIV infection in a population is by **reducing** its **spread**. HIV can be **spread** via **unprotected sexual intercourse**, through **infected bodily fluids** (e.g. like blood from sharing contaminated needles) and from a HIV-positive **mother** to her **fetus**. Not all babies from HIV-positive mothers are born infected with HIV and taking antiviral drugs during pregnancy can reduce the chance of the baby being HIV-positive.

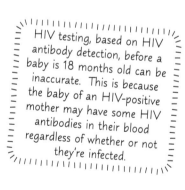
HIV testing, based on HIV antibody detection, before a baby is 18 months old can be inaccurate. This is because the baby of an HIV-positive mother may have some HIV antibodies in their blood regardless of whether or not they're infected.

Practice Questions

Q1 What type of cell does HIV replicate in?
Q2 Why can't antibiotics be used to treat HIV?

Exam Question

Q1 HIV is the virus that eventually causes AIDS. Describe the structure of HIV. [4 marks]

Viruses can be dangerous and hard to treat — they're just not funny...

Well, apart from rhinoviruses, which cause colds, but they're only funny because of the name. It's actually quite a logical name — rhino is from the Greek for nose. They're literally nose viruses. If I was a virus I'd choose somewhere better to infect. Anyway, understanding how HIV operates helps make sense of the symptoms and progression of AIDS.

DNA, Genes and Chromosomes

DNA can be cruel — it gave me two feet, but made me bad at football... OK, maybe that's not completely DNA's fault. These pages give you plenty of info on how DNA is packaged, what genes are and how they code for stuff.

DNA is **Stored Differently** in **Different Organisms**

Although the **structure** of DNA is the same in all organisms, **eukaryotic** and **prokaryotic** cells store DNA in slightly different ways. (For a recap on the differences between prokaryotic and eukaryotic cells see pages 38 and 44.)

Nuclear Eukaryotic DNA is Linear and Associated with Proteins

1) Eukaryotic cells contain **linear** DNA molecules that exist as **chromosomes** — thread-like structures, each made up of **one long molecule** of DNA. Chromosomes are found in the **nucleus**.

2) The DNA molecule is **really long** so, it has to be **wound up** so it can **fit** into the nucleus.

3) The DNA molecule is wound around **proteins** called **histones**.

4) Histone proteins also help to **support** the DNA.

5) The DNA (and protein) is then coiled up **very tightly** to make a **compact chromosome**.

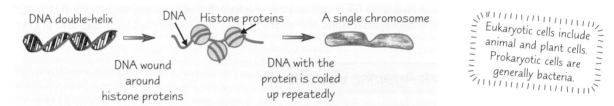

DNA double-helix → DNA wound around histone proteins → DNA with the protein is coiled up repeatedly → A single chromosome

Eukaryotic cells include animal and plant cells. Prokaryotic cells are generally bacteria.

6) The **mitochondria** and **chloroplasts** in eukaryotic cells also have their **own** DNA. This is pretty similar to prokaryotic DNA (see below) because it's **circular** and **shorter** than DNA molecules in the nucleus. It's **not associated** with **histone proteins**.

DNA Molecules are Shorter and Circular in Prokaryotes

1) Prokaryotes also carry DNA as **chromosomes** — but the DNA molecules are **shorter** and **circular**.

2) The DNA **isn't** wound around histones — it condenses to fit in the cell by **supercoiling**.

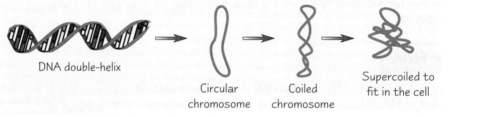

DNA double-helix → Circular chromosome → Coiled chromosome → Supercoiled to fit in the cell

If one more person confused Clifford with supercoiled DNA, he'd have 'em.

DNA Contains Genes

1) A **gene** is a **sequence** of **DNA bases** (see p. 32) that codes for either a **polypeptide** or **functional RNA** (see below).

2) The sequence of **amino acids** in a polypeptide forms the **primary structure** of a **protein** (see p. 17).

3) Different polypeptides have a **different number** and **order** of amino acids. It's the **order** of **bases** in a gene that determines the **order of amino acids** in a particular **polypeptide**.

4) Each amino acid is coded for by a sequence of **three bases** in a gene called a **triplet**. ⟹

5) To make a **polypeptide**, DNA is first copied into **messenger RNA** (mRNA). This is the first stage of **protein synthesis** (see p. 138).

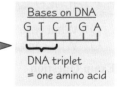

Bases on DNA
G T C T G A
DNA triplet
= one amino acid

6) Genes that don't code for a polypeptide code for **functional RNA** instead. Functional RNA is RNA molecules other than mRNA, which perform **special tasks** during protein synthesis, e.g. **tRNA** (see p. 138) and **ribosomal RNA** (rRNA), which forms part of ribosomes.

> A cell's **GENOME** is the **complete** set of **genes** in the cell.
> A cell's **PROTEOME** is the **full range** of **proteins** that the cell is able to produce.

DNA, Genes and Chromosomes

Most **DNA** in **Eukaryotic** Cells **Doesn't Code** for **Polypeptides**

1) **Some** genes don't code for **polypeptides** at all — they code for **functional RNA** (see previous page).

2) In **eukaryotic** DNA, genes that do code for **polypeptides** contain **sections** that **don't code** for **amino acids**.

3) These sections of DNA are called **introns**. There can be several introns within a gene.

4) All the bits of a gene that do code for amino acids are called **exons**.

5) **Introns** are **removed** during **protein synthesis** — so they **don't** affect the amino acid **order**. Their purpose isn't known for sure. (Prokaryotic DNA **doesn't** have introns.)

6) Eukaryotic DNA also contains regions of **multiple repeats** outside of genes.

7) These are DNA sequences that **repeat** over and over. For example: CCTTCCTTCCTT.

8) These areas **don't code** for amino acids either, so they're called **non-coding repeats**.

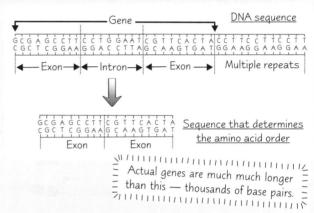

Genes **Can Exist in Different Forms Called Alleles**

1) A gene can exist in more than one form. These forms are called **alleles**.

2) The order of bases in each allele is slightly different, so they code for **slightly different versions** of the **same polypeptide**. For example, the gene that determines **blood type** exists as one of three alleles — one determines type O, another type A and the other type B.

Homologous pair of chromosomes

Allele for type A

Position of the gene for blood type

Allele for type B

In a **eukaryotic** cell nucleus, DNA is stored as **chromosomes**. Humans have **23 pairs** of chromosomes, 46 in total — two number 1s, two number 2s, two number 3s, etc. Pairs of matching chromosomes (e.g. the 1s) are called **homologous pairs**.
In a homologous pair, both chromosomes are the same size and have the **same genes**, although they could have **different alleles**. Alleles coding for the same characteristic will be found at the same **fixed position** (locus) on each chromosome in a homologous pair.

Practice Questions

Q1 What is a DNA triplet?

Q2 What is an intron?

Q3 What are non-coding repeats?

Q4 What is a locus?

Exam Questions

Q1 Describe how DNA is stored in eukaryotic cells. [5 marks]

Q2 A scientist is studying a DNA sequence that is made up of 3800 nucleotide pairs. Exons account for 672 of the nucleotide pairs. Introns account for 3128 of the nucleotide pairs. The sequence codes for a section of a polypeptide. How many amino acids will make up this section of the polypeptide? [2 marks]

Exons stay in, introns go out, in, out, in, out, and shake it all about...

Quite a few terms here, I'm afraid. Some are a bit confusing too. Just try to remember which way round they go. Introns are the non-coding regions, but exons are extremely important — they actually code for the polypeptide.

RNA and Protein Synthesis

Protein synthesis involves two stages — transcription and translation. They both involve RNA.

There's **More Than One** Type of **RNA**

Remember, RNA is a **single** polynucleotide strand and it contains **uracil** (**U**) as a base instead of thymine (see p. 32). Uracil **always pairs** with **adenine** during protein synthesis. RNA isn't all the same though. Here are two types:

Messenger RNA (mRNA)

mRNA is made during **transcription** (see below). It **carries the genetic code** from the DNA to the ribosomes, where it's used to make a **protein** during **translation** (see next page).

mRNA is a **single polynucleotide strand**.

In mRNA, groups of three adjacent bases are usually called **codons** (they're sometimes called **triplets** or **base triplets**).

Transfer RNA (tRNA)

tRNA is involved in **translation**. It **carries** the amino acids that are used to make **proteins** to the **ribosomes**. tRNA is a **single polynucleotide strand** that's folded into a **clover shape**. **Hydrogen bonds** between **specific base pairs** hold the molecule in this shape.

Every tRNA molecule has a **specific sequence** of **three bases** at one end called an **anticodon**. They also have an **amino acid binding site** at the other end.

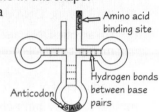

First Stage of Protein Synthesis — Transcription

During transcription, an **mRNA copy** of a gene is made from **DNA**. In **eukaryotic** cells, transcription takes place in the **nucleus**. (Prokaryotes don't have a nucleus, so transcription takes place in the cytoplasm.)

1) Transcription starts when **RNA polymerase** (an **enzyme**) **attaches** to the **DNA** double-helix at the **beginning** of a **gene**.

2) The **hydrogen bonds** between the two DNA strands in the gene **break**, **separating** the strands, and the DNA molecule **uncoils** at that point, **exposing** some of the **bases**.

3) **One** of the strands is then used as a **template** to make an **mRNA copy**.

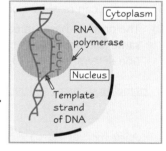

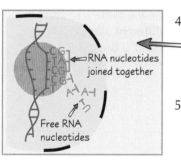

4) The RNA polymerase lines up **free RNA nucleotides** alongside the exposed bases on the template strand. The free bases are **attracted** to the exposed bases. Specific, **complementary base pairing** (see p. 33) means that the mRNA strand ends up being a **complementary copy** of the DNA template strand (except the base **T** is replaced by **U** in **RNA**).

5) Once the RNA nucleotides have **paired up** with their **specific bases** on the DNA strand, they're **joined together** by **RNA polymerase**, forming an **mRNA** molecule.

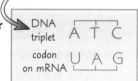

6) The RNA polymerase moves **along** the DNA, separating the strands and **assembling** the mRNA strand.

7) The **hydrogen bonds** between the uncoiled strands of DNA **re-form** once the RNA polymerase has passed by and the strands **coil back into a double-helix**.

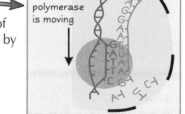

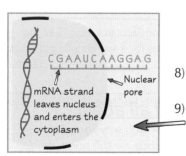

8) When RNA polymerase reaches a particular sequence of DNA called a **stop signal**, it stops making mRNA and **detaches** from the DNA.

9) In eukaryotes, **mRNA** moves **out** of the **nucleus** through a nuclear pore and attaches to a **ribosome** in the cytoplasm, where the next stage of protein synthesis takes place (see next page).

RNA and Protein Synthesis

Transcription Makes Different Products in Eukaryotes and Prokaryotes

1) In **eukaryotes**, the **introns** and **exons** are **both copied** into mRNA during transcription. mRNA strands containing introns and exons are called **pre-mRNA**. A process called **splicing** then occurs — **introns** are removed and the **exons** joined together — forming **mRNA** strands. This takes place in the **nucleus**. The mRNA then **leaves** the nucleus for the next stage of protein synthesis (**translation**).

2) In **prokaryotes**, mRNA is produced **directly** from the DNA — **without** splicing taking place. (There's no need for splicing because there are no introns in prokaryotic DNA.)

Turn to page 137 for more on introns and exons.

Second Stage of Protein Synthesis — Translation

Protein synthesis is also called polypeptide synthesis.

In both eukaryotes and prokaryotes, translation occurs at the **ribosomes** in the **cytoplasm**. During **translation**, **amino acids** are **joined together** to make a **polypeptide chain** (protein), following the sequence of **codons** (triplets) carried by the mRNA.

1) The **mRNA attaches** itself to a **ribosome** and **transfer RNA** (tRNA) molecules **carry amino acids** to it. **ATP** provides the energy needed for the **bond** between the **amino acid** and the **tRNA** molecule to form.

2) A **tRNA** molecule (carrying an amino acid), with an **anticodon** that's **complementary** to the **first codon** on the mRNA, attaches itself to the mRNA by **specific base pairing**.

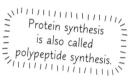

anticodon on tRNA U A C
codon on mRNA A U G

3) A second tRNA molecule attaches itself to the **next codon** on the mRNA in the **same way**.

4) The two amino acids attached to the tRNA molecules are **joined** by a **peptide bond**. The first tRNA molecule **moves away**, leaving its amino acid behind.

5) A third tRNA molecule binds to the **next codon** on the mRNA. Its amino acid **binds** to the first two and the second tRNA molecule **moves away**.

6) This process continues, producing a chain of linked amino acids (a **polypeptide chain**), until there's a stop signal on the mRNA molecule.

7) The polypeptide chain **moves away** from the ribosome and translation is complete.

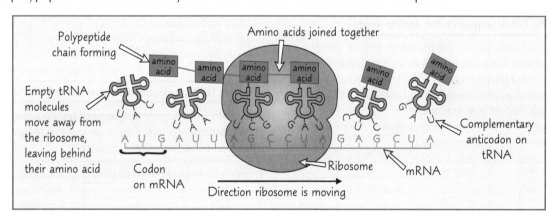

Practice Questions

Q1 Describe the structure of tRNA.

Q2 Where does transcription take place in eukaryotes?

Exam Question

Q1 A drug that inhibits cell growth is found to be able to bind to DNA, preventing RNA polymerase from binding. Explain how this drug will affect protein synthesis. [2 marks]

The only translation I'm interested in is a translation of this page into English

So you start off with DNA, lots of cleverness happens and bingo... you've got a protein. The only problem is understanding all that cleverness. Remember — an mRNA strand gets made during transcription. In translation, tRNA molecules act like little taxis, bringing amino acids to the mRNA strand, where they link to make a polypeptide.

The Genetic Code and Nucleic Acids

The genetic code is exactly as it sounds — a code found in your genes that tells your body how to make proteins. It can be interpreted, just like any other code. Don't get overexcited, but here's how to do it...

The Genetic Code is **Non-Overlapping**, **Degenerate** and **Universal**

1) The genetic code is the **sequence of base triplets** (codons) in **mRNA** which **code** for specific **amino acids**.

2) In the genetic code, each base triplet is **read** in sequence, **separate** from the triplet **before** it and **after** it. Base triplets **don't share** their **bases** — the code is **non-overlapping**.

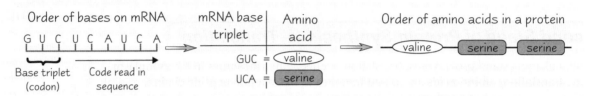

3) The genetic code is also **degenerate** — there are **more** possible combinations of **triplets** than there are amino acids (20 amino acids but 64 possible triplets). This means that some **amino acids** are coded for by **more than one** base triplet, e.g. tyrosine can be coded for by UAU or UAC.

4) Some triplets are used to tell the cell when to **start** and **stop** production of the protein — these are called **start** and **stop** signals (or **codons**). They're found at the **beginning** and **end** of the mRNA. E.g. UAG is a stop signal.

5) The genetic code is also **universal** — the **same** specific base triplets code for the **same** amino acids in **all living things**. E.g. UAU codes for tyrosine in all organisms.

Here's how to **Interpret Data** About **Nucleic Acids**

The table on the right shows the **mRNA codons** (triplets) for some amino acids. You can interpret information like this in different ways. Here's how to...

mRNA codon	Amino Acid
UCU	Serine
CUA	Leucine
UAU	Tyrosine
GUG	Valine
GCA	Alanine
CGC	Arginine

When interpreting data on nucleic acids remember that DNA contains T and RNA contains U.

...give the DNA sequence for amino acids

The mRNA codons for the amino acids are given in the table. Because **mRNA** is a **complementary copy** of the **DNA** template, the DNA sequence for each amino acid is made up of bases that would **pair** with the mRNA sequence:

mRNA codon	Amino Acid	DNA sequence (of template strand)
UCU	Serine	AGA
CUA	Leucine	GAT
UAU	Tyrosine	ATA
GUG	Valine	CAC
GCA	Alanine	CGT
CGC	Arginine	GCG

Sometimes you might need to work out the amino acids from a given DNA sequence and a table.

...give the tRNA anticodons from mRNA codons

tRNA anticodons are **complementary copies** of **mRNA codons**, so you can work out the tRNA anticodon from the mRNA codon:

mRNA codon	tRNA anticodon
UCU	AGA
CUA	GAU
UAU	AUA
GUG	CAC
GCA	CGU
CGC	GCG

You can also name the amino acid coded for by a tRNA anticodon using a table like the one above.

...write the amino acid sequence for a section of mRNA

To **work out** the sequence of **amino acids** from some mRNA, you need to break the genetic code into **codons** and then use the information in the table to work out what **amino acid** they code for.

Example

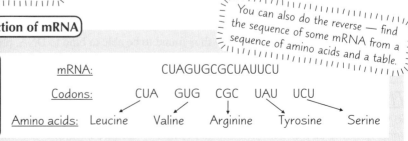

You can also do the reverse — find the sequence of some mRNA from a sequence of amino acids and a table.

The Genetic Code and Nucleic Acids

You Can **Interpret Data** About The **Role** of **Nucleic Acids**

Lots of experiments have been done to **investigate nucleic acids** and their **role** in **protein synthesis**. **Data** from experiments like these can be **interpreted** by **applying your knowledge** of how nucleic acids work. Here's an example:

Investigating the effect of new drugs on nucleic acids

1) To investigate **how** two new drugs affect **nucleic acids** and their **role** in protein synthesis, **bacteria** were **grown** in **normal conditions** for a few generations, then moved to media containing the drugs.

2) After a short period of time, the **concentration** of **protein** and **complete strands** of **mRNA** in the bacteria were analysed. The results are shown in the **bar graph**.

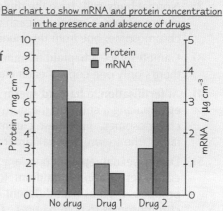

Bar chart to show mRNA and protein concentration in the presence and absence of drugs

3) Both mRNA **and** protein concentration were **lower** in the presence of **drug 1 compared** to the **no-drug control**. This suggests that drug 1 **affects the production** of **full length mRNA**, so there's no mRNA for protein synthesis during **translation**.

4) **mRNA production** in the presence of **drug 2** was **unaffected**, but **less protein** was produced — **3 mg cm^{-3}** compared to **8 mg cm^{-3}**. This suggests that drug 2 **interferes** with **translation**. **mRNA was produced**, but **less protein** was **translated** from it.

5) **Further tests** to establish the **nature** of the two drugs were carried out.

6) **Drug 1** was found to be a **ribonuclease** (an enzyme that **digests RNA**). This could **explain** the results of the first experiment — **any strands** of **mRNA** produced by the cell would be **digested** by drug 1, so **couldn't be used** in **translation** to make proteins.

7) **Drug 2** was found to be a **single-stranded, clover-shaped** molecule capable of binding to the **ribosome**. Again, this helps to **explain** the **results** from the first experiment — drug 2 could work by **binding** to the ribosome, **blocking tRNAs** from binding to it and so **preventing translation**.

A molecule capable of binding to mRNA would have had a similar effect to drug 1, since it would have prevented mRNA being read by the ribosomes and stopped it being translated.

Transcription and translation are on pages 138-139.

Practice Questions

Q1 What is the genetic code?
Q2 Why is the genetic code described as degenerate?
Q3 Why is the genetic code described as universal?

mRNA codon	amino acid
UGU	Cysteine
CGC	Arginine
GGG	Glycine
GUG	Valine
GCA	Alanine
UUG	Leucine
UUU	Phenylalanine

Exam Questions

Q1 The table shows the mRNA codons for some amino acids. Show your working for the following questions.
  a) Give the amino acid sequence for the mRNA sequence: GUGUGUCGCGCA. [2 marks]
  b) Give the DNA template strand sequence that codes for the amino acid sequence:
     valine, arginine, alanine. [3 marks]

Q2 An artificial mRNA was synthesised to code for a particular polypeptide. Part of the mRNA sequence was: UUGUGUGGGUUUGCAGCA. This produced the following sequence of amino acids: Leucine–Cysteine–Glycine–Phenylalanine–Alanine–Alanine. Use the table above to help you answer the following questions.
  a) Explain how the result suggests that the genetic code is based on triplets of nucleotides in mRNA. [2 marks]
  b) Explain how the result suggests that the genetic code is non-overlapping. [2 marks]

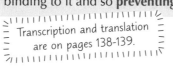

Yay — two pages with slightly fewer confusing terms and a lot less to remember. The key to interpreting the genetic code is understanding how DNA, mRNA and tRNA work together to make a protein. It also involves remembering that in complementary base pairing, C pairs with G and A pairs with T. Unless it's RNA — then A pairs with U instead.

Gametes and Fertilisation

Ahh, now on to some really exciting stuff — gametes (sex cells to you and me) and fertilisation. I won't tell you any more because it's all explained on these pages. You have to read it though — don't just giggle at the rude diagram...

DNA from One Generation is Passed to the Next by Gametes

1) **Gametes** are the **sperm** cells in males and **egg** cells in females. They join together at **fertilisation** to form a **zygote**, which divides and develops into a **new organism**.

2) Normal **body cells** have the **diploid number (2n)** of chromosomes — meaning each cell contains **two** of each chromosome, one from the mum and one from the dad.

3) **Gametes** have a **haploid (n)** number of chromosomes — there's only one copy of each chromosome.

4) At **fertilisation**, a **haploid sperm** fuses with a **haploid egg**, making a cell with the normal diploid number of chromosomes. Half these chromosomes are from the father (the sperm) and half are from the mother (the egg).

5) During sexual reproduction, any sperm can fertilise any egg — **fertilisation is random**. Random fertilisation produces zygotes with **different combinations of chromosomes** to both parents. This **mixing of genetic material** in sexual reproduction **increases genetic diversity** within a **species**.

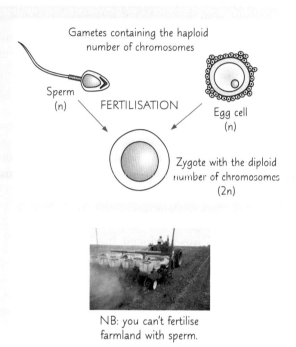

Gametes containing the haploid number of chromosomes

Sperm (n)   FERTILISATION   Egg cell (n)

Zygote with the diploid number of chromosomes (2n)

NB: you can't fertilise farmland with sperm.

Mammalian Gametes are Specialised for Their Function

Egg cells and sperm cells have all the **same organelles** as other **eukaryotic animal cells** (see pages 38-41), including a **nucleus** (which contains their genetic material) and a **cell-surface membrane**. But the structures of egg cells and sperm cells are also **specialised** for their **function** — bringing the **female** and **male DNA together** at **fertilisation** to form a **zygote**.

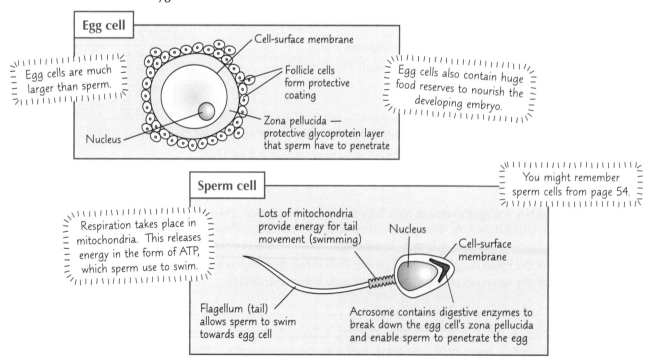

Egg cell

Egg cells are much larger than sperm.

Cell-surface membrane

Follicle cells form protective coating

Zona pellucida — protective glycoprotein layer that sperm have to penetrate

Nucleus

Egg cells also contain huge food reserves to nourish the developing embryo.

Sperm cell

You might remember sperm cells from page 54.

Respiration takes place in mitochondria. This releases energy in the form of ATP, which sperm use to swim.

Lots of mitochondria provide energy for tail movement (swimming)

Nucleus

Cell-surface membrane

Flagellum (tail) allows sperm to swim towards egg cell

Acrosome contains digestive enzymes to break down the egg cell's zona pellucida and enable sperm to penetrate the egg

Gametes and Fertilisation

In *Mammals* Fertilisation Occurs in the *Oviduct*

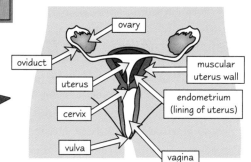

1) In mammals, **sperm** are deposited high up in the female **vagina** close to the entrance of the **cervix**.

2) Once there, they have to make their way up through the **cervix** and **uterus**, and into one of the **oviducts**. The diagram on the right shows the **human** female reproductive system.

3) Once the sperm are in the oviduct, **fertilisation** may occur. Here's how it works:

> 1) The **sperm swim** towards the **egg cell** in the oviduct.
>
> 2) Once **one** sperm makes contact with the **zona pellucida** of the egg cell (see previous page), the **acrosome reaction** occurs — this is where **digestive enzymes** are released from the acrosome of the sperm.
>
> 3) These enzymes **digest** the zona pellucida, so that the sperm can move through it to the cell membrane of the egg cell.

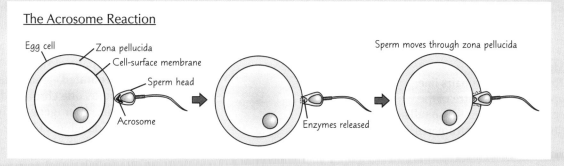

The Acrosome Reaction

> 4) The sperm head **fuses** with the **cell-surface membrane** of the egg cell. This triggers the **cortical reaction** — the egg cell releases the contents of vesicles called **cortical granules** into the space between the cell membrane and the zona pellucida.
>
> 5) The chemicals from the cortical granules make the zona pellucida **thicken**, which makes it **impenetrable** to other sperm. This makes sure that **only one** sperm fertilises the egg cell.
>
> 6) Only the **sperm nucleus** enters the egg cell — its **tail** is **discarded**.
>
> 7) The nucleus of the sperm **fuses** with the nucleus of the egg cell — this is **fertilisation**.

A **zygote** is now formed, which has the full number of chromosomes.
It immediately begins to divide by **mitosis** (see page 50) to develop into a fully formed organism.

Practice Questions

Q1 What is a gamete?
Q2 What is the zona pellucida?
Q3 Describe what happens in the acrosome reaction.

Exam Questions

Q1 Explain how sperm are specialised for their function. [3 marks]

Q2 Describe the process of fertilisation in mammals, following the acrosome reaction. [4 marks]

Reproduction isn't as exciting as some people would have you believe...

Hats off to the sperm and the eggs. You've gotta hand it to them — they're pretty well adapted for their function. It's a good job they are too, 'cause where would you and I be otherwise? Why not say some of these weird and wonderful words out loud — zona pellucida, acrosome, follicle, flagellum, vulva... OK, enough. Next page.

Meiosis

Right, now that you know what gametes are, I just know you're desperate to find out how they're formed. Luckily for you, these next two pages will make it all crystal clear (as long as you're wide awake with your learning head on first).

Meiosis Involves Two Divisions

1) **Meiosis** involves two divisions: **meiosis I** and **meiosis II**.
   Meiosis I is a **reduction division** — it halves the chromosome number.
2) Like **mitosis** (see page 50) meiosis I and meiosis II are each split
   into **prophase**, **metaphase**, **anaphase** and **telophase** stages.

The whole of meiosis begins with **interphase**. During interphase, the DNA **unravels** and **replicates** to produce double-armed chromosomes called **sister chromatids** (see page 50).

Meiosis I (first division)

Prophase I
The **chromosomes condense**, getting shorter and fatter. The chromosomes then arrange themselves into **homologous pairs** (see page 137) and **crossing-over** occurs (see below). Just like in mitosis, **centrioles** start moving to opposite ends of the cell, forming the **spindle fibres**. The **nuclear envelope breaks down**.

Metaphase I
The **homologous pairs line up** across the **centre** of the cell and **attach** to the **spindle fibres** by their **centromeres**.

Anaphase I
The **spindles contract**, separating the **homologous pairs** — **one** chromosome goes to **each end** of the cell.

Telophase I
A **nuclear envelope** forms around each group of chromosomes.

Cytokinesis (division of the cytoplasm) occurs and **two haploid daughter cells** are produced.

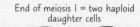

Meiosis II (second division)

The two daughter cells undergo **prophase II**, **metaphase II**, **anaphase II**, **telophase II** and **cytokinesis** — which are a lot like the stages in **mitosis**.

In **anaphase II**, the pairs of **sister chromatids** are **separated** — each **new** daughter cell inherits **one chromatid** from **each chromosome**. **Four (genetically different) haploid** daughter cells are produced — these are the **gametes**.

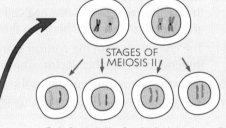

Chromatids Cross Over in Meiosis I

During meiosis I, **homologous pairs** of chromosomes come together and pair up. The chromatids twist around each other and bits of **chromatids** swap over. The chromatids still contain the **same genes** but now have a different combination of **alleles**.

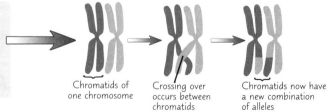

Meiosis

Meiosis Produces Cells that are Genetically Different

There are two main events during meiosis that lead to **genetic variation**:

①Crossing over of chromatids

The **crossing over** of chromatids in meiosis I means that each of the **four daughter cells** formed from meiosis contains chromatids with **different alleles**:

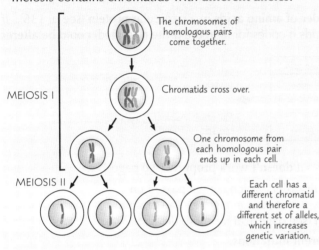

The chromosomes of homologous pairs come together.

MEIOSIS I

Chromatids cross over.

One chromosome from each homologous pair ends up in each cell.

MEIOSIS II

Each cell has a different chromatid and therefore a different set of alleles, which increases genetic variation.

②Independent segregation of chromosomes

1) Each **homologous pair** of chromosomes in your cells is made up of **one chromosome** from your mum (**maternal**) and **one chromosome** from your dad (**paternal**).

2) When the homologous pairs are **separated** in **meiosis I**, it's completely **random** which chromosome from each pair ends up in which daughter cell.

3) So the **four daughter cells** produced by meiosis have completely **different combinations** of those **maternal** and **paternal** chromosomes.

4) This is called **independent segregation** (separation) of the chromosomes.

5) This 'shuffling' of chromosomes leads to **genetic variation** in any **potential** offspring.

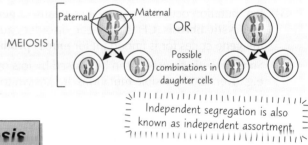

Paternal   Maternal   OR

MEIOSIS I

Possible combinations in daughter cells

Independent segregation is also known as independent assortment.

Meiosis Has a Different Outcome to Mitosis

	Outcomes:		
Mitosis	Produces cells with the **same number** of chromosomes as the parent cell.	Daughter cells are **genetically identical** to each other and to the parent cell.	Produces **two** daughter cells.
Meiosis	Produces cells with **half** the number of chromosomes as the parent cell.	Daughter cells are **genetically different** from one another and the parent cell.	Produces **four** daughter cells.

Mitosis and meiosis are different because **mitosis** only involves **one division** (which separates the sister chromatids) whereas **meiosis** has **two divisions** (which separate the homologous pairs and then the sister chromatids). There's **no pairing** or **separating** of **homologous chromosomes** in **mitosis**, and so **no crossing over** or **independent segregation of chromosomes**. This produces **genetically identical** daughter cells — unlike **meiosis**.

Practice Questions

Q1 Describe what happens at anaphase I in meiosis.

Exam Question

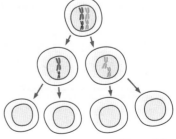

Q1 *Drosophila* (fruit flies) only have four chromosomes.
The diagram on the right summarises meiosis in *Drosophila*.

a) Complete the diagram to show the chromosomes in the four daughter cells. [1 mark]
b) Crossing over does not occur very frequently in male *Drosophila*.
Explain what crossing over is and how it leads to genetic variation. [4 marks]
c) Explain how independent segregation leads to genetic variation. [2 marks]

Independent segregation — choosing revision over going out...

The key thing to understand is that meiosis produces four genetically different haploid daughter cells. And that the genetic variation in the daughter cells occurs because of two processes — crossing over and independent segregation.

Mutations

Mutations can involve individual genes or whole chromosomes — some are useful, some not so.

Gene Mutations are Changes to the Base Sequence of DNA

Gene **mutations** involve a **change** in the **DNA base sequence** of chromosomes.

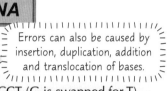
Errors can also be caused by insertion, duplication, addition and translocation of bases.

1) The **types** of errors that can occur include:

   Substitution — one base is substituted with another, e.g. ATGCCT becomes ATTCCT (G is swapped for T).

   Deletion — one base is deleted, e.g. ATGCCT becomes ATCCT (G is deleted).

2) The **order** of **DNA bases** in a gene determines the **order of amino acids** in a particular **protein** (see p. 136). If a mutation occurs in a gene, the **sequence** of **amino acids** it codes for (and the protein formed) could be **altered**:

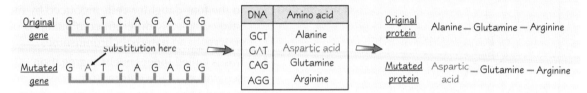

DNA	Amino acid
GCT	Alanine
GAT	Aspartic acid
CAG	Glutamine
AGG	Arginine

Original gene G C T C A G A G G
substitution here
Mutated gene G A T C A G A G G

Original protein: Alanine — Glutamine — Arginine
Mutated protein: Aspartic acid — Glutamine — Arginine

   This could **change** the final **3D shape** of the protein so it **doesn't work properly** (see page 17).

3) If a mutation occurs in a **gene** it can cause a **genetic disorder**, which is then **passed on**. E.g. **cystic fibrosis** (**CF**) is a genetic disorder caused by a mutation in a gene. The protein the gene codes for is important for **mucus production** (see page 150 for more details).

4) Some genetic disorders can be caused by lots of **different mutations**, e.g. over 1000 possible mutations are known to cause CF.

Not All Mutations Affect the Order of Amino Acids

The **degenerate nature** of the genetic code (see page 140) means that some amino acids are coded for by **more than one DNA triplet** (e.g. tyrosine can be coded for by TAT or TAC in DNA). This means that **not all** substitution mutations will result in a change to the amino acid sequence of the protein — some substitutions will still **code for** the **same amino acid**. For example:

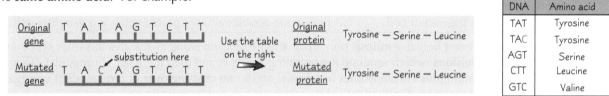

DNA	Amino acid
TAT	Tyrosine
TAC	Tyrosine
AGT	Serine
CTT	Leucine
GTC	Valine

Original gene T A T A G T C T T
substitution here
Mutated gene T A C A G T C T T

Use the table on the right

Original protein: Tyrosine — Serine — Leucine
Mutated protein: Tyrosine — Serine — Leucine

Substitution mutations **won't always** lead to changes in the amino acid sequence, but **deletions will** — the deletion of a base will change the **number** of bases present, which will cause a **shift** in all the triplets after it.

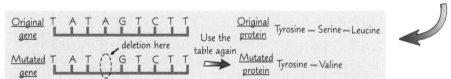

Original gene T A T A G T C T T
deletion here
Mutated gene T A T G T C T T

Use the table again

Original protein: Tyrosine — Serine — Leucine
Mutated protein: Tyrosine — Valine

Mutagenic Agents Increase the Rate of Mutation

Mutations occur **spontaneously**, e.g. when DNA is **misread** during **replication**. But some things can cause an **increase** in the **rate** of **mutations** — these are called **mutagenic agents**. **Ultraviolet radiation**, **ionising radiation**, some **chemicals** and some **viruses** are examples of mutagenic agents.

Looking at the rest of her herd, Nelly suspected she might have experienced one or two mutations.

Mutations

Chromosome Mutations are Caused by Errors in Cell Division

1) In humans, when meiosis **works properly**, all four daughter cells will end up with **23 whole chromosomes** — one from each homologous pair (1 to 23).

2) But sometimes meiosis **goes wrong** and the cells produced contain **variations** in the numbers of whole chromosomes or **parts** of chromosomes.

3) For example, two cells might have 23 whole chromosomes, one each of 1 to 23, but the other two might get a bit muddled up, one having two chromosome 6's and the other no chromosome 6.

4) This is called **chromosome mutation** and is caused by **errors** during meiosis.

5) Chromosome mutations lead to **inherited conditions** because the errors are present in the **gametes** (the hereditary cells).

One type of chromosome mutation is called **non-disjunction** — it's a **failure** of the **chromosomes** to **separate** properly. In humans, non-disjunction of **chromosome 21** during **meiosis** can lead to **Down's Syndrome**.

1) **Down's syndrome** is caused by a person having an **extra copy** of **chromosome 21** (or sometimes an extra copy of part of chromosome 21).

2) Non-disjunction means that chromosome 21 **fails to separate properly** during **meiosis**, so one cell gets an **extra copy** of 21 and another gets **none**.

3) When the gamete with the **extra copy** fuses to another gamete at **fertilisation**, the resulting zygote will have **three** copies of chromosome 21.

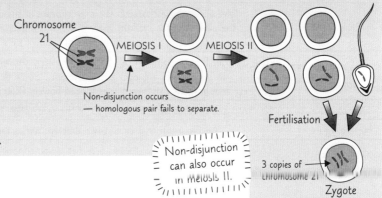

Chromosome 21 — MEIOSIS I — MEIOSIS II — Fertilisation

Non-disjunction occurs — homologous pair fails to separate.

Non-disjunction can also occur in meiosis II.

3 copies of chromosome 21 — Zygote

Practice Questions

Q1 What is a gene mutation?

Q2 Explain why mutations in genes can alter the proteins they code for.

Q3 What are mutagenic agents?

Q4 Give two examples of mutagenic agents.

DNA	Amino acid
AGT	Serine
TAT	Tyrosine
CTT	Leucine
AGG	Arginine

Exam Questions

Q1 A mutation occurred during DNA replication. The diagram on the right shows part of the original gene and the mutated gene.

a) What type of mutation has occurred? [1 mark]

b) Using the table provided, explain the effects that this mutation would have on the amino acid sequence. [2 marks]

Original gene   T A T A G T C T T

Mutated gene   T A T A G G C T T

Q2 Turner syndrome is a genetic condition affecting females. It is caused by non-disjunction of the sex chromosomes. Females usually have two X chromosomes. Some females with Turner syndrome have only one X chromosome.

Suggest and explain how chromosome non-disjunction could cause Turner syndrome. [3 marks]

What do you get if you cross James Bond with the Hulk™?*

DNA replication isn't perfect, which is how mutations can come about. Gene mutations can affect the sequence of amino acids produced, which can affect the protein produced. This isn't necessarily a bad thing (see natural selection, page 172) but it can cause problems, e.g. genetic disorders. Chromosome mutations include chromosome non-disjunction.

*A mutagenic agent

Genes and Inheritance

Now it's time find out the chances of certain characteristics being passed on when gametes are fertilised.
You're gonna need to draw a few diagrams, but first up there are quite a few terms to get your head around...

Here are Some Useful **Genetic Terms**:

There's more on genes on p. 136.

TERM	DESCRIPTION
Gene	A sequence of bases on a DNA molecule that codes for a protein, which results in a characteristic, e.g. the gene for eye colour.
Allele	A different version of a gene. Most plants and animals, including humans, have two copies of each gene, one from each parent. The two copies can be the same or they can be different. Different versions (alleles) have slightly different base sequences, which code for different versions of the same characteristic, e.g. brown eyes and blue eyes. They're represented using letters, e.g. the allele for brown eyes (B) and the allele for blue eyes (b).
Genotype	The alleles a person has, e.g. BB, Bb or bb for eye colour.
Phenotype	The characteristics displayed by an organism, e.g. brown eyes.
Dominant	An allele whose characteristic appears in the phenotype even when there's only one copy, e.g. the allele for brown eyes (B) is dominant — if a person's genotype is Bb or BB, they'll have brown eyes. Dominant alleles are shown by a capital letter.
Recessive	An allele whose characteristic only appears in the phenotype if two copies are present, e.g. the allele for blue eyes (b) is recessive — if a person's genotype is bb, they'll have blue eyes. Recessive alleles are shown by a lower case letter.
Incomplete Dominance	When the trait from a dominant allele isn't completely shown over the trait produced by the recessive allele, so both alleles influence the phenotype. Some flowers show incomplete dominance, e.g. snapdragons can have alleles for red flowers (RR), white flowers (rr) or pink flowers (Rr).
Homozygote	An organism that carries two copies of the same allele for a certain characteristic, e.g. BB or bb.
Heterozygote	An organism that carries two different alleles for a certain characteristic, e.g. Bb.
Carrier	If a recessive allele can cause disease, a carrier is someone who has one dominant and one recessive allele (heterozygous). They won't have the disease but they carry a copy of the allele for the disease.

Genetic Diagrams show the **Possible Alleles** of **Offspring**

Monohybrid inheritance is the inheritance of a **single characteristic** controlled by **different** alleles. **Genetic diagrams** can be used to predict the **genotypes** and **phenotypes** of the **offspring** produced if two parents are **crossed** (**bred**). Here's an example of how to **interpret** a genetic diagram:

Plant Height

1) The **height** of garden pea plants is controlled by a **single** gene with **two alleles**.
2) The allele for **tall** plants (**T**) is **dominant** over the allele for **dwarf** plants (**t**).
3) The diagram below shows the predicted genotypes and phenotypes of the offspring if **two heterozygous** pea plants (**Tt**) are crossed:

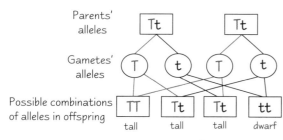

Parents' alleles — Tt, Tt
Gametes' alleles — T, t, T, t
Possible combinations of alleles in offspring — TT (tall), Tt (tall), Tt (tall), tt (dwarf)

See page 142 for more on gametes.

Predicted genotypes and phenotypes:
- 2 in 4 (**50%**) **chance** of offspring having the **genotype Tt** (phenotype = tall).
- 1 in 4 (**25%**) chance of offspring having the **genotype TT** (phenotype = **tall**).
- 1 in 4 (**25%**) chance of offspring having the **genotype tt** (phenotype = **dwarf**).

The phenotypic ratio is just the ratio of different phenotypes in the offspring.

So there's a **75%** (3 in 4) chance of offspring being **tall**, and the **phenotypic ratio** of tall to dwarf plants is **3 : 1**.

Genes and Inheritance

Homozygous Dominant x Homozygous Recessive = 100 % Heterozygous Offspring

Here's what happens if **two homozygous** pea plants (**TT** and **tt**) are crossed:

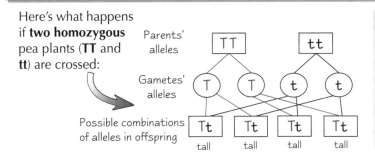

Parents' alleles

Gametes' alleles

Possible combinations of alleles in offspring

Predicted genotypes and phenotypes:

- 4 in 4 (**100%**) **chance** of offspring having the **genotype Tt** (**phenotype = tall**).
- 0 in 4 (**0%**) chance of offspring having the **genotype TT** (**phenotype = tall**).
- 0 in 4 (**0%**) chance of offspring having the **genotype tt** (**phenotype = dwarf**).

Some Genes are Linked

1) The **position** of a gene on a chromosome is called a **locus** (plural: **loci**) — see page 137. Independent segregation means that **genes** with loci on **different chromosomes** end up **randomly distributed** in the **gametes**.

2) But genes with loci on the **same chromosome** are said to be **linked** — because the genes are on the same chromosome, they'll stay together during **independent segregation** and their alleles will be **passed on to the offspring together**. The only reason this won't happen is if **crossing over** splits them up first.

A chromosome

Genes A, B and C are all linked.

Genes A and B are more closely linked than genes A and C.

3) The **closer together** the loci of two genes on a chromosome, the **more closely** they are said to be **linked**. This is because **crossing over** is **less likely** to split them up.

Some Characteristics are Sex-linked

1) A **characteristic** is said to be **sex-linked** when the **locus** of the **allele** that codes for it is on a **sex chromosome**.

2) In mammals, **females** have **two X chromosomes** (XX) and **males** have **one X** and **one Y** chromosome (XY).

3) The **Y chromosome** is **smaller** than the X chromosome and carries **fewer genes**. So most genes on the sex chromosomes are **only carried** on the X chromosome (called **X-linked** genes).

4) As **males** only have **one X chromosome**, they often only have **one allele** for sex-linked genes. So because they **only** have one copy, they **express** the **characteristic** of this allele even if it's **recessive**. This makes males **more likely** than females to show **recessive phenotypes** for genes that are sex-linked.

5) Genetic disorders caused by **faulty alleles** on sex chromosomes include **colour blindness** and **haemophilia**. The faulty alleles for both of these disorders are carried on the X chromosome — they're called **X-linked disorders**.

Practice Questions

Q1 Explain the difference between a dominant and a recessive allele.

Q2 What is incomplete dominance?

Q3 What is a sex-linked characteristic?

Exam Questions

Q1 The genes for eye colour and wing length in fruit flies are linked.

    a) What does it mean when two genes are linked? [1 mark]

    b) Explain how the loci of the genes affects the likelihood that they will stay linked following meiosis. [2 marks]

Q2 A garden pea plant is heterozygous for seed colour. The allele for yellow colour (Y) is dominant over the allele for green colour (y). Draw a genetic diagram to show the possible genotypes of the offspring produced if the heterozygous plant is crossed with a homozygous plant with green seeds. [3 marks]

Some genes are linked... so are some sausages...

There's quite a lot to get to grips with on these two pages — that list of genetic terms just goes on and on. You won't get much further in this section without them though, so just grin and bear it. Diagrams of genetic crosses might look a bit like spiders' webs, but they make predicting genotypes and phenotypes a piece of cake. Cake... Mmm... I'm hungry.

Cystic Fibrosis

Cystic fibrosis is a genetically inherited disease. You can use genetic pedigree diagrams to show how it's inherited.

Genetic Pedigree Diagrams Show How Traits Run in Families

1) Genetic pedigree diagrams show an **inherited trait** (characteristic) in a group of **related individuals**.

2) **Cystic fibrosis** (**CF**) is an inherited disorder that mainly affects the **respiratory**, **digestive** and **reproductive** **systems** (see next page). It's caused by a **recessive** allele (f), so a person will only have the disorder if they're **homozygous** for the allele (ff) — they must inherit one recessive allele **from each parent**. If a person is **heterozygous** (Ff), they **won't** have CF but they'll be a **carrier**.

3) Here are some **examples** of genetic pedigree diagrams for cystic fibrosis:

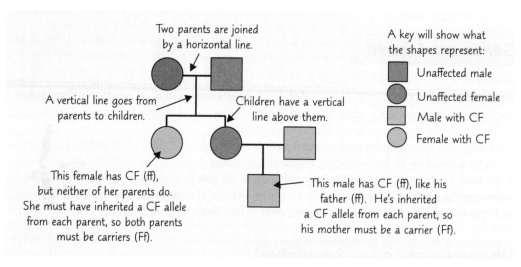

Sometimes carriers are also shown on the key:

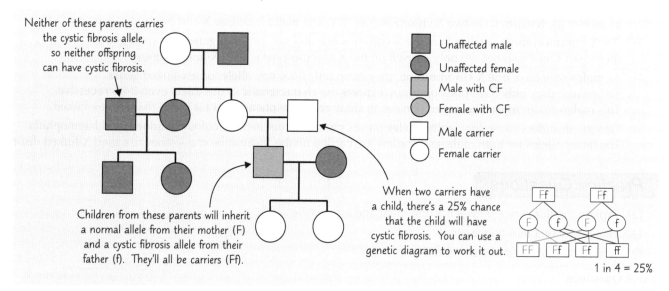

Cystic Fibrosis Causes the Production of Thick Sticky Mucus

1) Cystic fibrosis is caused by a **mutation** in the **gene** that codes for the **CFTR** protein (**C**ystic **F**ibrosis **T**ransmembrane Conductance **R**egulator).

See page 66 for more on osmosis.

2) CFTR is a **channel protein** (see page 60). It transports **chloride ions** out of cells and into mucus — this causes water to move **into** the mucus by **osmosis**, which makes mucus **watery**.

3) **Mutant** CFTR protein is much **less efficient** at transporting chloride ions **out** of the cell, so **less water moves out by osmosis**. This makes the mucus of people with CF abnormally **thick** and **sticky**.

4) This thick and sticky mucus causes **problems** in the **respiratory**, **digestive** and **reproductive systems** — see next page.

Cystic Fibrosis

Cystic Fibrosis Affects the **Respiratory System**...

Everybody has **mucus** in their respiratory system — it helps **prevent lung infections** by trapping **microorganisms**. The mucus (with the microorganisms) is transported towards the throat by **cilia** (small **hair-like** structures that beat to move mucus along). The abnormally **thick** and **sticky** mucus in people with CF causes some problems:

1) The cilia are **unable** to **move** the mucus towards the throat because it's so thick and sticky.
2) This means the **mucus builds up** in the **airways**.
3) Some airways can become completely **blocked** by the mucus — **gas exchange** can't take place in the area **below the blockage**.
4) This means that the **surface area** available for gas exchange is **reduced**, causing breathing difficulties.
5) People with CF are also more prone to **lung infections** as mucus containing microorganisms can't be removed.

See page 72 for more on gas exchange in the lungs.

People with CF can be given **antibiotics** to **kill** the **bacteria** trapped in mucus, and they can also have **physiotherapy** to help dislodge mucus and **improve gas exchange**.

...the **Digestive System**...

Everyone also has mucus in their digestive system. The abnormally thick mucus produced by people with CF can also cause **digestive problems** because:

1) The **tube** that connects the **pancreas** to the **small intestine** can become **blocked** with mucus — preventing **digestive enzymes** produced by the pancreas from **reaching** the small intestine. This reduces the ability of someone with CF to **digest food** and so **fewer nutrients** can be absorbed.
2) The mucus can cause **cysts** (growths) to form in the **pancreas**. These **inhibit** the **production** of **enzymes**, which also reduces the ability to digest food and absorb nutrients.
3) The mucus **lining** the **small intestine** is **abnormally thick** — this inhibits the **absorption** of nutrients.

...and the **Reproductive System**

Mucus is also secreted by the reproductive system — it helps to **prevent infections** and **transport sex cells** (sperm or eggs). The thick and sticky mucus of people with CF causes problems here because:

1) In some men with CF, the **tubes** connecting the **testicles** (where sperm are produced) to the **penis** are **absent** and can become **blocked** by the thick mucus in others. So, any **sperm** produced **can't reach the penis**.
2) In women, thickened **cervical mucus** can **prevent** the sperm from **reaching the egg**. The sperm has to travel through this mucus to reach the egg — thick mucus reduces the **motility** of the sperm, reducing its chances of **making it** to the egg.

Practice Questions

Q1 What is a genetic pedigree diagram?
Q2 Why do people with cystic fibrosis have abnormally thick and sticky mucus?

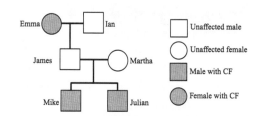

Exam Question

Q1 The genetic pedigree diagram above shows the inheritance of cystic fibrosis (CF) in one family.

a) Name one female who is homozygous for the CF allele and one individual who is a carrier. [2 marks]
b) If James and Martha have another child, what is the chance it will have CF? Show your working. [3 marks]
c)* Explain the effect of CF on the digestive system. [6 marks]

* You will be assessed on the quality of your written response in this question.

Pedigree Diagram — because your dog's worth it...

Genetic pedigree diagrams aren't as scary as they look, just work through them slowly. With recessive disorders affected individuals are always homozygous, so any children they have will always have at least one recessive allele.

Genetic Screening

Most genetic disorders can only be treated, not cured, so it's important to be able to screen for these conditions.

There are **Three Main Uses** of **Genetic Screening**

Genetic screening involves analysing **DNA** to see if it contains **alleles** for genetic disorders.
The **three** main uses are:

1. Identification of Carriers

1) **Carrier testing** is offered to individuals with a **family history** of genetic disorders.

2) It shows whether people **without** a disorder **carry an allele** that can cause a disorder (e.g. CF).

3) Couples can be tested **before having children** to determine the **chances** of any **future** children having the disorder, e.g. if both parents are **carriers** there's a **25%** chance their child will have the disorder.

4) Carrier testing allows people to make **informed decisions** about things like **whether to have children** and whether to carry out **prenatal testing** if the woman is pregnant (see below).

5) Carrier testing raises **social** and **ethical issues**:

- Finding out you're a carrier may cause **emotional stress** or affect your ability to **find a partner**.
- The tests **aren't** always 100% **accurate** — they could give a **false result**.
  This means decisions could be based on **incorrect information**.
- Other genetic **abnormalities** may be found, which could cause **further stress**.
- There are concerns that the **results** of genetic tests could be used by **employers** or **life insurance companies** — resulting in **genetic discrimination**.

2. Preimplantation Genetic Diagnosis (PGD)

1) **PGD** is carried out on **embryos** produced by *in vitro* **fertilisation (IVF)**.

2) It involves **screening** embryos for genetic disorders **before** they're implanted into the woman.

3) The **advantages** of PGD are that it **reduces** the chance of having a baby with a genetic disorder — only embryos **without** the genetic disorders tested for will be implanted. Also, because it's performed **before implantation**, it avoids the issue of **abortion** that could be raised by **prenatal testing** (see below).

4) PGD also raises **social** and **ethical issues**:

- It can be used to find out **other characteristics** (e.g. **gender, eye colour**) — leading to concerns that **in the future**, embryos may be selected for other characteristics (**designer babies**).
- **False results** could provide **incorrect information**.

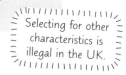
Selecting for other characteristics is illegal in the UK.

3. Prenatal Testing

1) Prenatal tests involve screening **unborn babies** (fetuses) for genetic disorders.

2) They're offered to pregnant women with a **family history** of genetic disease.

3) There are **two** types of test — **amniocentesis** and **chorionic villus sampling**.

Amniocentesis

1) This is usually carried out at **15-20 weeks** of pregnancy.

2) A sample of **amniotic fluid** (the fluid that surrounds the fetus) is obtained via the **abdomen** using a very fine **needle**.

3) This fluid contains fetal **cells**. The cells contain DNA, which can be **analysed**.

4) Amniocentesis has a **1% risk** of **miscarriage**.

5) Results aren't available until **2-3 weeks after** the sample is taken, although a **rapid test** (which only looks for a **few** of the **most common** disorders) can also be performed. The results of the rapid test are usually available in **3-4 days**.

Genetic Screening

Chorionic Villus Sampling (CVS)

1) CVS is usually performed at **11-14 weeks** of pregnancy.

2) Because it can take place **earlier** in a pregnancy than amniocentesis, an earlier **decision** to abort can be made, meaning that the procedure is less physically traumatic.

3) A sample of **cells** is taken from the **chorionic villi** (part of the fetus that connects it to its mother). The cells contain fetal **DNA**, which can be **analysed**.

4) This procedure is done via either the **abdomen** (using a fine **needle**) or the **vagina** (using a **catheter** — a thin flexible tube).

5) CVS has a **1-2% risk** of **miscarriage**, which is greater than with amniocentesis.

6) **Initial** results (which tell you whether any **obvious major issues** have been found) are available in a **few days**, but the results of more **in-depth** and **detailed** tests can take **two weeks** or **more**.

Testing Allows People to **Make Decisions**

1) Prenatal testing allows parents to make **informed decisions**. If the test is positive, the parents may decide to **have the child** or to have an **abortion**. The results can also help parents to **prepare for the future care** of the child — any **medical treatment** available could be started as soon as the child is born.

2) As with the other forms of testing, prenatal testing raises **social** and **ethical issues**:

   - Prenatal tests slightly **increase** the risk of **miscarriage**.
   - **False results** could provide **incorrect information**.
   - Some people consider it **unethical** to **abort** a fetus because it has a genetic disorder.

Practice Questions

Q1 What is genetic screening?

Q2 Describe one ethical issue raised by prenatal testing.

Exam Questions

Q1 Which of the following is true about chorionic villus sampling (CVS)?

   A It has a lower risk of miscarriage and can be carried out earlier than amniocentesis.
   B It has a higher risk of miscarriage and is carried out later than amniocentesis.
   C It has a higher risk of miscarriage and can be carried out earlier than amniocentesis.
   D It has a lower risk of miscarriage and is carried out later than amniocentesis.   [1 mark]

Q2 Duchenne muscular dystrophy is a genetic disorder caused by a recessive allele.
   It is caused by a mutated gene, which normally codes for a protein needed for healthy muscle tissue.

   a) Explain why an individual with a family history of Duchenne muscular dystrophy may be offered carrier testing.   [3 marks]

   b) Preimplantation genetic diagnosis is available for Duchenne muscular dystrophy.

      i)   Explain what preimplantation genetic diagnosis is.   [1 mark]
      ii) Describe one benefit of preimplantation genetic diagnosis.   [1 mark]
      iii) Describe two social or ethical issues raised by preimplantation genetic diagnosis.   [2 marks]

Carrier testing — which bag has the strongest handles?

Phew. That's a pretty deep way to end a section. And those prenatal procedures don't sound too pleasant either — I've never been a fan of needles. Whatever your personal opinion, remember to consider both the advantages and the ethical issues surrounding genetic screening if you get asked about it in your exam. Chin up, kettle on, and back to it.

Stem Cells and Differentiation

If I had to choose a favourite type of cell, I'd choose a stem cell and here's why...

Stem Cells are Unspecialised Cells

1) **Multicellular organisms** are made up from many **different** cell types that are **specialised** for their function, e.g. liver cells, muscle cells, white blood cells.

2) **All** these specialised cell types originally came from **stem cells**.

3) Stem cells are **unspecialised** cells — they can develop into **different types** of cell.

4) **All** multicellular organisms have some form of **stem cell**.

5) In **humans**, stem cells are found in **early embryos** and in a few places in **adults**. Stem cells in **early embryos** can develop into **any type** of human cell. Stem cells in **adults** can only develop into a **limited range** of cells (see next page).

Tina, Joe and Bex knew their cells were specialised — specialised to look good.

Stem Cells Differentiate into Specialised Cells

1) Stem cells **divide** to become **new cells**, which then become **specialised**.

2) The process by which a cell becomes specialised for its job is called **differentiation**.

3) In animals, adult stem cells are used to replace **damaged cells**, e.g. to make **new skin** or **blood cells** (see below).

4) **Plants** are always growing, so stem cells are needed to make **new shoots** and **roots** throughout their lives. Stem cells in plants can **differentiate** into various plant tissues including **xylem and phloem** (see below).

5) Stem cells are also able to **divide** to produce **more** undifferentiated **stem cells**, i.e. they can **renew** themselves.

Cells in the Bone Marrow Differentiate into Blood Cells

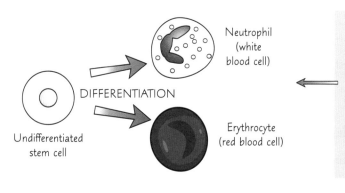

DIFFERENTIATION

Neutrophil (white blood cell)

Erythrocyte (red blood cell)

Undifferentiated stem cell

1) **Bones** are living organs, containing nerves and **blood vessels**.

2) The main bones of the body have **marrow** in the **centres**.

3) Here, **adult stem cells** divide and **differentiate** to replace worn out blood cells — **erythrocytes** (red blood cells) and **neutrophils** (white blood cells that help to fight infection).

Cells in the Meristems Differentiate into Xylem and Phloem

1) In plants, **stem cells** are found in the **meristems** (parts of the plant where growth can take place).

2) In the root and stem, stem cells of the **vascular cambium** divide and **differentiate** to become **xylem vessels** and **phloem sieve tubes**.

Root or shoot

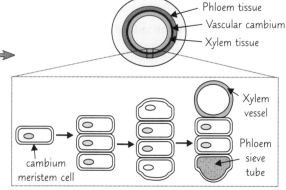

Phloem tissue
Vascular cambium
Xylem tissue

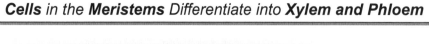

The vascular cambium is a meristem that runs up the length of the roots and shoots of many plants.

There's more about the function of xylem and phloem on p. 94-95.

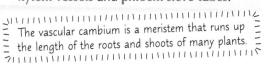

cambium meristem cell

Xylem vessel

Phloem sieve tube

Meristem cells divide and begin to differentiate

Xylem and phloem differentiate on either side of the meristem

Stem Cells and Differentiation

The **Ability** of Stem Cells to **Differentiate** is Called **Potency**

1) **Different types** of stem cells have **different potencies**. Here are two examples:

   1) **Totipotency** — the ability to produce **all cell types**, including all the **specialised cells** in an organism and **extraembryonic cells** (cells of the placenta and umbilical cord).

   2) **Pluripotency** — the ability of a stem cell to produce all the **specialised cells** in an organism (but **not** extraembryonic cells, because the genes for these cell types have become inactivated — see below).

2) **Totipotent** stem cells are **only** present in mammals in the **first few cell divisions** of an **embryo**. After this point the **embryonic stem cells** become **pluripotent**. They can still specialise into **any** cell in the body, but **lose** the **ability** to become the cells that make up the **placenta** and **umbilical cord**.

3) Stem cells are also found in **some adult** mammalian tissues (where they become **specialised cells** that need to be **replaced**, e.g. stem cells in the intestines constantly replace intestinal epithelial cells). Adult stem cells are much **less flexible** than embryonic stem cells though — they can only develop into **some** cell types.

Stem Cells Become **Specialised** Through **Differential Gene Expression**

A cell **doesn't express** (make proteins from) **all the genes** in its **genome** (see page 136). Stem cells become **specialised** because **different genes** in their DNA **become active** and get **expressed**:

1) **Stem cells** all contain the **same genes**, but not all of them are **expressed** because not all of them are **active**.

2) Under the **right conditions**, some **genes** are **activated** and others are **inactivated**.

3) **mRNA** is only **transcribed** from the **active genes**.

4) The mRNA from the active genes is then **translated** into **proteins**.

5) These proteins **modify the cell** — they determine the **cell structure** and **control cell processes** (including the activation of **more** genes, which produces more proteins).

6) **Changes** to the cell produced by these proteins cause the cell to become **specialised** (differentiate). These changes are **difficult** to **reverse**, so once a cell has specialised it **stays** specialised.

Transcription is when DNA is copied into mRNA. Translation is when proteins are produced using the code in mRNA. See pages 138-139 for more.

All of the girls expressed different jeans.

Practice Questions

Q1 What are stem cells?
Q2 What is the name of the process by which a stem cell becomes specialised?
Q3 Stem cells in bone marrow can differentiate into other cell types. Name two of these cell types.
Q4 Name one part of a plant where stem cells are found.

Exam Questions

Q1 Describe, with an example, the role of stem cells in adult mammals. [3 marks]

Q2 During the development of a human embryo, stem cells specialise to become all the different types of cell that make up the body. During very early development, stem cells are totipotent, but they soon become pluripotent.
   a) Explain the difference between totipotent stem cells and pluripotent stem cells. [3 marks]
   b)* Describe how differential gene expression results in the production of specialised cells from stem cells. [6 marks]

* You will be assessed on the quality of your written response in this question.

And you thought differentiation was just boring maths stuff...

Stem cells are pretty amazing when you think about it — they can differentiate to become any cell in the whole body. Totipotent stem cells are the coolest cells though — they can divide and differentiate into a whole organism.

Stem Cells in Medicine

These pages are about how stem cells can be used in medicine to replace damaged cells. It's got me thinking... perhaps I could grow another brain from some of my stem cells — then I'd be twice as clever.

Stem Cells Could be Used to Treat Some Diseases

1) **Stem cells** can develop into **any** specialised cell type, so scientists think they could be used to **replace damaged tissues** in a **range** of **diseases**.

2) Some stem cell therapies **already exist**. For example, the treatment for **leukaemia** (a cancer of the bone marrow) kills all the **stem cells** in the bone marrow, so **bone marrow transplants** can be given to patients to **replace** them.

3) Scientists are **researching** the use of stem cells as a **treatment** for lots of conditions, including:

- **Spinal cord injuries** — stem cells could be used to repair damaged **nerve tissue**.
- **Heart disease** and **damage caused by heart attacks** — stem cells could be used to replace damaged heart tissue.
- **Neurological disorders** like **Alzheimer's** and **Parkinson's**:

With **Alzheimer's**, **nerve cells** in the brain **die** in increasing numbers. This results in severe **memory loss**. Researchers are hoping to use stem cells to **regrow healthy nerve cells** in people with Alzheimer's.	Patients with **Parkinson's** suffer from **tremors** that they can't control. The disease causes the loss of a particular type of **nerve cell** found in the **brain**. These cells release a **chemical** called **dopamine**, which is needed to **control movement**. **Transplanted stem cells** may help to **regenerate** the dopamine-producing cells.

4) Stem cells are also used by scientists researching **developmental biology**, i.e. how organisms **grow** and **develop**. Studying stem cells can help us to understand more about things like **developmental disorders** and **cancer**.

5) People who make **decisions** about the **use** of stem cells in medicine and research have to consider the **potential benefits** of stem cell therapies:

- They could **save** many **lives** — e.g. many people waiting for organ transplants **die** before a **donor organ** becomes available. Stem cells could be used to **grow organs** for those people awaiting transplants.
- They could **improve** the **quality of life** for many people — e.g. stem cells could be used to replace damaged cells in the eyes of people who are **blind**.

Human Stem Cells Can Come from Adult Tissue or Embryos

In order to **use stem cells** in medicine and research, scientists have to get them from somewhere. There are **two** potential **sources** of human stem cells:

1) Adult stem cells

1) These are obtained from the **body tissues** of an **adult**. For example, adult stem cells are found in **bone marrow**.

2) They can be obtained in a relatively **simple operation** — with very **little risk** involved, but quite **a lot of discomfort**. The **donor** is anaesthetised, a **needle** is **inserted** into the centre of a **bone** (usually the hip) and a **small quantity** of bone marrow is **removed**.

3) Adult stem cells **aren't** as **flexible** as embryonic stem cells — they can only develop into a **limited** range of cells (see page 155).

4) However, if a **patient** needs a stem cell transplant and their **own** adult stem cells can be used (from elsewhere in their body) there's **less risk of rejection**.

2) Embryonic stem cells

1) These are obtained from **early embryos**.

2) Embryos are created in a **laboratory** using *in vitro* fertilisation (IVF) — egg cells are **fertilised** by sperm **outside the womb**.

3) Once the embryos are approximately **4 to 5 days old**, **stem cells are removed** from them and the rest of the embryo **is destroyed**.

4) Embryonic stem cells can develop into **all types** of specialised cells (see p.155).

Rejection of transplants occurs quite often and is caused by the patient's immune system recognising the cells as foreign and attacking them.

Stem Cells in Medicine

The Use of Embryonic Stem Cells Raises Ethical Issues

1) Obtaining stem cells from **embryos** created by IVF raises **ethical issues** because the procedure results in the **destruction** of an embryo that's **viable** (could become a fetus if placed in a womb).

2) Many people believe that at the moment of **fertilisation** a **genetically unique individual** is formed that has the **right** to **life** — so they believe that it's **wrong** to **destroy** embryos.

3) Some people have **fewer objections** to stem cells being **obtained** from **egg cells** that **haven't** been fertilised by sperm, but have been **artificially activated** to start dividing. This is because the cells **couldn't survive** past a few days and **wouldn't** produce a fetus if placed in a womb.

4) Some people think that **scientists** should **only use** adult stem cells because their production **doesn't** destroy an embryo. But adult stem cells **can't** develop into all the specialised cell types that embryonic stem cells can.

Society Makes Decisions About the Use of Stem Cells in Medicine

Society has to consider all the arguments **for** and **against** stem cell research before allowing it to go ahead. To help society make these decisions, **regulatory authorities** have been established to consider the **benefits** and **ethical issues** surrounding embryonic stem cell research. The work of regulatory authorities includes:

1) Looking at proposals of **research** and deciding if they should be **allowed**, taking the **ethical issues** surrounding the work **into account** — this ensures that any research involving embryos is carried out for a **good reason**. This also makes sure research isn't unnecessarily **repeated** by different groups.

2) **Licensing** and **monitoring centres** involved in embryonic stem cell research — this ensures that only **fully trained staff** carry out the research. These staff will understand the **implications** of the research and **won't** waste precious resources, such as embryos. This also helps to **avoid unregulated research**.

3) Producing **guidelines** and **codes of practice** — this ensures all scientists are working in a **similar manner** (if scientists don't use similar methods their results can't be compared). It also ensures that the scientists are using an **acceptable source** of stem cells and that the **methods** they use to **extract** the cells are **controlled**. This includes regulating the **maximum age** of an **embryo** that can be used as a source of stem cells.

4) **Monitoring developments** in scientific research and advances — this ensures that any changes in the field are **regulated appropriately** and that all the **guidelines** are **up to date** with the latest in scientific understanding.

5) Providing **information** and **advice** to governments and professionals — this helps to **promote** the science involved in embryo research, and it helps **society** to **understand** what's involved and why it's important.

Practice Questions

Q1 Describe how stem cells could be used to treat a range of diseases.

Q2 Name two potential sources of human stem cells.

Q3 Give three ways in which regulatory authorities help society to consider the benefits and ethical issues of embryonic stem cell research.

Exam Question

Q1 Stem cell research is permitted in the UK, but it is regulated by a number of authorities.

   a) Give one potential benefit of using stem cells in medicine. [1 mark]

   b) Embryonic stem cells can be used for research.

      i) Explain one benefit of using embryonic stem cells for research rather than adult stem cells. [2 marks]

      ii) State two reasons why some people are opposed to using stem cells from embryos. [2 marks]

Stem cells — I think they prove that we all evolved from plants...

Stem cells have the potential to cure or relieve the symptoms of many diseases, but their use raises ethical issues.

Gene Expression

You may remember from page 155 that cells become specialised because different genes get expressed.
Well, here's how the cell controls which genes get expressed and which don't. Read on — it's thrilling stuff.

Transcription Factors Can Control the Expression of Genes

1) **Gene expression** can be **controlled** by **altering** the rate of **transcription** of genes.
   E.g. **increased** transcription produces **more mRNA**, which can be used to make **more protein**.

2) This is controlled by **transcription factors** — proteins that **bind** to **DNA** and **activate** or **deactivate** genes by **increasing** or **decreasing** the **rate** of **transcription**.

3) Factors that **increase** the rate of transcription are called **activators** and those that **decrease** the rate are called **repressors**. **Activators** often work by helping **RNA polymerase bind** to the **DNA** and **begin** transcription. **Repressors** often work by **preventing** RNA polymerase from **binding** and so **stopping** transcription.

4) In **eukaryotes**, such as **animals** and **plants**, transcription factors bind to **specific DNA sites** near the **start** of their **target genes** — the genes they **control** the **expression** of. In **prokaryotes**, control of gene expression often involves transcription factors binding to **operons**.

5) An **operon** is a **section** of **DNA** that contains a cluster of **structural genes**, that are **transcribed together**, as well as **control elements** and sometimes a **regulatory gene**:

   - The **structural genes** code for **useful proteins**, such as **enzymes**.
   - The **control elements** include a **promoter** (a DNA sequence located **before** the structural genes that **RNA polymerase** binds to) and an **operator** (a DNA sequence that **transcription factors** bind to).
   - The **regulatory gene** codes for an **activator** or **repressor**.

6) The **lac operon** in **E. coli** is an example of how gene expression can be controlled:

   1) *E. coli* is a bacterium that **respires glucose**, but it can use **lactose** if glucose isn't available.
   2) The genes that produce the **enzymes** needed to **respire lactose** are found on an operon called the *lac* operon.
   3) The *lac* operon has **three structural genes** — *lacZ*, *lacY* and *lacA*, which produce proteins that help the bacteria digest lactose (including β-**galactosidase** and **lactose permease**).

Lactose NOT present

The **regulatory** gene (*lacI*) produces the *lac* **repressor**, which is a **transcription factor** that **binds** to the **operator** site when there's **no lactose** present. This **blocks transcription** because RNA polymerase can't bind to the promoter.

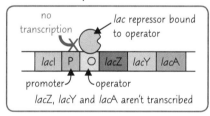

Lactose present

When **lactose is present**, it **binds** to the **repressor, changing** the repressor's **shape** so that it can **no longer bind** to the operator site. **RNA polymerase** can now **begin transcription** of the structural genes.

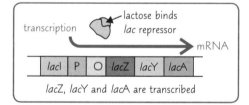

Changes in the Environment Can Cause Changes in Gene Expression

1) In **eukaryotes**, **epigenetic control** can also determine **whether** certain genes are expressed, **altering** an organism's **phenotype** (the characteristics it displays).

2) Epigenetic control **doesn't** alter the **base sequence** of **DNA**. It works by **attaching** or **removing** chemical groups **to** or **from** the **DNA**. This alters how **easy** it is for the **enzymes** and other proteins needed for **transcription** to **interact** with and **transcribe** genes.

3) **Epigenetic changes** to gene expression play a **role** in lots of normal **cellular processes**. They can also occur in **response** to **changes** in the **environment** — e.g. pollution and availability of food.

Gene Expression

Increased Methylation of DNA Represses a Gene

1) One method of **epigenetic control** is **methylation** of **DNA** — this is when a **methyl group** is **attached** to the **DNA** coding for a **gene**.

2) The group always attaches at a **CpG site**, which is where a **cytosine** and **guanine** base are **next to** each other in the DNA.

A methyl group is a -CH₃ group.

3) **Increased** methylation **changes** the **DNA structure**, so that the **proteins** and **enzymes** needed for transcription **can't bind to** the gene — so the gene is **not expressed** (i.e. it's **repressed** or **inactivated**).

Modification of Histones Also Affects Gene Expression

Histones are **proteins** that DNA **wraps around** to form **chromatin**, which makes up **chromosomes** (see page 136). Chromatin can be **highly** condensed or **less** condensed. How **condensed** it is affects the **accessibility** of the **DNA** and whether or not the **proteins** and **enzymes** needed for transcription can **bind** to it.

Epigenetic modifications to histones include the **addition** or **removal** of **acetyl** groups:

1) When histones are **acetylated**, the chromatin is **less condensed**. This means that the proteins involved in transcription can bind to the DNA, allowing genes to be **transcribed** (i.e. the genes are **activated**).

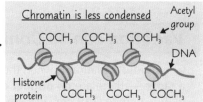

Chromatin is less condensed

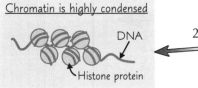

Chromatin is highly condensed

2) When **acetyl groups** are **removed** from the histones, the chromatin becomes **highly condensed** and genes in the DNA **can't** be **transcribed** because the transcription proteins **can't** bind to them — the genes are **repressed**.

Epigenetic Changes Can be Passed On After Cell Division

1) When a cell **divides** and **replicates**, **epigenetic changes** to its gene expression may be **passed on** to the resulting **daughter cells**. For example, **methyl groups** are usually **removed** from DNA during the production of gametes, but some **escape the removal process** and end up in the sperm or egg cells.

2) If epigenetic changes get passed on, it means that certain **genes** that are **activated** or **deactivated** in the **original cell** will also be **activated** or **deactivated** in the **daughter cells**.

3) If an epigenetic change occurred in **response** to a **change** in the **environment**, this means that the **daughter cells** will be **equipped** to deal with the **changed environment** in the same way as the **original cell** was.

Practice Questions

Q1 What is a transcription factor?

Q2 What do the structural genes on the *lac* operon do?

Q3 What is epigenetic control?

Q4 How can methylation of DNA affect gene expression?

Exam Question

Q1 Some cancers can be caused by epigenetic modifications to histones associated with genes related to cell division. Describe how histone modifications can affect the transcription of the genes that the histones are associated with. [2 marks]

Histones are great, but hisrhythm is way off...

DNA is pretty clever but transcription factors, well — they control which genes are activated, so which proteins are made. Epigenetic changes can also affect gene expression and can even be passed on. Whoever would've thought...

Variation

Ever wondered why no two people are exactly alike? No, well nor have I actually, but it's time to start thinking about it. This variation is partly genetic and partly due to differences in the environment.

Variation Exists Between All Individuals

Variation is the **differences** that exist between **individuals**. Every individual organism is **unique** — even **clones** (such as identical twins) show some **variation**. It can occur:

No matter what anyone said, Malcolm knew size was important.

1) <u>Within species</u> — Variation within a species is called **intraspecific** variation. For example, **individual** European robins weigh **between** 16 g and 22 g and show some variation in many other characteristics including length, wingspan, colour and beak size.

2) <u>Between species</u> — The variation between **different species** is called **interspecific** variation. For example, the **lightest** species of bird is the bee hummingbird, which weighs around 1.6 g on average. The **heaviest** species of bird is the ostrich, which can weigh up to 160 kg (100 000 times as much).

Here's how I remember which is which — Int-er means diff-er-ent species.

Variation can be Continuous...

Continuous variation is when the **individuals** in a population vary **within a range** — there are **no distinct categories**, e.g. **humans** can be **any height** within a range (139 cm, 175 cm, 185.9 cm, etc.), **not just** tall or short. Here are some more examples:

The categories are not distinct

Number of people (vertical axis) vs **Height** (horizontal axis)

Animals

1) **Milk yield** — e.g. cows can produce any volume of milk within a range.
2) **Mass** — e.g. humans can be any mass within a range.

Plants

1) **Surface area of leaves** — the surface area of a leaf can be any value within a range.
2) **Mass** — e.g. the mass of the seeds from a flower head varies within a range.

Microorganisms

1) **Width** — e.g. the width of *E. coli* bacteria varies within a range.
2) **Length** — e.g. the length of the flagellum (see p. 44) can vary within a range.

Characteristics that show continuous variation are often controlled by several genes — they're polygenic.

...or Discontinuous

Discontinuous variation is when there are two or more **distinct categories** — each individual falls into **only one** of these categories, there are **no intermediates**. Here are some examples:

Four distinct blood groups

Number of people (vertical axis) vs **Blood group** (A, B, AB, O)

Animals

Blood group — e.g. humans can be group A, B, AB or O.

Plants

1) **Colour** — e.g. courgettes are either yellow, dark green or light green.
2) **Seed shape** — e.g. some pea plants have smooth seeds and some have wrinkled seeds.

Characteristics that show discontinuous variation are often controlled by only one gene — they're monogenic.

Microorganisms

1) **Antibiotic resistance** — e.g. bacteria are either resistant or not.
2) **Pigment production** — e.g. some types of bacteria can produce a coloured pigment, some can't.

Variation

Variation can be Caused by Genes, the Environment, or Both

Variation can be caused by **genetic factors**, **environmental factors** or a combination of **both**:

(1) Genetic factors

1) **Different species** have **different genes**.
2) Individuals of the **same species** have the **same genes**, but **different versions** of them (called **alleles**).
3) The genes and alleles an organism has make up its **genotype**.
4) The differences in **genotype** result in **variation** in **phenotype** — the **characteristics** displayed by an organism.
5) Examples of variation caused **only** by genetic factors include **blood group** in humans (O, A, B or AB) and **antibiotic resistance** in bacteria.
6) You **inherit** your genes from your parents. This means variation caused by genetic factors is **inherited**.

(2) Environmental factors

1) Variation can also be caused by **differences in the environment**, e.g. climate, food, lifestyle.
2) Characteristics controlled by environmental factors can **change** over an organism's life.
3) Examples of variation caused **only** by environmental factors include **accents** and whether people have **pierced ears**.

(3) Both

Genetic factors determine the characteristics an organism's **born with**, but **environmental factors** can **influence** how some characteristics **develop**. For example:

1) **Height** — genes determine how tall an organism **can grow** (e.g. tall parents tend to have tall children). But **diet or nutrient availability** affect how tall an organism **actually grows**.
2) **Flagellum** — genes determine if a microorganism **can grow** a flagellum, but some will only **start to grow** them in **certain environments**, e.g. if metal ions are present.

Practice Questions

Q1 What is variation?

Q2 Describe what is meant by continuous variation and give one example.

Q3 Describe what is meant by discontinuous variation and give one example.

Q4 Give an example of how variation can be caused by the environment.

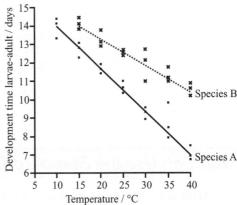

Exam Question

Q1 The graph shows the results of an investigation into the effects of temperature on the length of time it took for ladybird larvae to emerge as adults. Two species of ladybird were investigated, species A and species B.

a) Describe the results of the study. [2 marks]

b) Explain what causes the variation within each species. [1 mark]

Environmental Factor — the search is on for the most talented environment...

It's amazing to think how many factors and genes influence the way we look and behave. It's the reason why every single organism is unique. My parents have often said they're glad they'll never have another child as 'unique' as me.

Investigating Variation

If you do lots of work collecting data about variation from different populations, then you're probably going to want to analyse your data to see what it shows. Ok, you might not want to, especially cos it involves a fair bit of maths, but I'll explain how to do it anyway just in case you change your mind...

You Can Use the **Mean** to Look for **Variation Between Samples**

1) To **investigate variation** you usually take **samples** of a population (see page 180).

2) The **mean** is an **average** of the values collected in a sample. It can be used to tell if there is **variation between samples**. For example:

> The **mean height** of a species of **tree** in woodland A = **26 m**,
> in woodland B = **32 m** and in woodland C = **35 m**.
> So the **mean height varies**.

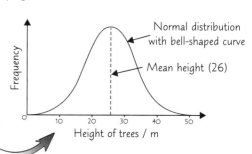

3) Most samples will include values **either side** of the **mean**, so you end up with a **bell-shaped graph** — this is called a **normal distribution**. A normal distribution is **symmetrical** about the mean.

The **Standard Deviation** Tells You About **Variation Within a Sample**

1) The **standard deviation** tells you how much the **values** in a **single sample vary**. It's a measure of the **spread** of **values** about the **mean**.

2) Sometimes you'll see the mean written as, e.g. **9 ± 3**. This means that the **mean** is **9** and the **standard deviation** is **3**, so most of the **values** are spread between **6** and **12**.

3) A **large standard deviation** means the values in the sample **vary a lot**. A **small standard deviation** tells you that most of the sample data is around the mean value, so **varies little**.

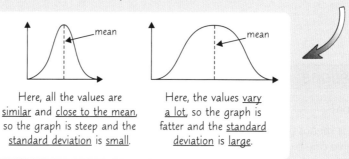

Here, all the values are similar and close to the mean, so the graph is steep and the standard deviation is small.

Here, the values vary a lot, so the graph is fatter and the standard deviation is large.

You Can Use the **Standard Deviation** to Draw **Error Bars**

1) **Standard deviations** can be **plotted** on a graph or chart of **mean values** using **error bars**, e.g.

2) Error bars extend **one standard deviation above** and **one standard deviation below** the mean (so the total **length** of an error bar is **twice the standard deviation**).

3) The **longer** the **bar**, the **larger** the **standard deviation** and the **more spread out** the sample data is from the mean.

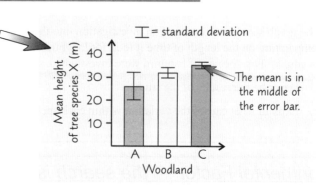

Investigating Variation

You Can Find the **Standard Deviation** Using the **Formula**

This is the formula for finding the standard deviation of a group of values:

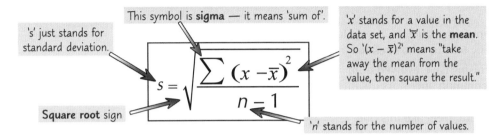

This symbol is **sigma** — it means 'sum of'.

's' just stands for standard deviation.

$$s = \sqrt{\frac{\sum (x - \bar{x})^2}{n - 1}}$$

'x' stands for a value in the data set, and $\bar{x}$ is the **mean**. So '$(x - \bar{x})^2$' means "take away the mean from the value, then square the result."

Square root sign

'n' stands for the number of values.

Example:

The table shows the height of four different trees in a forest. To find the **standard deviation**:

Tree	Height (m)
A	22
B	27
C	26
D	29

① Write out the **equation**. $s = \sqrt{\dfrac{\sum (x - \bar{x})^2}{n - 1}}$

② Work out the **mean** height of the trees, $\bar{x}$. $(22 + 27 + 26 + 29) \div 4 = \mathbf{26}$

③ Work out $(x - \bar{x})^2$ for each value of x.   A: $(22 - 26)^2 = (-4)^2 = \mathbf{16}$ B: $(27 - 26)^2 = 1^2 = \mathbf{1}$
For each tree height in the table, you need to take away the mean, then square the answer.   C: $(26 - 26)^2 = 0^2 = \mathbf{0}$ D: $(29 - 26)^2 = 3^2 = \mathbf{9}$

④ **Add up** all these numbers to find $\sum(x - \bar{x})^2$. $16 + 1 + 0 + 9 = \mathbf{26}$

⑤ Divide this number by the number of values, n, minus 1. Then take the **square root** to get the answer. $26 \div 3 = 8.66...$
$\sqrt{8.66...} = \mathbf{2.9}$ **to 2 s.f.**

Practice Questions

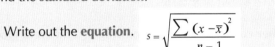

Q1 Describe the shape of a graph with a normal distribution.

Q2 What does the standard deviation of a data set tell us?

Q3 What does a small standard deviation indicate about sample data?

Germination Time (Days)	
Species A	Species B
8	12
11	10
9	6
10	12
7	15
9	11

Exam Question

Q1 A student was investigating the variation in germination time for two plant species. The student recorded the germination time for six seedlings from species A and six from species B. The results are shown in the table.

a) Calculate the mean germination time for each species.   [2 marks]

b) The standard deviation for species A is 1.3 and for species B is 2.7 (to 1 decimal place). What conclusions can you draw from this information?   [2 marks]

Sex and drugs and rock and roll — it's all just standard deviation...

Bet you thought you'd finished with maths — 'fraid not. Luckily, calculating the mean is a reasonably easy bit of maths. To interpret — a bigger difference in the means, tells you there's a bigger difference <u>between</u> the populations sampled. A bigger standard deviation, tells you there's a bigger difference <u>within</u> the population. There, it's not that bad really.

Classification of Organisms

For hundreds of years people have been putting organisms into groups to make it easier to recognise and name them. For example, my brother is a member of the species Idioto bigearian (Latin for idiots with big ears).

Phylogeny Tells Us About the Evolutionary History of Organisms

1) **Phylogeny** is the study of the **evolutionary history** of groups of **organisms**.
Phylogeny tells us **who's related** to whom and how **closely related** they are.

2) All organisms have **evolved** from shared **common ancestors** (relatives). This can be shown on a **phylogenetic tree**, like this one.

   First branch point

   Orangutan
   Human
   Chimpanzee
   Bonobo
   Gorilla

3) This tree shows the **relationship** between members of the Hominidae family (great apes and humans).
The **first branch point** represents a **common ancestor** of **all** the family members.
This ancestor is now **extinct**. **Orangutans** were the first group to **diverge** (evolve to become a different species) from this common ancestor.

4) Each of the following branch points represents **another common ancestor** from which a **different group diverged**. Gorillas diverged next, then humans, closely followed by bonobos and chimpanzees.

5) Closely related species **diverged** away from each other **most recently**. E.g. humans and **chimpanzees** are **closely** related, as they diverged very **recently**. You can see this because their branches are **close** together.

Classification is All About Grouping Together Related Organisms

Taxonomy is the science of classification. It involves **naming** organisms and **organising them** into **groups**. This makes it **easier** to **identify** and **study** them. Scientists now take into account **phylogeny** when classifying organisms, and group organisms according to their **evolutionary relationships**.

1) There are **eight** levels of groups used to classify organisms.
These groups are called **taxa**. Each group is called a **taxon**.

2) The groups are arranged in a **hierarchy**, with the **largest groups** at the **top** and the smallest groups at the bottom. Organisms can only belong to **one group** at **each level** in the hierarchy — there's **no overlap**.

3) Organisms are first sorted into **three** large groups (or taxa) called **domains** — the **Eukarya**, **Bacteria** and **Archaea**.

4) **Related organisms** in a domain are then sorted into **slightly smaller groups** called **kingdoms**, e.g. all animals are in the animal kingdom. **More closely related** organisms from that kingdom are then grouped into a **phylum**, then grouped into a **class**, and **so on** down the eight levels of the hierarchy.

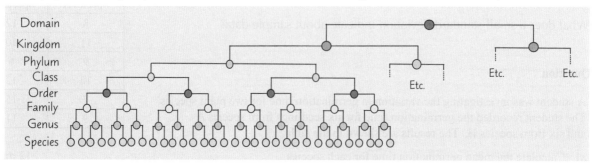

5) As you move **down** the hierarchy, there are **more groups** at each level but **fewer organisms** in each group. The organisms in each group also become **more closely related**.

6) The hierarchy **ends** with **species** — the groups that contain only **one type** of organism (e.g. humans, dogs, *E. coli*). The biological definition of a **species** is:

> **A species is a group of similar organisms able to reproduce to give fertile offspring.**

7) Scientists constantly **update** classification systems because of **discoveries** about new species and new **evidence** about known organisms (e.g. **DNA sequence** data — see page 160).

Classification of Organisms

The Binomial Naming System is Used in Classification

1) The **nomenclature** (**naming system**) used for classification is called the **binomial system** — all organisms are given **one** internationally accepted scientific **name** in **Latin** that has **two parts**.

2) The **first part** of the name is the **genus** name and has a capital letter. The **second part** is the **species** name and begins with a lower case letter. E.g. using the binomial system humans are *Homo sapiens*. Names are always written in *italics* (or they're **underlined** if they're **handwritten**).

3) The binomial system helps to avoid the **confusion** of using **common names**. E.g. over 100 different plant species are called **raspberries** and one species of buttercup has over 90 different common names.

Organisms Can be Placed into One of Five Kingdoms

Here are the **general characteristics** of organisms in each of the **five kingdoms**:

KINGDOM	EXAMPLES	FEATURES
Prokaryotae	bacteria	prokaryotic, unicellular (single-celled), no nucleus, less than 5 μm
Protoctista	algae, protozoa	eukaryotic cells, usually live in water, single-celled or simple multicellular organisms
Fungi	moulds, yeasts, mushrooms	eukaryotic, chitin cell wall, saprotrophic (absorb substances from dead or decaying organisms), single-celled or multicellular organisms
Plantae	mosses, ferns, flowering plants	eukaryotic, multicellular, cell walls made of cellulose, can photosynthesise, contain chlorophyll, autotrophic (produce their own food)
Animalia	nematodes (roundworms), molluscs, insects, fish, reptiles, birds, mammals	eukaryotic, multicellular, no cell walls, heterotrophic (consume plants and animals)

Plants are also known as photoautotrophs — they produce their own food using light.

Practice Questions

Q1 List the groups of the phylogenetic hierarchy in order, starting with domain.

Q2 Give two features of the kingdom Fungi.

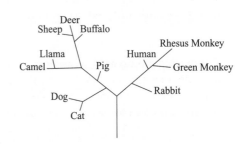

Exam Questions

Q1 The brown trout is part of the Salmonidae family. Its Latin name is *Salmo trutta*. It is part of the kingdom Animalia.
   a) What genus does the brown trout belong to? [1 mark]
   b) Give two features that the brown trout must have to place it in the kingdom Animalia. [2 marks]

Q2 The phylogenetic tree above shows the evolutionary history of some mammalian species.
   a) Which species shown on the tree is most closely related to humans? Explain how you know this. [2 marks]
   b) On the tree, circle the most recent common ancestor of both camels and deer. [1 mark]

Snozcumber kingdom features — long, thin, green, filled with snot...

Make sure that you really understand all the basics on these pages before delving any deeper into this section. Learning the order of the levels in the taxonomic hierarchy is about as easy as licking your elbow... try making up a mnemonic to help (like 'Dopey King Prawns Can't Order Fried Green Sausages' for Domain, Kingdom, Phylum, Class, Order, Family, etc).

Evolution of Classification Systems

Classification systems and the groups organisms are placed in aren't set in stone. New technology and new evidence can lead to changes in these systems and the reclassification of organisms.

Courtship Behaviour can be Used to Help Classify Species

1) **Courtship behaviour** is carried out by organisms to **attract** a mate of the **right species**.
2) It can be fairly simple, e.g. **releasing chemicals**, or quite complex, e.g. a series of **displays**.
3) Courtship behaviour is **species specific** — only members of the same species will do and respond to that courtship behaviour. This allows members of the **same species** to **recognise** each other, preventing **interbreeding** and making reproduction **more successful** (as mating with the wrong species won't produce **fertile** offspring).
4) Because of this specificity, courtship behaviour can be used to **classify organisms**.
5) The more **closely related** species are, the **more similar** their courtship behaviour.
   Some examples of courtship behaviour include:

Geoff's jive never failed to attract a mate.

1) **Fireflies** give off **pulses of light**. The pattern of flashes is specific to each species.
2) **Crickets** make **sounds** that are similar to Morse code, the code being different for different species.
3) **Male peacocks** show off their **colourful tails**. This tail pattern is only found in peacocks.
4) **Male butterflies** use **chemicals** to attract females. Only those of the correct species respond.

Advances in Techniques Can Change How Organisms are Classified

As well as information on **behaviour**, scientists now collect **other types** of information in order to classify organisms — such as **genome sequencing data**. Collecting this data often involves using **advanced** technologies. **New** or **improved technologies** can result in **new discoveries** being made and the **evolutionary relationships** between organisms being **clarified**. This can lead to **classification systems** being **updated**. Technologies that have been useful for clarifying evolutionary relationships include:

<u>Genome sequencing</u> — Advances in genome sequencing have meant that the entire base sequence of an organism's DNA can be determined. The DNA base sequence of one organism can then be compared to the DNA base sequence of another organism, to see how closely related they are. Closely related species will have a higher percentage of similarity in their DNA base order, e.g. humans and chimps share around 94%, humans and mice share about 86%.

Genome sequencing has clarified the relationship between skunks and members of the Mustelidae family (e.g. weasels and badgers). Skunks were classified in the Mustelidae family until their DNA sequence was revealed to be significantly different to other members of that family. So they were reclassified into the family Mephitidae.

<u>Comparing amino acid sequence</u> — Proteins are made of **amino acids**. The **sequence** of amino acids in a protein is coded for by the **base sequence** in DNA (see p. 136). **Related organisms** have similar DNA sequences and so **similar amino acid sequences** in their proteins. E.g. **cytochrome C** is a short protein found in many species. The more **similar** the **amino acid sequence** of cytochrome C in two different species, the **more closely related** the species are likely to be.

<u>Immunological comparisons</u> — **Similar proteins** will also bind the same **antibodies** (see p. 123). E.g. if antibodies to a **human version** of a protein are added to isolated samples from some other **species**, any protein that's like the human version will also be **recognised** (bound) by that antibody.

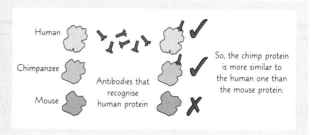

So, the chimp protein is more similar to the human one than the mouse protein.

Evolution of Classification Systems

Five Kingdoms Vs Three Domains

The **five kingdom classification system** shown on page 165 has now been replaced with the **three domain system**:

1) In the older **system** the **largest groups** were the **five kingdoms** — all organisms were placed into **one of** these groups.

2) In 1990, the **three domain system** was proposed. This new system has three domains — **large superkingdoms** that are **above** the kingdoms in the **taxonomic hierarchy** (see p. 164).

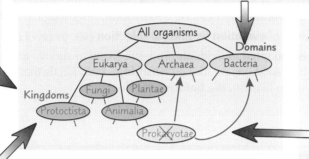

3) In the three domain system, organisms that were in the kingdom **Prokaryotae** (which contains unicellular organisms **without a nucleus**) are separated into two domains — the **Archaea** and **Bacteria**.

4) Organisms with cells that **contain a nucleus** are placed in the domain **Eukarya** (this includes four of the five kingdoms).

5) The **lower** hierarchy stays the **same** — Kingdom, Phylum, Class, Order, Family, Genus, Species.

Molecular Evidence Led to the Proposal of the Three Domain System

1) The three domain system was proposed because of **new evidence**, mainly molecular. E.g. the **Prokaryotae** were **reclassified** into **two domains** because new evidence showed large differences between the Archaea and Bacteria. The new evidence included:

- <u>Molecular evidence</u> — The enzyme **RNA polymerase** (needed to make RNA) is **different** in Bacteria and Archaea. **Archaea**, but **not Bacteria**, have similar **histones** (see p. 136) to **Eukarya**.
- <u>Cell membrane evidence</u> — The **bonds** of the **lipids** (see p. 14) in the **cell membranes** of Bacteria and Archaea are **different**. The **development** and composition of **flagellae** (see p. 44) are also **different**.

2) Most scientists now **agree** that Archaea and Bacteria **evolved separately** and that Archaea are **more closely related** to Eukarya than Bacteria. The three domain system reflects how **different** the Archaea and Bacteria are.

3) The development of the three domain system is an example of how **scientific knowledge** is always **changing** and **improving** (see page 2).

Practice Questions

Q1 Give one technological advance that has helped to clarify evolutionary relationships.

Q2 What is meant by a domain?

Exam Questions

Q1 A gibbon is a type of ape. Describe one way in which scientists could use molecular evidence to determine how closely gibbons are related to humans. [2 marks]

Q2 The three domain system of classification places Cyanobacteria in the domain Bacteria. Describe three differences between organisms in the Bacteria and Archaea domains. [3 marks]

Five kingdoms, three domains — all the makings of a great TV series...

Molecular evidence has a lot to answer for — imagine thinking you were a Prokaryote, then waking up one morning and discovering you were an Archaeon. It's enough to give anyone issues. Remember, the more similar the DNA and proteins, the more closely related two species are (because relatives have similar DNA, which codes for similar proteins).

Adaptations

All the variation between and within species means that some organisms are better adapted to their environment than others...

Adaptations make Organisms Well Suited to Their Environment

1) Being **adapted** to an environment means an organism has features that **increase** its **chances of survival** and **reproduction**, and also the chances of its **offspring reproducing successfully**.

2) These features are called **adaptations** and can be behavioural, physiological and anatomical (see below).

3) Adaptations develop because of **evolution** by **natural selection** (see page 172).

4) In each generation, the **best-adapted individuals** are more likely to survive and reproduce — passing their adaptations on to their **offspring**. Individuals that are less well adapted are more likely to **die before reproducing**.

Adaptations can be Behavioural, Physiological and Anatomical

Behavioural adaptations

Ways an organism **acts** that increase its chance of survival. For example:

- **Possums** sometimes '**play dead**' — if they're being threatened by a **predator** they play dead to **escape attack**. This **increases** their chance of **survival**.
- **Scorpions dance** before **mating** — this makes sure they attract a mate of the **same species**, increasing the likelihood of **successful mating**.

Bob and Sue were well adapted to hiding in candyfloss shops.

Physiological adaptations

Processes inside an organism's body that increase its chance of survival. For example:

- **Brown bears hibernate** — they **lower their rate of metabolism** (all the chemical reactions taking place in their body) over **winter**. This **conserves energy**, so they don't need to look for **food** in the months when it's scarce — **increasing** their chance of **survival**.
- **Some bacteria** produce **antibiotics** — these **kill** other species of bacteria in the area. This means there's **less competition**, so they're **more likely** to **survive**.

Anatomical (structural) adaptations

Structural features of an organism's body that increase its chance of survival. For example:

- **Otters** have a **streamlined shape** — making it easier to **glide** through the **water**. This makes it easier for them to **catch prey** and **escape predators**, increasing their chance of **survival**.
- **Whales** have a **thick layer** of **blubber** (fat) — this helps to keep them **warm** in the cold sea. This increases their chance of survival in places where their **food** is found.

Different Taxonomic Groups May Have Similar Features

1) Organisms from **different** taxonomic groups may have **similar** features even though they're **not closely related**.

2) This is usually because the organisms have **evolved** in **similar environments** and to fill **similar ecological niches**.

3) The example on the next page is of **marsupial** and **placental moles**.

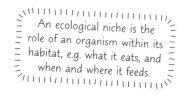

An ecological niche is the role of an organism within its habitat, e.g. what it eats, and when and where it feeds.

Adaptations

Marsupial and Placental Mammals Have Evolved Separately

1) There are **three different groups** of mammals. Most mammals are **placental mammals**, while some are **marsupials** (and a very few are egg-laying monotremes).

2) Marsupials are found mainly in **Australia** and the **Americas**. They **diverged** from placental mammals many **millions of years ago** and have been **evolving separately** ever since.

Marsupial mammals (e.g. kangaroos):

- have a **short gestation period** (pregnancy).
- don't develop a **full placenta**.
- are born **early** in their development and climb into their mother's **pouch**. Here they become attached to a **teat** and receive milk while they **continue** to **develop**.

Placental mammals (e.g. humans):

- have a **longer gestation period**.
- develop a **placenta** during pregnancy, which allows the **exchange of nutrients** and **waste products** between the fetus and the mother.
- are born more **fully developed**.

Marsupial and Placental Moles Look Alike But Aren't Closely Related

1) **Marsupial** moles and **placental** moles **aren't closely related** — they **evolved independently** on different **continents**.

2) They do share **similar anatomical features** though (i.e. they look alike). That's because they've both evolved to live in **similar environments**:

When two species evolve similar characteristics independently of one another (because they've adapted to live in similar environments) it's called convergent evolution.

Both types of mole live in **tunnels** in the ground. They **burrow** to reach their **food supply** (e.g. earthworms, insects and other invertebrates). Their **adaptations** to this lifestyle include:

- **Small** or **nonexistent eyes** because they don't need to be able to see underground.
- **No external ears**, to keep a streamlined head for burrowing.
- **Scoop-shaped** and **powerful front paws**, which are good for digging.
- **Claws** that are specialised for digging.
- A **tube shaped body** and **cone shaped head**, which makes it easier to push through sand or soil.

Practice Questions

Q1 What is meant by the term adaptation?

Q2 Describe the differences between behavioural, physiological and anatomical adaptations.

Q3 Explain why marsupial moles and placental moles share similar anatomical features, even though they are not closely related.

Q4 Give two anatomical features marsupial and placental moles have in common.

Exam Question

Q1 a) Both whales and sharks have developed a streamlined body and fins, despite being from different taxonomic groups. Suggest why. [1 mark]

b) Like humans, whales are mammals. This means they can't breathe underwater and have to come to the surface for air. However, whales have developed the ability to exchange up to 90% of the oxygen in their lungs compared to the human average of 10-15%.

Suggest why humans haven't developed the same oxygen-exchanging ability as whales. [1 mark]

I'm perfectly adapted — for staying in bed...

Adaptations are features that make an organism more likely to survive and reproduce. Repetitive? Yes, but that's why it's so easy to learn. Features that are adaptive for an organism might not stay the same, though, which is why genetic diversity is so important — you can read all about this on the next couple of pages, you lucky thing...

Genetic Diversity

Genetic diversity describes the number of alleles in a species or population. Events that reduce genetic diversity can affect the ability of a population to adapt to the environment by natural selection — see pages 172-173.

Lots of Different Alleles Means a High Genetic Diversity

1) Remember, there can be **different versions** of a single **gene** — these are called **alleles** (see page 137).
2) **Genetic diversity** is the number of **different alleles** of genes in a species or population.
3) Genetic diversity **within** a **population** is increased by:

A population is a group of organisms of one species living in a particular habitat.

- **Mutations** in the DNA — forming **new alleles**.
- **Different alleles** being **introduced** into a population when individuals from another population **migrate into them** and reproduce. This is known as **gene flow**.

4) Genetic diversity is what allows **natural selection** to occur (see page 172).

Genetic Bottlenecks Reduce Genetic Diversity

1) A **genetic bottleneck** is an event that causes a big **reduction** in a population, e.g. when a large number of organisms within a population **die** before reproducing.
2) This reduces the number of **different alleles** in the **gene pool** and so reduces **genetic diversity**.

The gene pool is the complete range of alleles in a population.

3) The survivors **reproduce** and a larger population is created from a few individuals.

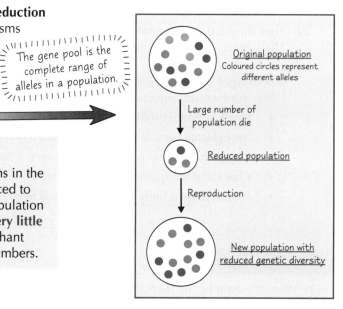

Original population
Coloured circles represent different alleles

Large number of population die

Reduced population

Reproduction

New population with reduced genetic diversity

Example — Northern Elephant Seals

Northern elephant seals were hunted by humans in the late 1800s. Their **original population** was reduced to around **50 seals** who have since produced a population of around 170 000. This new population has **very little** genetic diversity compared to the southern elephant seals who never suffered such a **reduction** in numbers.

The Founder Effect is a Type of Genetic Bottleneck

1) The **founder effect** describes what happens when just a **few** organisms from a population start a **new colony** and there are only a **small number** of **different alleles** in the **initial gene pool**.
2) The **frequency** of each allele in the **new colony** might be **very different** to the frequency of those alleles in the original population — for example, an allele that was **rare** in the original population might be **more common** in the new colony. This may lead to a **higher incidence** of **genetic disease**.
3) The founder effect can occur as a result of **migration** leading to geographical **separation** or if a new colony is separated from the original population for **another reason**, such as **religion**.

Example — The Amish

The **Amish population** of North America are all descended from a **small** number of Swiss who **migrated** there. The population shows **little genetic diversity**. They have remained **isolated** from the surrounding population due to their **religious beliefs**, so **few new alleles** have been introduced. The population has an unusually high incidence of certain **genetic disorders**.

Genetic Diversity

Gene Technologies Have Changed the Way Genetic Diversity is Assessed

You might remember from pages 166-167 that the way in which organisms are **classified** has **evolved** over time with **changing technologies** — well the same is true for assessing **genetic diversity**:

1) Early **estimates** of genetic diversity were made by looking at the **frequency** of **measurable** or **observable characteristics** in a population, e.g. the number of different eye colours in a population and the number of people with each particular eye colour.

2) Since different **alleles** determine different **characteristics** a **wide variety** of **each characteristic** in a population indicates a **high number** of different **alleles** — and so a **high genetic diversity**.

3) However gene technologies have now been developed that allow us to **measure genetic diversity directly**:

There weren't many people with Sid's observable characteristics.

For example:

- **Different alleles** of the same gene will have **slightly different DNA base sequences**. Comparing the DNA base sequences of the same gene in **different organisms** in a population allows scientists to find out **how many alleles** of that gene there are in that population.

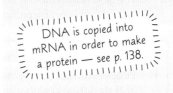

DNA is copied into mRNA in order to make a protein — see p. 138.

- Different alleles will also produce slightly different **mRNA base sequences**, and may produce **proteins** with slightly different **amino acid sequences**, so these can also be compared.

4) These **new technologies** can all be used to give more **accurate estimates** of genetic diversity within a population or species.

5) They also allow the genetic diversity of **different species** to be **compared** more easily.

Practice Questions

Q1 What events does the founder effect describe?

Q2 How has the way in which genetic diversity is assessed changed over time?

Q3 Explain how comparing amino acid sequences can allow us to compare the genetic diversity of organisms.

Exam Questions

Q1 Which of the following best defines the term 'genetic diversity'?

   A The number of different alleles in a species or population.

   B The number of different alleles in an organism.

   C The number of different genes in a species or population.

   D The number of different genes in an organism.   [1 mark]

Q2 Describe what a genetic bottleneck is and explain how it causes
   reduced genetic diversity within a population.   [3 marks]

These pages have a PG classification — Protein Guidance...

...on genetic diversity — it's the latest release... Having lots of different alleles for a gene in a population can be a really good thing. It means that if there is a sudden change in the environment, then it's more likely that at least some individuals will have alleles that allow them to survive and reproduce — there's more on this on the next page...

Evolution and Speciation

All the variation between organisms means that some are better adapted to their ecological niche (see page 168) than others — which can lead to evolution by natural selection...

Adaptations Become More Common by Evolution

Useful adaptations become more common in populations of species because of **evolution** by **natural selection**:

1) **Mutations** (see page 146) can introduce **new alleles** into a population, so individuals within a population show **variation** in their **phenotypes** (characteristics). Some of these alleles determine **characteristics** that can make the individual **more likely** to **survive**.

2) **Selection pressures** such as **predation**, **disease** and **competition** create a **struggle for survival**.

3) Individuals **without** the advantageous alleles **don't survive**. This means there are **fewer individuals** and **less competition** for **resources**.

A selection pressure is anything that affects an organism's chance of survival and reproduction.

4) Individuals with **better adaptations** (characteristics that give a selective advantage, e.g. being able to run away from predators faster) are **more likely** to **survive**, **reproduce** and **pass on** their advantageous alleles to their **offspring**.

5) Over time, the **number** of individuals with the advantageous alleles **increases**.

6) Over generations this leads to **evolution** as the **frequency** of the advantageous **alleles** in the population **increases** and the favourable adaptations become **more common**.

How often an allele occurs in a population is called the allele frequency.

<u>Example — Peppered Moths</u>

1) Peppered moths show **variation** in **colour** — there are **light** ones (with alleles for light colour) and **dark** ones (with alleles for dark colour, which arose from **mutations**).

2) Before the 1800s, there were **more light moths** than dark moths.

3) During the 1800s, **pollution** had **blackened** many of the trees.

4) Dark coloured moths were now **better adapted** to this environment — the alleles for dark colour made them better **camouflaged** from predators.

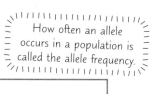
That colour is marvellous on you, really darling.

5) The light coloured moths were **more susceptible** to **predation** (the selection pressure) as they **stood out** against the **blackened** tree bark, meaning that they were **less likely** to survive. This meant the dark moths had **less competition** for resources (such as food).

6) So the dark moths were more likely to **survive**, reproduce and **pass on** the **alleles** for their dark colouring to their offspring.

7) Over time, the **frequency** of the **alleles** for **dark colour** in the population **increased** and the **dark moths** became **more common**.

Charles Darwin came up with the original theory of evolution by natural selection. Over time the theory has become **increasingly accepted** as more **evidence** has been found to support it, and no evidence has been shown to disprove it. Evidence increases scientists' **confidence** in a theory — the more evidence there is, the more chance of something becoming an **accepted scientific explanation** (see page 2). There's more on Darwin and the evidence supporting his theory on page 174.

Speciation is the Development of a New Species

1) Remember, a **species** is a group of **similar organisms** that can **reproduce** to give **fertile offspring** (see page 164).

2) **Speciation** is the development of a **new species**.

3) It occurs when **populations** of the **same species** become **reproductively isolated** — the **changes** in the alleles and phenotypes of the populations **prevent** them from **successfully breeding together**. These changes include:

- **Seasonal changes** — individuals from the same population develop different **flowering** or **mating** seasons, or become **sexually active** at **different times** of the year.
- **Mechanical changes** — changes in **genitalia** prevent successful mating.
- **Behavioural changes** — a group of individuals develop **courtship rituals** that **aren't attractive** to the main population.

4) A population could become **reproductively isolated** due to **geographical isolation** (see next page) or **random mutations** that introduce **new alleles** to the population, resulting in the changes mentioned above.

Evolution and Speciation

Geographical Isolation can lead to Speciation

1) Geographical isolation happens when a **physical barrier divides** a population of a species — **floods**, **volcanic eruptions** and **earthquakes** can all cause barriers that isolate some individuals from the main population.

2) **Conditions** on either side of the barrier will be slightly **different**.
   For example, there might be a **different climate** on each side.

3) Because the environment is different on each side, **different characteristics** will become **more common** due to **natural selection** (because there are **different selection pressures**):

   - Because different **characteristics** will be **advantageous** on each side, the **allele frequencies** will change in each population, e.g. if one allele is more advantageous on one side of the barrier, the frequency of that allele on that side will **increase**.

   - **Mutations** will take place **independently** in each population, also changing the **allele frequencies**.

   Remember, an organism's phenotype is the characteristics that it displays.

   - The changes in allele frequencies will lead to changes in **phenotype frequencies**, e.g. the advantageous characteristics (**phenotypes**) will become more common on that side.

4) Eventually, the different populations will have become **genetically distinct**. Individuals from the different populations will have changed so much that they won't be able to breed with one another to produce **fertile** offspring — they'll have become **reproductively isolated**.

5) The two groups will have become separate **species**.

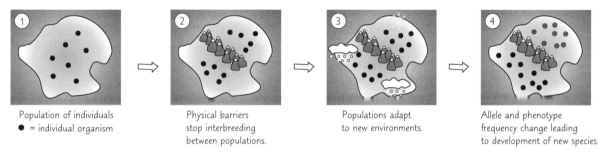

| Population of individuals
● = individual organism | Physical barriers stop interbreeding between populations. | Populations adapt to new environments. | Allele and phenotype frequency change leading to development of new species. |

Practice Questions

Q1 Give an example of a selection pressure.

Q2 Give an example of a physical barrier that could geographically isolate a population of a species.

Exam Questions

Q1 The diagram shows an experiment conducted with fruit flies. One population was split in two and each population was fed a different food. After many generations the two populations were placed together and it was observed that they were unable to breed together.

   a) What evidence shows that the formation of a new species occurred? [1 mark]

   b) Explain why the experiment resulted in the formation of a new species. [3 marks]

Group fed starch-based food

Many generations pass

Single species of fruit fly

Group fed maltose-based food

Q2 Tawny owls show variation in colour. There are light grey owls and darker brown owls. Before the 1970s there were more grey owls than brown owls in Finland. Since then, climate change has been causing a decrease in the amount of snowfall in Finland. During this period, the darker brown owls have become more common.

   Explain how natural selection has led to the brown owls becoming more common. [5 marks]

I've evolved to revise for hours and still not remember things...

Basically, natural selection leads to adaptation and evolution — if an organism has alleles that make it better adapted, it's more likely to survive, reproduce and pass on those advantageous alleles, increasing their frequency in the population. If a population gets split up for any reason, the organisms might even evolve into separate species.

More on Evolution

You might remember from page 172 that Charles Darwin came up with the original theory of evolution by natural selection. He wasn't the only scientist involved in developing the theory though — as you're about to find out...

Darwin Published his Theory of Evolution by Natural Selection in 1859

Darwin made **four** key observations about the world around him:

1) Organisms produce **more offspring** than **survive**.
2) There's **variation** in the characteristics of members of the **same species**.
3) Some of these characteristics can be **passed on** from one generation to the next.
4) Individuals that are **best adapted** to their environment are more likely to **survive**.

Darwin wrote his theory of **evolution by natural selection** to **explain** his observations, but he didn't have all of the information on **genes** and **alleles** that we have now (so he couldn't explain how characteristics were passed on). These details were **added** to the theory, as other scientists made **new discoveries**.

Wallace Contributed to the Theory of Evolution

Alfred Russel Wallace, a scientist working at the **same time** as Darwin, played an important part in developing the **theory of evolution by natural selection**.

- He **independently** came up with the idea of **natural selection** and wrote to Darwin about it.
- He and Darwin **published** their **papers** on evolution **together** and acknowledged each other's work — although they **didn't always agree** about the mechanisms involved in natural selection.
- Wallace's **observations** provided lots of **evidence** to **support** the theory of evolution by natural selection. For example, he realised that **warning colours** are used by some species (e.g. butterflies) to deter predators from eating them and that this was an example of an **advantageous adaptation** that had evolved by natural selection.

Unfortunately for Wallace, it wasn't until Darwin published his famous book **'On the Origin of Species'** that other **scientists** began to pay **attention** to the theory. In this book Darwin gave lots of **evidence** to support the theory and expanded on it. E.g., he wrote about all the **species** that he had **observed** during his voyage to South America and the Galápagos Islands in the 1830s. The book is partly why **Darwin** is usually **better remembered** than Wallace — even though **Wallace helped** to come up with the **theory**.

There's Plenty of Evidence to Support Evolution

Fossil Record Evidence:

Fossils are the **remains** of organisms **preserved in rocks**. By arranging fossils in chronological (date) order, **gradual changes** in organisms can be observed that provide **evidence** of evolution.

For example: the fossil record of the **horse** shows a **gradual change** in characteristics, including increasing **size** and **hoof** development.

DNA Evidence:

The theory of evolution suggests that all organisms have evolved from shared **common ancestors**. Closely related species **diverged** (evolved to become different species) more recently. Evolution is caused by **gradual changes** in the **base sequence** of an organisms' DNA. Organisms that diverged away from each other more recently, should have **more similar DNA**, as **less time** has passed for changes in the DNA sequence to occur. This is exactly what scientists have found.

For example: humans, chimps and mice all evolved from a common ancestor. Humans and mice diverged a **long time ago**, but humans and chimps diverged **quite recently**. The **DNA base sequence** of humans and chimps is 94% the same, but human and mouse DNA is only 85% the same.

Molecular Evidence:

In addition to DNA, the similarities in **other molecules** provide evidence. Scientists compare the **sequence** of **amino acids** in **proteins**, and compare **antibodies**. Organisms that diverged away from each other **more recently** have **more similar molecules**, as **less time** has passed for changes in proteins and other molecules to occur.

More on Evolution

Populations of Insects can Evolve Resistance to Pesticides

Pesticides are chemicals that **kill pests** (e.g. insects that damage crops). Scientists have observed the evolution of **pesticide resistance** in many species of insect. For example, some populations of **mosquito** have **evolved resistance** to the pesticide **DDT**. And some populations of **pollen beetles** (which damage the crop oilseed rape) are resistant to **pyrethroid** pesticides.

The evolution of **pesticide resistance** can be explained by **natural selection**:

1) There is **variation** in a population of insects. **Genetic mutations** create **alleles** that make some insects naturally **resistant** to a pesticide.

2) If the population is exposed to that pesticide only the individuals with resistance will **survive** to **reproduce**.

3) The **alleles** which cause the pesticide resistance will be **passed on** to the next generation, and so the population will **evolve** — more individuals will carry the allele than in the previous generation.

The pesticide acts as a selection pressure — without a selection pressure, natural selection won't take place.

The Evolution of Pesticide Resistance has Implications for Humans

1) **Crop infestations** with **pesticide-resistant** insects are **harder** to **control** — some insects are resistant to **lots of different pesticides**. It takes farmers a while to figure out which pesticide will kill the insect and in that time **all** the crop could be **destroyed**. If the insects are resistant to specific pesticides (ones that only kill that insect), farmers might have to use **broader pesticides** (those that kill a range of insects), which could kill beneficial insects.

2) If **disease-carrying** insects (e.g. mosquitoes) become pesticide-resistant, the **spread of disease** could **increase**.

3) A population of insects could **evolve resistance** to **all** pesticides in use. To prevent this **new pesticides** need to be **produced**. This takes **time** and costs **money**.

The Evolution of Drug Resistance Has Implications for Humans Too

1) You might remember from page 128 that scientists have observed the **evolution** of **antibiotic resistance** in many species of **bacteria**, e.g. MRSA.

2) **Other pathogens** have **evolved resistance** to specific **drugs** too. For example, some of the **protoctists** that cause **malaria** (see page 118) are **resistant** to several drugs used to treat malaria.

3) **Infections** caused by drug-resistant microorganisms are **harder** to **treat** — especially if the microorganism is resistant to **lots of different drugs**. It can take doctors a while to figure out which drugs will get rid of the infection, and in that time the **patient** could become **very ill** or **die**.

4) There could come a point where a pathogen has become resistant to **all the drugs** we currently use against it. To prevent this, **new drugs** need to be **developed**. This takes **time** and costs a lot of **money**.

Practice Questions

Q1 What four key observations did Darwin make?
Q2 Briefly describe how fossil evidence supports the theory of evolution.

Exam Question

Q1 The diamondback moth is a pest of many crops. In 1953 it became resistant to the pesticide DDT and by 1981 it had become resistant to 36 other pesticides.
a) Explain how the diamondback moth populations could have developed DDT resistance. [4 marks]
b) Describe two possible implications of the diamondback moth developing resistance to pesticides. [2 marks]

The fossil record — it rocks...

Evolution is great — you and I certainly wouldn't be here, working through this book, without it. The evolution of pests and disease-causing microorganisms is causing us one or two problems though. Ah well. Can't have everything.

Investigating Selection

Now you get to apply what you know about natural selection to bacteria and babies (amongst other things).
Natural selection affects different populations in different ways, as you'll soon discover...

Different Types of *Natural Selection* Lead to *Different Frequency Patterns*

Natural selection alters the **allele frequency** in a population. **Directional selection** and **stabilising selection** are **types** of **natural selection** that affect **allele frequency** in different ways. Here are two examples:

Antibiotic Resistance Shows *Directional* Selection

Directional selection is where individuals with alleles for characteristics of an **extreme type** are more likely to **survive** and **reproduce**. This could be in response to an **environmental change**. **Bacteria** evolving **antibiotic resistance** is an example of **directional selection**. Here's how it works:

1) Some individuals in a population have alleles that give them **resistance** to an **antibiotic**.

2) The population is **exposed** to the antibiotic, **killing** bacteria **without** the resistant allele.

3) The **resistant bacteria survive** and **reproduce** without competition, passing on the **allele** that gives antibiotic resistance to their offspring.

4) After some time, **most** organisms in the population will carry the **antibiotic resistance allele**.

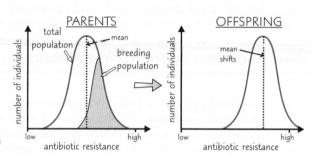

Human Birth Weight Shows *Stabilising* Selection

Stabilising selection is where individuals with alleles for characteristics towards the **middle** of the range are more likely to **survive** and **reproduce**. It occurs when the environment **isn't changing**, and it **reduces the range** of possible **characteristics**. An example of **stabilising selection** is **human birth weight**.

1) Humans have a **range** of **birth weights**.

2) Very **small babies** are **less likely** to **survive** — partly because they find it **hard** to **maintain** their **body temperature**.

3) Giving birth to **large babies** can be difficult, so large babies are **less likely** to **survive** too.

4) Conditions are **most favourable** for **medium**-sized babies — so weight of human babies tends to **shift towards** the **middle** of the range.

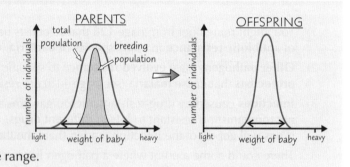

The *Effects* of *Selection* Can be Interpreted from *Data* — *Example*:

There is a population of **rabbits** with **varying fur length**. **Longer fur** helps to keep the rabbits **warmer**. The graph shows how the **average fur length** of the rabbits **changed** over a period of six years, which had particularly **cold winters**. The **bars** span the **difference** between the **shortest** and **longest fur lengths** recorded.

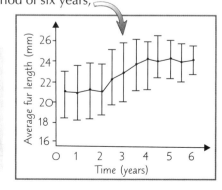

<u>Describing the data:</u>
Over the first two years the average fur length is about 21 mm. However, the average length gradually increases from 21 mm to 24 mm. This shows <u>directional selection</u>.
<u>Possible explanation:</u>
The rabbits with the <u>longer fur</u> are <u>more likely</u> to <u>survive</u> the <u>cold winters</u> than the <u>short-furred rabbits</u>. This makes them more likely to <u>reproduce</u> and, when they do, they <u>pass on</u> the <u>allele</u> for <u>longer fur</u> to the next generation. Over time, the allele for longer fur becomes <u>more common</u> in the population and the <u>average fur length</u> of the rabbits <u>increases</u>.

Investigating Selection

You Can **Investigate** the **Effects** of **Antibiotics** on **Bacterial Growth**

Here's how you would **investigate** the effect of **antimicrobial substances** (e.g. antibiotics, antiseptics or disinfectants) on **microbial growth**, using **aseptic techniques**.

This method can also be used to investigate the effects of antimicrobial substances produced by some plants.

Test the Effects of **Antibiotics** Using **Agar Plates**

1) The bacteria you will use are likely to have been grown in a **liquid broth** (a mixture of distilled water, bacterial culture and nutrients).

2) Use a **wire inoculation loop** to **transfer** the bacteria from the broth to an **agar plate** — a **Petri dish** containing **agar jelly**. Spread the bacteria over the plate using the loop.

3) Place paper discs **soaked** with different **antibiotics** spaced apart on the plate. Various **concentrations** of antibiotics should be used. Make sure you add a **negative control** disc soaked only in **sterile water**. (See page 4 for more on negative controls.)

4) **Tape** a **lid** onto the Petri dish, invert, and **incubate** the plate at about **25 °C** for **24-48 hours**. This allows the bacteria to **grow** (forming a 'lawn'). Anywhere the bacteria **can't grow** can be seen as a **clear patch** in the lawn of bacteria. This is called an **inhibition zone**.

5) The size of an **inhibition zone** tells you how well an antibiotic works. The **larger** the zone, the **more** the bacteria were inhibited from growing.

6) A **similar technique** can be used to test the effects of **antiseptics** or **disinfectants** on microbial growth.

This diagram shows an agar plate with **meticillin**, **tetracycline** and **streptomycin** discs **after** it has been **incubated**.

125 mg   250 mg
Meticillin — Inhibition zone
— Agar plate
Tetracycline
Streptomycin
Negative control (soaked in water)
Disc — Lawn of bacteria

- The **tetracycline** discs have **no** inhibition zones, so the bacteria are **resistant** to tetracycline up to 250 mg.
- The **streptomycin** discs have **small** inhibition zones, with the zone at 250 mg slightly larger than the one at 125 mg. So streptomycin has **some effect** on the bacteria.
- The **meticillin** discs have the **largest** inhibition zones, so meticillin has the **strongest effect** on these bacteria.

Always Use **Aseptic Techniques** to **Prevent Contamination** of Microbial Cultures

Aseptic techniques are used to **prevent contamination** of cultures by **unwanted** microorganisms. This is important because contamination can affect the **growth** of the microorganism that you're **working** with. It's also important to avoid contamination with **disease-causing microbes** that could make you **ill**. When carrying out the investigation above, you need to use the following **aseptic techniques**:

- Regularly **disinfect** work surfaces to minimise contamination.
- Work **near** a **Bunsen flame**. **Hot air rises**, so any microbes in the air should be drawn away from your culture.
- **Sterilise** the **wire inoculation loop before** and **after** each use by passing it through a **hot** Bunsen burner **flame** for 5 seconds. This will kill any microbes on the loop.
- Briefly **flame** the neck of the glass **container of broth** just after it's **opened** and just before it's **closed** — this causes air to move out of the container, preventing **unwanted** organisms from **falling in**.
- **Sterilise** all glassware before and after use, e.g. in an **autoclave** (a machine which steams equipment at high pressure).

You should also take steps to protect yourself, e.g. wash your hands thoroughly before and after handling cultures.

Practice Questions

Q1 Describe how you could investigate the effects of antibiotics on bacterial growth.

Exam Question

Q1 A group of scientists monitored how the colour of oyster shells on a beach changed over time. The graph shows the colour of the oyster shells in the scientists' initial sample and in their final sample. The oysters were mainly found on the sand, which was a mid-brown colour.

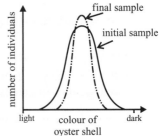

a) What type of selection is shown in the graph? Explain your answer. [3 marks]

b) Suggest how the changes shown in the graph might have taken place. [4 marks]

One Directional selection — the shift in the population of teenage girls...
Quite a bit on these pages — maybe try the whole cover, scribble, check thing to make sure you remember the details.

The Hardy-Weinberg Principle

Since natural selection affects the frequency of alleles in a population, by calculating the allele frequencies for a population you can see whether the population is changing. That's where those fellows Hardy and Weinberg come in...

Evolution is a Change in Allele Frequency

1) Remember, allele frequency is how **often** an **allele occurs** in a population. It's usually given as a **percentage** of the total population, e.g. 35%, or a **number**, e.g. 0.35.
2) The **frequency** of an **allele** in a population **changes** over time — this is **evolution**.
3) The **allele frequencies** of a population can be **calculated** using the **Hardy-Weinberg equations** (see below) and used to see if the population is **changing** over time (see next page).

The Hardy-Weinberg Principle Predicts Allele Frequencies Won't Change

1) The **Hardy-Weinberg principle** predicts that the **frequencies** of **alleles** in a population **won't change** from **one generation** to the **next**.
2) But this prediction is **only true** under **certain conditions** — it has to be a **large population** where there's **no immigration**, **emigration**, **mutations** or **natural selection**. There also needs to be **random mating** — all possible genotypes can breed with all others.
3) The **Hardy-Weinberg equations** (see below) are based on this principle. They can be used to **estimate the frequency** of particular **alleles**, **genotypes** and **phenotypes** within populations.
4) If the allele frequencies **do change** between generations in a large population then immigration, emigration, natural selection or mutations have happened.

The Hardy-Weinberg Equations Can be Used to Predict Allele Frequency...

When a gene has two alleles, you can **figure out** the frequency of one of the alleles of the gene if you **know the frequency of the other allele**, using this equation:

$$p + q = 1$$

Where: **p** = the **frequency** of the **dominant** allele
q = the **frequency** of the **recessive** allele

For more on dominant and recessive alleles — see pages 148-149.

The total frequency of all possible alleles for a characteristic in a certain population is 1.0. So the frequencies of the individual alleles (e.g. the dominant one and the recessive one) must add up to 1.0.

E.g. a species of plant has either **red** or **white** flowers. Allele **R** (red) is **dominant** and allele **r** (white) is **recessive**. If the frequency of R is **0.4**, then the frequency of r is: 1 – 0.4 = **0.6**.

... and to Predict Genotype and Phenotype Frequency

You can **figure out** the frequency of one genotype if you **know the frequencies of the others**, using this equation:

$$p^2 + 2pq + q^2 = 1$$

Where: p^2 = the **frequency** of the **homozygous dominant genotype**
$2pq$ = the **frequency** of the **heterozygous genotype**
q^2 = the **frequency** of the **homozygous recessive genotype**

The total frequency of all possible genotypes for one characteristic in a certain population is 1.0. So the frequencies of the individual genotypes must add up to 1.0.

E.g. if there are **two alleles** for **flower colour** (R and r), there are **three possible genotypes** — **RR, Rr** and **rr**. If the frequency of genotype **RR** (p^2) is **0.34** and the frequency of genotype **Rr** ($2pq$) is **0.27**, the frequency of genotype **rr** (q^2) must be: 1 – 0.34 – 0.27 = **0.39**.

Genotype frequencies can then be used to work out **phenotype frequencies** (the frequencies of observable traits).

E.g. the frequency of **red flowers** is equal to the genotype frequencies of **RR** and **Rr** added together (0.34 + 0.27 = **0.61**) and the frequency of **white flowers** is equal to the genotype frequency of **rr** (**0.39**).

The Hardy-Weinberg Principle

Sometimes You Need to Use **Both Hardy-Weinberg Equations**

EXAMPLE

The **frequency** of **cystic fibrosis** (genotype ff) in the UK is currently approximately **1 birth in every 2500**. From this information you can estimate the **percentage** of people in the UK that are cystic fibrosis **carriers** (Ff). To do this you need to find the **frequency** of **heterozygous genotype Ff**, i.e. **2pq**, using **both** equations:

$$p + q = 1$$ $$p^2 + 2pq + q^2 = 1$$

First calculate q:
Frequency of cystic fibrosis (homozygous recessive, ff) is 1 in 2500
$ff = q^2 = 1 \div 2500 = 0.0004$
So, $q = \sqrt{0.0004} = 0.02$

Next calculate p:
Using $p + q = 1$, $p = 1 - q$
$p = 1 - 0.02 = 0.98$

Then calculate 2pq:
$2pq = 2 \times 0.98 \times 0.02 = 0.039$

The **frequency** of genotype Ff is **0.039**, so the **percentage** of the UK population that are **carriers** is **3.9%**.

Allele Frequencies Show if a Population is Changing Over Time

EXAMPLE

If the **frequency** of **cystic fibrosis** is measured **50 years later** it might be found to be **1 birth in 3500**. From this information you can estimate the **frequency** of the **recessive allele** (f) in the population, i.e. **q**. ⟹

The frequency of the recessive allele is now **0.017**, compared to **0.02** currently (see above).

To calculate q:
Frequency of cystic fibrosis (homozygous recessive, ff) is 1 in 3500
$ff = q^2 = 1 \div 3500 = 0.00029$
So, $q = \sqrt{0.00029} = 0.017$

As the frequency of the allele has **changed** between generations the **Hardy-Weinberg principle doesn't apply** so there must have been some **factors** affecting **allele frequency**, e.g. **immigration**, **emigration**, **mutations** or **natural selection**.

Practice Questions

Q1 What is the relationship between allele frequency in a population and evolution?

Q2 What conditions are needed for the Hardy-Weinberg principle to apply?

Q3 Which term represents the frequency of the heterozygous genotype in the Hardy-Weinberg equation $p^2 + 2pq + q^2$?

Exam Questions

Q1 A breed of dog has either a black or brown coat. Allele B (black) is dominant and allele b (brown) is recessive. The frequency of the recessive allele is 0.23. The Hardy-Weinberg equation is $p^2 + 2pq + q^2 = 1$.
Find the frequency of the heterozygous (Bb) genotype.   [1 mark]

Q2 Cleft chins are controlled by a single gene with two alleles. The allele coding for a cleft chin (T) is dominant over the allele coding for a non-cleft chin (t). In a particular population the frequency of the homozygous dominant genotype for cleft chin is 0.14. The Hardy-Weinberg equation is $p^2 + 2pq + q^2 = 1$.
a) What is the frequency of the recessive allele in the population?   [1 mark]
b) What is the frequency of the homozygous recessive genotype in the population? [1 mark]
c) What percentage of the population have a cleft chin?   [1 mark]

This stuff's surely not that bad — Hardly worth Weining about...

Not many of you will be thrilled with the maths content on these pages, but don't worry. If you know what to use each Hardy-Weinberg equation for and what the different terms mean, then you can just plug the numbers you're given into the right places. You'll probably need a calculator too — unless you can calculate the square root in your head...

Studying Biodiversity

Bet you've noticed how there are loads of different living things in the world — well that's biodiversity in a nutshell.

Biodiversity is the Variety of Organisms

Before you can sink your teeth into the real meat of biodiversity, there are a few definitions you need to know:

1) **Biodiversity** — the **variety** of **living organisms** in an **area**.
2) **Species** — a group of **similar organisms** able to **reproduce** to give **fertile offspring**.
3) **Habitat** — the **area inhabited** by a species. It includes the **physical** factors, like the soil and temperature range, and the **living** (biotic) factors, like availability of food or the presence of predators.

Areas with a **high** biodiversity are those with lots of **different species**.

Pete wasn't sure that the company's new increased biodiversity policy would be good for productivity.

Biodiversity Can be Considered at Different Levels

1) **Habitat diversity** — the number of **different habitats** in an **area**. For example, a particular area could contain many different habitats — sand dunes, woodland, meadows, streams, etc.
2) **Species diversity** — the number of **different species** (species richness) and the **abundance** of each species (species evenness) in an **area**. For example, a woodland could contain many different species of plants, insects, birds and mammals.
3) **Genetic diversity** — the variation of **alleles** within a species (or a population of a species). For example, the variation of alleles within the dog species gives rise to different breeds, such as a Labrador or poodle.

Sampling Can be Used to Measure Biodiversity

In most cases it'd be **too time-consuming** to count every individual organism in a habitat. Instead, a **sample** of the population is taken. **Estimates** about the whole habitat are based on the sample. Here's what sampling involves:

1) **Choose** an **area** to **sample** — a small area within the habitat being studied.
2) **Count** the number of individuals of **each species**. How you do this depends on **what** you're counting, for example:→
3) **Repeat** the process — take as many samples as possible. This gives a better indication of the **whole habitat**.
4) Use the results to **estimate** the total number of individuals or the total number of different species in the habitat being studied.
5) When sampling **different habitats** and comparing them, always use the **same sampling technique**.

- For plants you'd use a quadrat (a frame which you place on the ground).
- For flying insects you'd use a sweep net (a net on a pole).
- For ground insects you'd use a pitfall trap (a small pit that insects can't get out of).
- For aquatic animals you'd use a net.

You could **investigate** the **impact** of **mowing** on the **biodiversity** of your school playing fields by sampling a mowed and an un-mowed field, then calculating the biodiversity for each field using an index of diversity (see next page).

Sampling Can be Random or Non-Random

1) To avoid **bias** in your results, the **sample** should be **random**. For example, if you were looking at plant species in a field, you could pick random sample sites by dividing the field into a **grid** using **measuring tapes** and using a **random number generator** to select **coordinates**.
2) However, sometimes it's **necessary** to take a **non-random sample**. E.g. when there's a lot of variety in the distribution of species in the habitat and you want to make sure all the different areas are sampled.
3) There are **three** types of **non-random** sample:
   - **Systematic** — This is when samples are taken at **fixed intervals**, often along a **line**. E.g. **quadrats** could be placed along a line (called a **transect**) from an area of shade in the corner to the middle of the field.
   - **Opportunistic** — This is when samples are **chosen** by the **investigator**. It's used because it is **simple** to carry out, but the data will be **biased**.
   - **Stratified** — This is when **different areas** in a habitat are **identified** and **sampled** separately in **proportion** to their part of the **habitat** as a **whole**. E.g. a heathland may have patches of gorse in it — the heath and gorse areas would be sampled separately according to how much of each there was in the habitat.

Studying Biodiversity

Species Richness and Species Evenness Affect Biodiversity

The **greater** the **species richness** and **species evenness** in an area, the **higher** the biodiversity.

Species richness is the number of **different species** in an area. The **higher** the number of species, the **greater** the species richness. It's measured by taking random samples of a habitat (see previous page) and counting the number of different species.

Species evenness is a measure of the **relative abundance** of **each species** in an area. The **more** similar the **population size** of each species, the **greater** the species evenness. It's measured by taking random samples of a habitat, and counting the **number of individuals** of each different species.

Example — Habitat X and habitat Y both contain **two different species** and **30 individual organisms**.

	Habitat X	Habitat Y
species 1	28	15
species 2	2	15
total	30	30

- **Species richness** in the two habitats is the **same** — 2.
- In **habitat Y** the individual organisms are **more evenly distributed** between the different species — it has **greater species evenness**.

Biodiversity Can be Measured Using an Index of Diversity

1) **Species richness** is a very **simple measure** of biodiversity. But species present in a habitat in very **small** numbers shouldn't be treated the same as those with **bigger** populations.

2) An **index of diversity** is another way of measuring biodiversity. It's calculated using an equation that takes into account both **species richness** and **species evenness**.

3) You can **calculate** an index of diversity (d) using this formula:

$$d = \frac{N(N-1)}{\sum n(n-1)}$$

This isn't the only formula for calculating an index of diversity. Check with your teacher which one you're supposed to learn for your exams.

N = Total **number** of organisms of **all** species
n = Total **number** of organisms of **one** species
$\sum$ = 'Sum of' (i.e. added together)

4) When calculating an index of diversity using this formula, the **higher** the **number** you end up with, the **more diverse** the area is. If all the individuals are of the **same species** (i.e. no biodiversity) **this index** will have a value of **1**. For example:

There are 3 different species of flower in this field — a red species, a white and a blue. There are 11 organisms altogether, so N = 11. There are 3 of the red species, 5 of the white and 3 of the blue.

So the species diversity index of this field is:

$$d = \frac{11(11-1)}{3(3-1)+5(5-1)+3(3-1)} = \frac{110}{6+20+6} = 3.44$$

Simpson's Index of Diversity gives you a value between 0 and 1. For Simpson's Index, the closer to 1 the index is, the more diverse the area.

Practice Questions

Q1 What is biodiversity?

Q2 What is stratified sampling?

Exam Question

Site 1 — No Field Margins		Site 2 — Enhanced Field Margins	
Bombus lucorum	15	*Bombus lucorum*	35
Bombus lapidarius	12	*Bombus lapidarius*	25
Bombus pascuorum	24	*Bombus pascuorum*	34
		Bombus ruderatus	12
		Bombus terrestris	26

Q1 A study was conducted to investigate the impact of introducing enhanced field margins on the diversity of bumblebees. Enhanced field margins are thick bands of land around the edges of fields that are not farmed, but instead are planted with plants that are good for wildlife. Scientists studied two wheat fields, one where the farmer sowed crops right to the edge of the field and another where the farmer created enhanced field margins. The scientists counted the number of bees of different species at each site. Their results are shown in the table above.

a) Use the data in the table and the formula on the right $d = \dfrac{N(N-1)}{\sum n(n-1)}$ to calculate the index of diversity for each site. [4 marks]

b) What conclusions can be drawn from the findings of this study? [2 marks]

Species richness — goldfish and money spiders top the list...

That index of diversity formula looks a bit scary, but it's really just a case of plugging the right numbers in the right places.

More on Biodiversity

Advances in genetics mean we can now assess genetic diversity (see page 171). This helps us to understand the human impacts on global biodiversity (the total number of species on Earth).

Genetic Diversity Can be Assessed

1) You already know that **genetic diversity** is the **variation** of **alleles** within a **species** (or within a population of a species).

2) You can do **calculations** to work out the **genetic diversity** of a **population**.

3) This is important because if a population has **low genetic diversity**, they might **not** be able to **adapt** to a **change in the environment** and the **whole population** could be **wiped out** by a single event (e.g. a disease).

4) Populations in which genetic diversity may be low include **isolated populations** such as those bred in **captivity** (e.g. in zoos, and pedigree animals and rare breeds).

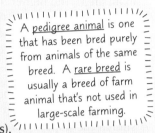

A <u>pedigree animal</u> is one that has been bred purely from animals of the same breed. A <u>rare breed</u> is usually a breed of farm animal that's not used in large-scale farming.

5) **Calculations** can be used to **monitor** the **genetic diversity** of these populations over time and efforts can be made to **increase** the genetic diversity of the population if needed. E.g. **breeding programmes** in **zoos** are very closely **managed** to **maximise** genetic **diversity**.

Genetic Polymorphism is Used to Measure Genetic Diversity

1) You know that **alleles** are different versions of a **gene**. **Alleles** of the **same gene** are found at the **same point** (called a **locus**) on a chromosome (see page 137).

2) **Polymorphism** describes a **locus** that has **two or more alleles**.

3) Working out the **proportion** of **polymorphic gene loci** in an organism (i.e. those points on a chromosome which can have more than one allele) gives you a **measure** of **genetic diversity**.

4) There's a nifty **formula** you can use:

$$\text{proportion of polymorphic gene loci} = \frac{\text{number of polymorphic gene loci}}{\text{total number of loci}}$$

Example:
If 40 of the genes sampled in a population are polymorphic out of 100 genes sampled in total, then the proportion of polymorphic gene loci $= \frac{40}{100} = \textbf{0.4}$.

5) If you **multiply** the **proportion** of polymorphic gene loci in a sample **by 100**, you'll get the **percentage** of genes in the sample that have alleles.

6) You could also calculate the **heterozygosity index** (**H**) to estimate genetic diversity. A **heterozygote** is an individual with **two different alleles** at a **particular locus**. The formula is:

$$H = \frac{\text{number of heterozygotes}}{\text{number of individuals in the population}}$$

7) The **higher** the value of **H**, the **greater** the **genetic diversity** in the population.

Factors Affecting Global Biodiversity Include...

1) Human Population Growth

The **human population** of the planet has **grown hugely** in the last couple of centuries and is **continuing to rise**. This is **decreasing global biodiversity** because of the following factors:

1) **Habitat loss** — human development is **destroying habitats**, e.g. there is deforestation in the Amazon to make way for grazing and agriculture. This **decreases habitat diversity**.

2) **Over-exploitation** — a **greater demand** for **resources** (such as food, water and energy) means a lot of resources are being **used up faster** than they can be **replenished**. E.g. industrial fishing can deplete the populations of certain fish species and may even cause extinction (a species to die out). This **decreases genetic diversity** within populations, as well as **decreasing species diversity** (as a result of extinction).

3) **Urbanisation** — sprawling cities and major road developments can **isolate species**, meaning populations are unable to **interbreed** and **genetic diversity** is decreased.

4) **Pollution** — high amounts of **pollutants** can **kill species** or **destroy habitats**, e.g. high levels of **fertiliser** flowing into a river can lead to a **decrease** in **fish species** in that river. This **decreases biodiversity**.

More on Biodiversity

2) *Increased Use* of *Monoculture* in *Agriculture*

In order to **feed** an ever growing number of **people**, **large areas** of land are devoted to **monoculture** — the growing of a **single variety** of a **single crop**. E.g. in Africa, large areas of land are used for palm oil plantations. This leads to a **decline** in **global biodiversity** because of the following factors:

1) **Habitats** are **lost** as **land** is **cleared** to make way for the large fields, **reducing habitat diversity**.

2) **Local** and naturally occurring **plants** and **animals** are seen as **weeds** and **pests**, and so are destroyed with **pesticides** and **herbicides**, **reducing species diversity**.

3) **Heritage** (traditional) **varieties** of crops are **lost** because they **don't make enough money** and so are not **planted** any more, which **reduces species diversity**.

3) *Climate Change*

1) **Climate change** is the **variation** in the Earth's climate, e.g. things like changes in **temperature** and **rainfall patterns**.

2) It occurs **naturally**, but the **scientific consensus** is that the climate change we're **experiencing at the moment** is **caused** by **humans** increasing emissions of **greenhouse gases** (such as **carbon dioxide**).

3) Greenhouse gases cause **global warming** (**increasing global average temperature**), which causes **other types** of climate change, e.g. changing rainfall patterns.

4) Climate change will affect **different areas** of the world in **different ways** — some places will get **warmer**, some **colder**, some **wetter** and others **drier**. All of these are likely to **affect global biodiversity**:

- Most species need a particular **climate** to survive.

- A change in climate may mean that an area that was previously **inhabitable** becomes **uninhabitable** (and **vice versa**).

- This may cause an **increase** or **decrease** in the **range** of some species (the area in which they live). This could increase or decrease biodiversity.

- Some species may be forced to **migrate** to a more suitable area, causing a change in **species distribution**. Migrations usually **decrease** biodiversity in the areas the species migrate from, and **increase** biodiversity in the areas they migrate to.

- If there isn't a suitable habitat to migrate to, the species is a plant and **can't migrate**, or if the change is **too fast**, the species may become **extinct**. This will **decrease** biodiversity.

Range change example

The southern **range** limit of the **Sooty Copper Butterfly** has **moved** 60 miles north in recent decades.

Extinction example

Corals die if water temperature **changes** by just one or two degrees. In 1998 a coral reef near Panama was badly damaged because the water **temperature** had **increased** — at least one species of coral became **extinct** as a result.

Practice Questions

Q1 What is the formula used to work out the proportion of polymorphic gene loci?

Q2 Give two ways in which climate change affects global biodiversity.

Exam Questions

Q1 In a population of Species A, a sample of 80 gene loci were tested for polymorphism. 36 of the genes were found to be polymorphic. What is the proportion of polymorphic gene loci in this sample? [1 mark]

Q2* Describe how human population growth and monoculture during the last 30 years could have decreased global biodiversity. [6 marks]

* You will be assessed on the quality of your written response in this question.

Extinction — coming soon to a habitat near you...

All of this makes the future look a bit bleak — deforestation, loads of different species dying out and climate change. Now you know why biodiversity's at risk, it's time to take a look at why it's so important and worth saving...

Importance of Biodiversity

You're probably wondering what all this fuss about biodiversity is for. Well, it turns out that everything is connected, so if you eliminate even just one species you might just end up with all sorts of problems you'd never even thought of.

Maintaining Biodiversity is Important for Ecological Reasons...

The ecological reasons for maintaining biodiversity are all down to the **complex relationships** between **organisms** and their **environments**.

1) To Protect Species, Including Keystone Species

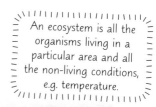
An ecosystem is all the organisms living in a particular area and all the non-living conditions, e.g. temperature.

Organisms in an ecosystem are **interdependent** — they depend on each other to survive. This means that the loss of **just one species** can have pretty **drastic effects** on an ecosystem, such as:

1) **Disruption** of **food chains**, e.g. some species of bear feed on salmon, which feed on herring. If the number of herring decline it can affect both the salmon and the bear populations.

2) **Disruption** of **nutrient cycles**, e.g. decomposers like worms improve the **quality of soil** by recycling nutrients. If worm numbers decline, soil quality will be affected. This will affect the **growth** of plants and the **amount of food** available to animals.

There are some species on which many of the other species in an ecosystem **depend** and without which the ecosystem would **change dramatically** — these are called **keystone species**. Keystone species are often **predators** — keeping the population of prey in check, but can also be **modifiers** — maintaining the environment needed for the ecosystem (e.g. beavers building dams), or **hosts** — plants that provide a particular environment, such as palm trees.

Example: The **wolf** is a **keystone species** in America. **Wolf populations** were **eliminated** in most American states during the 20th century. Without the wolves to hunt them, **elk populations increased**, leading to **overgrazing**. This led to the **loss of plant species**, as well as the loss of species that depend on those plants such as **beavers** and **songbirds**. The situation has since been reversed in some national parks.

2) To Maintain Genetic Resources

Genetic resources refer to any **material** from **plants**, **animals** or **microorganisms**, containing **genes**, that we find **valuable**. Genetic resources could be crops, plants used for medicines, micro-organisms used in industrial processes, or animal breeds. We need to **maintain** genetic resources for the following reasons:

1) Genetic resources provide us with a **variety** of **everyday products**, such as:

- **Food** and **drink** — plants and animals are the source of almost all **food** and some **drinks**.
- **Clothing** — a lot of **fibres** and **fabrics** are made from plants and animals (e.g. cotton from plants and leather from animals).
- **Drugs** — many are made from plant compounds (e.g. the painkiller **morphine** is made from **poppies**).
- **Fuels** — we use a number of organisms to produce **renewable** fuels, including ethanol and biogas. Fossil fuels are **non-renewable** (they'll run out), so other sources are of **major economic importance**.
- **Other industrial materials** — a huge variety of other materials are produced from plant and animal species, including **wood, paper, dyes, adhesives, oils, rubber** and chemicals such as **pesticides**.

Many genetic resources are important to the **global economy**. Products derived from plant and animal species are traded on a local and global scale.

2) Genetic resources allow us to **adapt** to **changes in the environment**. For example, **climate change** (see page 183) may mean that some crops won't be able to grow in the same areas as they do now, e.g. there might be **droughts** in those areas. However, we may be able to use **genes** from a plant that's **resistant** to droughts to genetically engineer a **drought-resistant crop** — that's if we have such genetic resources to choose from.

Importance of Biodiversity

...Economic Reasons...

To Reduce Soil Depletion

1) **Monoculture** is growing a **single variety** of a **single crop** (see page 183).
2) **Continuous monoculture** involves planting the **same crop** in the **same field** without interruption.
3) Continuous monoculture causes **soil depletion** because the **nutrients** required by the crop are gradually **used up**. (In more traditional farming methods crops are rotated with other types of crops, so that the **nutrients** and **organic** matter are **replaced**.)
4) The **economic costs** of soil depletion include **increased spending** on **fertilisers** (to artificially replace nutrients) and **decreased yields** (in the long run and if fertilisers are not used).

'Yield' is the amount of a crop produced.

...and Aesthetic Reasons

Some people believe we should conserve biodiversity because it brings **joy** to millions of people.

1) Areas **rich** in biodiversity provide pleasant, **attractive landscapes** that people can enjoy. By maintaining biodiversity we **protect** these beautiful **landscapes**.
2) The more biodiversity in an area the more **visitors** the area is likely to **attract** — this also has economic advantages.

There are lots of aesthetic reasons for maintaining biodiversity... this isn't one of them

Practice Questions

Q1 What is meant when we say that organisms in an ecosystem are 'interdependent'?

Q2 What is a genetic resource?

Q3 Give two reasons why it's important to maintain genetic resources.

Q4 Give an economic reason for the conservation of biodiversity.

Q5 Give an aesthetic reason for the conservation of biodiversity.

Exam Questions

Q1 Sea otters live in the Pacific northwest. Part of their food web is shown below.

$$\text{kelp (seaweed)} \longrightarrow \text{sea urchin} \longrightarrow \text{sea otter}$$

Sea otters are described as a keystone species.
a) What is a keystone species? [1 mark]
b) Use the information above to give one reason why the otter is a keystone species. [1 mark]

Q2 Explain why reducing biodiversity through continuous monoculture can come at an economic cost. [4 marks]

All biodiversity is important — even spider diversity...

So, it turns out biodiversity is pretty important. Without it, not only would your life lack its little luxuries, like tissues with aloe vera, and designer clothes, just surviving would be tricky — there'd be nothing to eat and fewer medicines. Bad news.

Conservation and Biodiversity

Places like zoos and botanic gardens help preserve biodiversity through conservation — they help species that are endangered get out of the woods, or back into the woods, depending how you look at it...

In Situ *Conservation* Keeps Species in Their *Natural Habitat*

In situ conservation means **on site** conservation — it involves protecting species in their **natural habitat**. Conservation is important to **ensure the survival** of **endangered species** — species which are at risk of **extinction** because of a **low** population, or a **threatened habitat**. Methods of *in situ* conservation include:

1) Establishing **protected areas** such as **national parks** and **wildlife reserves** (also known as nature reserves) — habitats and species are protected in these areas by **restricting urban development, industrial development** and **farming**. A similar idea has been introduced to **sea** ecosystems with **Marine Conservation Zones**, where human activities (like fishing) are **controlled**.

2) **Controlling** or **preventing the introduction** of species that **threaten** local biodiversity. For example, grey squirrels are not native to Britain. They **compete** with the native red squirrel and have caused a population **decline**. So they're controlled in some areas.

3) **Protecting habitats** — e.g. controlling water levels to conserve wetlands and coppicing (trimming trees) to conserve woodlands. This allows organisms to **continue living** in their **natural habitat**.

4) **Promoting** particular species — this could be by protecting **food sources** or **nesting sites**.

5) Giving **legal protection** to **endangered species**, e.g. making it illegal to kill them (see next page).

Jim reckoned he'd seen the last of those red squirrels — but he hadn't counted on their friends turning up.

One advantage of *in situ* conservation is that often both the **species** and their **habitat** are conserved. **Larger populations** can be protected and it's **less disruptive** than removing organisms from their habitats. The chances of the population **recovering** are **greater** than with *ex situ* **methods** (see below).

But it can be **difficult to control** some factors that are **threatening** a species (such as poaching, predators, disease or climate change).

Ex Situ *Conservation Removes* Species from Their *Natural Habitat*

Ex situ conservation means **off site** conservation — it involves protecting a species by **removing** part of the population from a **threatened habitat** and placing it in a **new location**. *Ex situ* conservation is often a **last resort**. Methods of *ex situ* conservation include:

1) **Relocating** an organism to a **safer area**, e.g. five white rhinos were recently relocated from the Congo to Kenya because they were in danger from **poachers** who kill them for their ivory.

2) **Breeding** organisms in **captivity** then **reintroducing** them to the wild when they are **strong enough**, e.g. sea eagles have been reintroduced to Britain through a captive breeding programme. Breeding is carried out in **animal sanctuaries** and **zoos**.

3) **Botanic gardens** are controlled environments used to grow a variety of **rare** plants for the purposes of **conservation, research, display** and **education**. **Endangered** plant species as well as species that are **extinct in the wild** can be grown and **reintroduced** into suitable habitats.

4) **Seed banks** — seeds can be frozen and stored in seed banks for over a century without losing their **fertility**. Seed banks provide a useful source of seeds if **natural reserves** are **destroyed**, for example by **disease** or other **natural disasters**.

The advantages of *ex situ* conservation are that it can be used to protect individual animals in a **controlled environment** — things like predation and hunting can be managed more easily. It can also be used to **reintroduce** species that have **left an area**.

But, there are disadvantages — usually only a **small number** of individuals can be cared for. It can be **difficult** and **expensive** to create and **sustain** the **right environment**. In fact, animals that are habituated (used to) human contact may be less likely to exhibit natural behaviour and may be more likely to catch a disease from humans. *Ex situ* conservation is usually **less successful** than *in situ* methods — many species can't **breed successfully** in captivity, or don't **adapt** to their new environment when moved to a new location.

Conservation and Biodiversity

International Cooperation is Important in Species Conservation

Information about threats to biodiversity needs to be shared and countries need to decide on conservation methods and implement them together. Here are a couple of examples of successful international cooperation:

Rio Convention on Biological Diversity (CBD)

1) It aims to **develop international strategies** on the conservation of biodiversity and how to use animal and plant resources in a **sustainable** way.

2) The convention made it part of **international law** that conserving biodiversity is **everyone's responsibility**.

3) It also provides **guidance** to governments on how to conserve biodiversity.

CITES Agreement

1) CITES (**Convention** on **International Trade** in **Endangered Species**) is an agreement designed to increase **international cooperation** in **regulating trade** in wild animal and plant specimens.

2) The member countries all agreed to make it **illegal** to **kill** endangered species.

3) The agreement helps to **conserve** species by **limiting** trade through **licensing**, and by making it **illegal** to trade in products made from endangered animals (such as rhino ivory and leopard skins).

4) It's also designed to **raise awareness** of threats to biodiversity through **education**.

International cooperation is really **important** — it'd be pointless making hunting endangered species illegal in one country if poachers could just go and hunt them in another country.

Local Conservation Agreements Protect Special Areas in the UK

Whilst international cooperation is important, schemes at the **local** level are vital too. Here is an example from the UK:

The Countryside Stewardship Scheme (CSS)

1) The **Countryside Stewardship Scheme** was introduced in 1991. Some of its aims were to conserve wildlife and biodiversity, and to improve and extend wildlife habitats by promoting specific management techniques to landowners.

2) The Government offered 10-year agreements to **pay landowners** who followed the **management techniques** they were suggesting. For example, to **regenerate hedgerows**, to leave **grassy margins** around the edges of fields where **wildflowers** could grow, and to **graze upland** areas to keep down **bracken**.

3) In the year 2000, there were 10 000 agreements in England. Since the introduction of the scheme, various **species** have begun to rebuild in numbers, including **birds** such as the **stone curlew**, **black grouse** and **bittern**.

Practice Questions

Q1 Describe how botanic gardens and seed banks help in the conservation of biodiversity.

Q2 What is CITES and how does it help to conserve endangered species?

Q3 What is the Countryside Stewardship Scheme and how does it help to conserve endangered species?

Exam Question

Q1 The hawksbill turtle is an endangered species of sea turtle threatened by hunting and loss of nesting sites. They have slow reproductive, growth and development rates and their numbers are in rapid decline. The hawksbill turtle could be conserved using *in situ* or *ex situ* methods.

   a) Suggest how the hawksbill turtle could be conserved by *in situ* methods. [3 marks]

   b) Describe the disadvantages of using *ex situ* conservation methods. [4 marks]

The path of true conservation ne'er did run smooth...

I'm sure the animals being forcibly removed from their homes are just as bemused as you are right now but there you go. Don't be put off by things like 'in' or 'ex' situ — that's just a way of saying 'on' or 'off' site that makes people feel clever when they say them. In fact, I'm feeling rather clever right now.

Answers

Development of Practical Skills

Page 9

1 a) Any three from: e.g. the concentration of amylase solution used. / The concentration of starch solution used. / The volume of amylase solution used. / The volume of starch solution used. / The procedure used to mix the amylase and starch solutions together. / The volume of the sample added to the spot tile. / The volume of iodine solution added to each sample.
[1 mark for each correct answer.
Maximum of three marks available.]

b) It is an anomalous result *[1 mark]*.

c) Any two from: e.g. the solutions of amylase and starch were mixed together before they were placed in the water bath, so the reaction started before the test temperature was reached *[1 mark]*. This could be improved by putting the solutions in the water bath and bringing them both to the desired temperature before they are mixed together *[1 mark]*. / The samples were only tested every minute which means the results may not be very accurate *[1 mark]*. This could be improved by testing the samples at more regular intervals *[1 mark]*. / The colour change depends heavily on personal judgement so the results may not be reproducible *[1 mark]*. This could be improved by making sure the same person determines the colour change each time/using a colorimeter to record the colour change *[1 mark]*.

d) Between 10 °C and 40 °C the time taken for amylase to break down starch decreases slowly *[1 mark]*. From 40 °C to 60 °C the time taken for amylase to break down starch increases rapidly *[1 mark]*.

Section 1 — Biological Molecules

Page 11 — Water

1 a) As the water evaporates from the surface of the elephant's body *[1 mark]*, some of the elephant's heat energy is used to break the hydrogen bonds which hold the water molecules together *[1 mark]*. This cools the surface of the elephant's body *[1 mark]*.

b) There is strong cohesion between water molecules *[1 mark]*. This results in water having a high surface tension when in contact with air, causing it to form droplets *[1 mark]*.

Page 13 — Carbohydrates

1 B *[1 mark]*
Remember a hexose monosaccharide is one with six carbon atoms and carbohydrates don't contain nitrogen, so the chemical formula must be $C_6H_{12}O_6$.

2 Glycogen is a polysaccharide of alpha-glucose, which is used to store excess glucose in animals *[1 mark]*. It has a branched structure, meaning glucose can be released quickly *[1 mark]*. It's also a very compact molecule, so it's good for storage *[1 mark]*.

Page 15 — Lipids

1 They arrange themselves into a (phospholipid) bilayer/double layer *[1 mark]*, with fatty acid tails facing towards each other *[1 mark]*. This is because the fatty acid tails are hydrophobic (water-repelling), forcing them to face inwards, away from the water on either side of the membrane *[1 mark]*.

2 a) The flattened shape allows the cholesterol molecules to fit in between the phospholipids, causing the phospholipids to pack together more tightly *[1 mark]*, which makes the membrane less fluid and more rigid *[1 mark]*.

b) The hydrophobic tails force triglycerides to clump together in the cytoplasm as insoluble droplets *[1 mark]*. This means they can be stored in cells without affecting the cell's water potential *[1 mark]*.

Page 18 — Proteins

1 D *[1 mark]*

2 *5-6 marks:*
The answer fully describes four different bonds that may be in the tertiary structure and explains clearly how the structure of HSA makes it suited to its role.
The answer has a clear and logical structure.
The information given is relevant and detailed.
3-4 marks:
The answer describes two or three of the bonds that may be in the tertiary structure and explains briefly how the structure of HSA makes it suited to its role.
The answer has some structure. Most of the information given is relevant and there is some detail involved.
1-2 marks:
The answer briefly describes one of the bonds that may be in the tertiary structure and there is an attempt to link the structure of HSA to its role.
The answer has no clear structure. The information given is basic and lacking in detail. It may not all be relevant.
0 marks:
No relevant information is given.
Here are some points your answer may include:
The tertiary structure may contain ionic bonds. These are attractions between negatively-charged R groups and positively-charged R groups on different parts of the molecule. It may also contain disulfide bonds, which form when the sulfur atoms in two nearby cysteine molecules bond. There may also be hydrogen bonds, which are weak bonds between slightly positively-charged hydrogen atoms in some R groups, and slightly negatively-charged atoms in other R groups on the polypeptide chain. The tertiary structure will also contain hydrophobic and hydrophilic interactions. Hydrophobic R groups clump together, meaning that hydrophilic R groups are more likely to be pushed to the outside. This will make HSA soluble in water, which makes it suited for its role of transporting molecules in the blood.

Page 19 — Inorganic Ions

1 hydrogencarbonate *[1 mark]*, HCO_3^- *[1 mark]*
If a H_2CO_3 molecule loses a hydrogen ion (H^+) it will become HCO_3^-. (You're told in the question an anion is made, so you should definitely know to add the minus sign.)

Answers

Page 21 — Biochemical Tests for Molecules

1 a) Solution C *[1 mark]*
Solution C has the lowest absorbance. It therefore has the least amount of Benedict's reagent <u>left</u> — so it had the most reducing sugar <u>before</u> the Benedict's test.

  b) Any two from, e.g: the amount of Benedict's reagent used in each test tube *[1 mark]*. / The concentration of Benedict's reagent used *[1 mark]*. / The length of time each solution is left for *[1 mark]*.

Page 23 — Biochemical Tests and Separating Molecules

1 a) A concentrated spot of the sugar solution was placed on the line at the bottom of the paper *[1 mark]*. The bottom of the paper was then dipped in a solvent *[1 mark]*. The paper was taken out when the solvent had nearly reached the top of the paper *[1 mark]*.

  b) The substances in the sugar solution travel different distances in the mobile phase *[1 mark]*.

  c) R_f value = $\dfrac{\text{distance travelled by spot}}{\text{distance travelled by solvent}}$

= 2.5 cm ÷ 10.4 cm = **0.24** *[2 marks for 0.24 or 1 mark for the correct calculation]*
The carbohydrate in spot X is fructose *[1 mark]*.
Fructose has a R_f value of 0.24 in the table of R_f values, so the carbohydrate in spot X is fructose.

Section 2 — Enzymes

Page 25 — Action of Enzymes

1 Dextran binds to the active site of the dextranase enzyme *[1 mark]*. As it does so, dextran makes the active site change shape slightly to fit more closely around it *[1 mark]*. Amylose is not able to fit into dextranase's active site and make it change shape in the right way, so dextranase won't catalyse its breakdown *[1 mark]*.

Page 28 — Factors Affecting Enzyme Activity

1 65 °C gradient = 40 cm³ ÷ 4 s = **10 cm³ s⁻¹**
(accept between 8 cm³ s⁻¹ and 13 cm³ s⁻¹) *[1 mark]*.

2 a) She could add a buffer solution of a different pH to each of the test tubes containing the milk powder solution *[1 mark]*.

  b) Any one from, e.g. the volume of milk powder solution used in each test tube / the concentration of milk powder solution used in each test tube / the volume of trypsin used / the concentration of trypsin used / the temperature *[1 mark]*.

  c) Any four valid points from: above the optimum pH, the OH⁻ ions in the alkaline solution *[1 mark]* will interfere with the ionic/hydrogen bonds that hold trypsin's tertiary structure in place *[1 mark]*. This will make the active site change shape *[1 mark]*, so the rate of reaction will decrease *[1 mark]*. The enzyme will eventually denature *[1 mark]*. *[Maximum of 4 marks available.]*

Page 31— Cofactors and Enzyme Inhibition

1 C *[1 mark]*
Galactose is a product inhibitor of ß-galactosidase. This means it's reversible, so it must bind to the enzyme via weak hydrogen or ionic bonds. Galactose is a competitive inhibitor because it binds to the active site of ß-galactosidase.

2 a) Magnesium ions are a cofactor for hexokinase *[1 mark]*. They help the enzyme and substrate bind together *[1 mark]*.

  b) Aluminium ions are an enzyme inhibitor for hexokinase *[1 mark]*. They bind to the enzyme and prevent the enzyme-substrate complex from forming *[1 mark]*.

  c) Because they inhibit respiration, which is a metabolic reaction *[1 mark]*.

3 Ritonavir will prevent the HIV virus from replicating *[1 mark]*, because the virus will not be able to break down the proteins and use the products to make new viruses *[1 mark]*. The Ritonavir molecules are a similar shape to the protease enzyme's substrate so it will act as a competitive inhibitor *[1 mark]* / it will bind to the active site of the enzyme and block it so the substrate cannot fit in *[1 mark]*.
[Maximum of 3 marks available.]

Section 3 — Nucleotides and Nucleic Acids

Page 34 — DNA, RNA and ATP

1

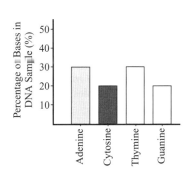

[1 mark for a bar drawn for thymine at 30%. 1 mark for a bar drawn for guanine at 20%]
Remember, thanks to complementary base pairing, there are always equal amounts of adenine and thymine in a DNA sample and equal amounts of cytosine and guanine. Double-check your answer by making sure the percentages of all four bases add up to 100%.

2 a) Nucleotides are joined between the phosphate group of one nucleotide and the (deoxyribose) sugar of the next *[1 mark]* by phosphodiester bonds *[1 mark]* in a condensation reaction *[1 mark]*.

  b) Two polynucleotide strands join through hydrogen bonding between the base pairs *[1 mark]*. Base pairing is complementary (e.g. A always pairs with T and C always pairs with G) *[1 mark]*. The two antiparallel polynucleotide strands twist to form a DNA double helix *[1 mark]*.

Answers

Page 37— DNA Replication and Purification

1   Any five from: e.g. DNA helicase breaks the hydrogen bonds between the two DNA strands and the DNA helix unwinds *[1 mark]*. / Each strand acts as a template for a new strand *[1 mark]*. / Individual free DNA nucleotides join up along the template strand by complementary base pairing *[1 mark]*. / DNA polymerase joins the individual nucleotides together, so that the sugar-phosphate backbone forms *[1 mark]*. / Hydrogen bonds then form between the bases on each strand and the strands twist to form a double-helix *[1 mark]*. / Two identical DNA molecules are produced *[1 mark]*. / Each of the new molecules contains a single strand from the original DNA molecule and a single new strand *[1 mark]*.

Section 4 — Cell Structure and Division

Page 43 — Eukaryotic Cells and Organelles

1   B *[1 mark]*
2 a) i) mitochondrion *[1 mark]*
     ii) Golgi apparatus *[1 mark]*
   b) Mitochondria are the site of aerobic respiration *[1 mark]*. The Golgi apparatus processes and packages new lipids and proteins / makes lysosomes *[1 mark]*.
3   D *[1 mark]*
4 a) chloroplast *[1 mark]*
   b) It is the site where photosynthesis takes place *[1 mark]*.
5   In order: rough endoplasmic reticulum *[1 mark]*, Golgi apparatus *[1 mark]*, Golgi vesicle *[1 mark]*, cell-surface membrane *[1 mark]*.
6   Any three from: supports the cell's organelles *[1 mark]*. / Strengthens the cell/maintains its shape *[1 mark]*. / Transports materials around the cell *[1 mark]*. / Enables cell movement *[1 mark]*.

Page 45 — Prokaryotic Cells and Viruses

1 a) murein *[1 mark]*
   b) Any three from: e.g. *Vibrio cholerae* replicates its circular DNA and its plasmids *[1 mark]*. / The cell gets bigger and the DNA moves to opposite poles *[1 mark]*. / New cell walls begin to form *[1 mark]*. / The cytoplasm divides to make two daughter cells *[1 mark]*. / This process is called binary fission *[1 mark]*.
      Vibrio cholerae is a prokaryotic organism, so its cell wall must be made from murein and it must replicate by binary fission.
   c) Having a capsule may help to protect *Vibrio cholerae* from attack by the immune system cells of the people it infects *[1 mark]*.

Page 47 — Analysis of Cell Components

1   Magnification = image size ÷ object size
                    = 80 mm ÷ 0.5 mm *[1 mark]*
                    = × 160 *[1 mark]*
     Always remember to convert everything to the same units first — the insect is 0.5 mm long, so the length of the image needs to be changed from 8 cm to 80 mm.
2   Image size = magnification × object size
                 = 100 × 0.059 mm *[1 mark]*
                 = **5.9 mm** *[1 mark]*
     Hint: To convert 59 µm into mm, divide by 1000.
3 a) mitochondrion *[1 mark]* and nucleus *[1 mark]*
      The resolution of light microscopes is not good enough to show objects smaller than 0.2 µm *[1 mark]*.
   b) All of the organelles in the table would be visible *[1 mark]*. The resolution of SEMs is good enough to resolve objects down to about 0.002 µm in size *[1 mark]*.

Page 49 — Analysis of Cell Components

1   It should be kept ice-cold to reduce the activity of enzymes that break down organelles *[1 mark]*. It should be kept isotonic to prevent damage to the organelles through osmosis *[1 mark]*.

Page 51 — Cell Division — Mitosis

1 a) A — Metaphase *[1 mark]*, B — Telophase *[1 mark]*, C — Anaphase *[1 mark]*.
   b) X — Chromosome/Chromatid *[1 mark]*, Y — Centromere *[1 mark]*, Z — Spindle fibre *[1 mark]*.

Page 53 — Cell Division — Investigating Mitosis

1   32 ÷ 42 = **0.76** *[2 marks for the correct answer or 1 mark for the correct calculation.]*

Page 55 — Cellular Organisation

1   It has many chloroplasts to absorb light for photosynthesis *[1 mark]*. It has thin cell walls, so carbon dioxide can easily enter *[1 mark]*.
2   It's best described as an organ *[1 mark]* as it is made of many tissues working together to perform a particular function *[1 mark]*.

Answers

Section 5 — Transport Across Cell Membranes

Page 57 — Cell Membranes

1 The membrane is described as fluid because the phospholipids are constantly moving *[1 mark]*. It is described as a mosaic because the proteins are scattered throughout the membrane like tiles in a mosaic *[1 mark]*.

2 Any two from: Proteins form channels in the cell membranes which allow small or charged particles through *[1 mark]*. / Carrier proteins transport molecules and ions across the cell membrane *[1 mark]*. / Proteins can act as receptors for molecules, e.g. hormones, which are important in cell signalling *[1 mark]*.

Page 59 — Cell Membranes

1 a) Cut five equal-sized pieces of beetroot and rinse them to remove any pigment released during cutting *[1 mark]*. Make up five test tubes with alcohol concentrations 0, 25, 50, 75 and 100% *[1 mark]*. Place a piece of beetroot in each test tube for the same length of time *[1 mark]*. Remove the piece of beetroot from each tube and use a colorimeter to measure how much light is absorbed by each of the remaining solutions *[1 mark]*.

b) As the concentration of alcohol increased the absorbance also increased *[1 mark]*. This means that more pigment was released by the beetroot as the alcohol concentration increased, which suggests that the cell membrane became more permeable *[1 mark]*.

c) E.g. Increasing the concentration of alcohol increases the permeability of the cell membrane because the alcohol dissolves the lipids in the membrane causing it to lose its structure *[1 mark]*.

Page 62 — Diffusion and Facilitated Diffusion

1 a) Any two from: e.g. the concentration of hydrochloric acid solution *[1 mark]*. / The temperature of the hydrochloric acid and gelatine cubes *[1 mark]*. / The concentration of cresol red in each gelatine cube *[1 mark]*.

b) As surface area to volume ratio decreases, rate of diffusion decreases *[1 mark]*. *[Opposite explanation also gets 1 mark.]*
You can see from the results of the experiment that as the surface area to volume ratio of the cubes gets smaller, the time taken for the gelatine cubes to turn yellow gets longer. Therefore the rate at which the hydrochloric acid is diffusing through the gelatine blocks is decreasing.

c) Any one from: e.g. observing the colour change is a matter of opinion *[1 mark]*. / It is hard to say exactly when the colour change has occurred *[1 mark]*. / It would be difficult to cut the blocks to exactly the same size every time *[1 mark]*.

Page 65 — Active Transport and Endocytosis

1 a) Solute X. E.g. because the concentration of solute X inside the cell continues to increase over time, showing uptake against a concentration gradient *[1 mark]*. / Because the concentration of solute Y levels off, which does not happen in active transport *[1 mark]*.
Solute Y is being transported by some form of diffusion. Once the concentration of solute Y inside the cell reaches equilibrium with the concentration outside the cell, the rate levels off. This doesn't happen with active transport.

b) Energy is needed because the solute is being transported against its concentration gradient *[1 mark]*.

c) Energy is released by the hydrolysis of ATP *[1 mark]* into ADP and P_i/inorganic phosphate *[1 mark]*.

2 Endocytosis takes in substances from outside the cell *[1 mark]* via vesicles formed from the plasma membrane *[1 mark]*. Exocytosis secretes substances from the cell *[1 mark]* via vesicles made from the Golgi apparatus *[1 mark]*.
Make sure you don't get these two processes mixed up — try to remember endo for 'in' and exo for 'out'.

Page 67 — Osmosis

1 a) The water potential of the sucrose solution was higher than the water potential of the potato *[1 mark]*. Water moves by osmosis down a water potential gradient / from a solution of higher water potential to a solution of lower water potential *[1 mark]*. So water moved into the potato, increasing its mass *[1 mark]*.

b) The water potential of the potato and the water potential of the solution was the same *[1 mark]*.

c) – 0.4 g *[1 mark]*. The difference in water potential between the solution and the potato is the same as with the 1% solution, so the mass difference should be about the same, but negative / mass should be lost not gained *[1 mark]*.
A 5% sucrose solution has a lower water potential than the potato. This means that water will move out of the potato into the sucrose solution, decreasing the mass of the potato.

Section 6 — Gas Exchange

Page 69 — Specialised Exchange Surfaces

1 A small mammal has a bigger surface to volume ratio than a large mammal *[1 mark]*. This means that heat is lost more easily from a small mammal *[1 mark]*. So a smaller mammal needs a relatively high metabolic rate, in order to generate enough heat to maintain a constant body temperature *[1 mark]*.

Page 72 — Adaptations of Gas Exchange Surfaces

1 To provide support *[1 mark]*.

2 Any two from: e.g. the lungs contain millions of tiny air sacs called alveoli, creating a large surface area for gas exchange *[1 mark]*. / The alveolar epithelium is only one cell thick, which means there is a short diffusion pathway *[1 mark]*. / The alveoli are surrounded by a dense network of capillaries, which maintains a steep concentration gradient of oxygen and carbon dioxide between the alveoli and the blood *[1 mark]*.

Answers

Page 74 — The Gas Exchange System — Mammals

1 a) The trachea will contain large C-shaped pieces of cartilage in its walls *[1 mark]*. The walls of the bronchi will contain smaller pieces of cartilage *[1 mark]* and the large bronchiole will not contain any cartilage *[1 mark]*.

   b) E.g. the student will be able to see goblet cells / ciliated epithelium / smooth muscle in the tissue sample from the largest bronchiole, but not the sample from the smaller bronchiole *[1 mark or opposite argument accepted for 1 mark.]*

2 a) If the elastic fibres are destroyed, the walls of the alveoli may not recoil properly on breathing out *[1 mark]*. This may make it difficult for the person to exhale/breathe out fully *[1 mark]*. *Destruction of the elastic fibres means the alveoli can't recoil to expel air as well, so more air than normal remains trapped in the lungs.*

   b) Any two from, e.g. it could cause mucus to build up in the lungs/airways *[1 mark]*. / It could prevent dust/microorganisms from being cleared out of the lungs/airways *[1 mark]*. / It could increase the chances of a lung infection developing *[1 mark]*.

Page 77 — Ventilation

1 The external intercostal muscles contract *[1 mark]*, making the ribs move up and out *[1 mark]* and the diaphragm contracts/flattens *[1 mark]*. This increases the volume of the thorax *[1 mark]*, so the pressure inside decreases, drawing air into the lungs *[1 mark]*.

2 The fish opens its mouth, which lowers the floor of the buccal cavity *[1 mark]*. This increases the volume of the buccal cavity *[1 mark]*, decreasing the pressure *[1 mark]*. Water then flows into the buccal cavity *[1 mark]*.

Page 79 — Interpreting Lung Disease Data

1 a) The daily death rate increased rapidly after 4th December *[1 mark]* peaking around the 7th, then decreasing afterwards *[1 mark]*. Both pollutants followed the same pattern *[1 mark]*. *You could also get the marks by saying it the other way round — the pollutants rose and peaked around the 7th then decreased, with the death rates following the same pattern.*

   b) There is a link/correlation between the increase in sulfur dioxide and smoke concentration and the increase in death rate *[1 mark]*.
   Don't go saying that the increase in sulfur dioxide and smoke caused the increase in death rate — there could have been another reason for the trend, e.g. there could have been other pollutants responsible for the deaths.

Section 7 — Exchange and Transport in Animals

Page 81 — Digestion and Absorption

1 a) lactase *[1 mark]*

   b) The digestion products of lactose/glucose and galactose are absorbed across the epithelial cells of the ileum by active transport with sodium ions *[1 mark]* via a co-transporter protein *[1 mark]*.

Page 83 — Circulatory Systems

1 The blood flows through the body in vessels *[1 mark]*.

2 Beetles are insects, so they have an open circulatory system *[1 mark]*. The blood is pumped into the body cavity where it circulates freely *[1 mark]*.

3 a) It is a closed system *[1 mark]*.

   b) It is a single circulatory system, not a double one *[1 mark]*.

Page 85 — Blood Vessels

1 D *[1 mark]*

2 The hydrostatic pressure in the capillary is greater than the hydrostatic pressure in the spaces around the cells *[1 mark]*, so fluid moves out of the capillary and into spaces around the cells *[1 mark]*.

Page 88 — The Heart

1 a) 0.2 - 0.4 seconds *[1 mark]*.
   The AV valves are shut when the pressure is higher in the ventricles than in the atria.

   b) 0.3 - 0.4 seconds *[1 mark]*.
   When the ventricles relax the volume of the chamber increases and the pressure falls. The pressure in the left ventricle was 16.5 kPa at 0.3 seconds and it decreased to 7.0 kPa at 0.4 seconds, so it must have started to relax somewhere between these two times.

   c) $16.5 - 0.5 = 16$
   $(16 \div 0.5) \times 100 = $ **3200%** *[1 mark for the correct answer.]*
   In this question you need to calculate the percentage increase from 0.5 kPa (blood pressure at 0.0 s) to 16.5 kPa (blood pressure at 0.3 s). To do this you find the difference between the two blood pressures (16 kPa), divide this by the starting blood pressure (0.5 kPa), and multiply the whole thing by 100.

Page 89 — Investigating Heart Rate

1 Any two from: e.g. invertebrates are considered to be simpler than vertebrates *[1 mark]*. / They're more distantly related to humans than other vertebrates *[1 mark]*. / They have less sophisticated nervous systems than vertebrates, so may feel less/no pain *[1 mark]*.

Page 91 — Heart Activity

1 a) The sino-atrial node acts as a pacemaker/initiates heartbeats *[1 mark]*.

   b) The Purkyne tissue conducts electrical impulses through the ventricle walls *[1 mark]*.

2 The ventricles are not contracting properly *[1 mark]*. This could be because of muscle damage / because the AVN is not conducting impulses to the ventricles properly *[1 mark]*.

Answers

Page 93 — Haemoglobin

1 a) It is composed of more than one polypeptide chain *[1 mark]*.
The reason that haemoglobin has a quaternary structure is because it has <u>more than one</u> polypeptide chain. The fact that it's made up of four polypeptides isn't important.

b) i), ii)

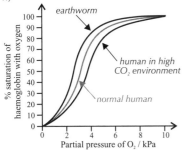

i) The curve for a human in a high carbon dioxide environment should look like a normal human dissociation curve that has shifted right (see graph above) *[1 mark]*. This is the Bohr effect *[1 mark]*. High concentrations of carbon dioxide increase the rate of oxygen unloading and the saturation of blood with oxygen is lower for a given pO_2 *[1 mark]*.

ii) The curve for the earthworm should be drawn to the left of the human one (see graph above) *[1 mark]*.
The earthworm lives in an environment with a low partial pressure of oxygen, so it needs haemoglobin with a higher affinity for oxygen than human haemoglobin.

Section 8 — Plant Biology

Page 95 — Xylem and Phloem

1 Any two from: e.g. xylem vessel cells have no end walls *[1 mark]*, so they form an uninterrupted tube that allows water to pass through easily *[1 mark]*. / The vessel cells are dead and contain no cytoplasm *[1 mark]*, which allows water to easily pass through *[1 mark]*. / Their walls are thickened with a woody substance called lignin *[1 mark]*, which helps support the xylem vessels/stop them collapsing inwards *[1 mark]*. / The vessel walls have small holes called pits *[1 mark]*, which allow substances to pass in and out of the vessels *[1 mark]*.

Page 97 — Plant Fibres and Sustainability

1 The cell wall contains cellulose microfibrils in a net-like arrangement *[1 mark]*. The strength of the microfibrils and their arrangement in the cell wall makes plant fibres strong *[1 mark]*.

Page 99 — Water Transport in Plants

1 When water evaporates from the leaf this creates tension that pulls more water molecules into the leaf *[1 mark]*. This then causes water to move through the xylem and into the leaf to replace water that has been lost from the plant *[1 mark]*. Cohesive forces between water molecules mean that they are attracted to each other *[1 mark]*. This means that when water molecules move through the xylem, they move as a continuous column *[1 mark]*.

2 Blocking the plasmodesmata would prevent water from travelling between cells via the symplast pathway *[1 mark]*. This would mean that water would only be able to travel via the apoplast pathway *[1 mark]*.

Page 101 — Transpiration

1 'Hairs' on the epidermis *[1 mark]* trap moist air round the stomata, which reduces the water potential gradient and so reduces transpiration *[1 mark]*. A thick waterproof cuticle *[1 mark]* stops water evaporating through it *[1 mark]*.

Page 103 — Translocation

1 a) Leaves can act as a source because they are a part of a plant where solutes/products of photosynthesis are made *[1 mark]*.

b) Radioactive solutes/products of photosynthesis have been translocated to the fruits because the fruits are acting as a sink *[1 mark]*.

Page 104 — Plant Minerals

1 1 — Nutrient broth containing all essential nutrients except magnesium ions.
2 — Nutrient broth containing all essential nutrients except nitrate ions.
[1 mark for both specific mineral deficient broths.]
3 — Nutrient broth containing all essential nutrients.
4 — Broth lacking all essential nutrients.
[1 mark for both control broths.]

Page 105 — Drugs from Plants and Drug Testing

1 William Withering made a chance observation — a patient suffering from dropsy made a good recovery after being treated with a traditional remedy containing foxgloves *[1 mark]*. Digitalis is found in foxgloves *[1 mark]*. He tested different versions of the remedy containing different concentrations of digitalis *[1 mark]*. He found that too much digitalis poisoned his patients, while too little had no effect *[1 mark]*. Through this trial and error method, he discovered the right amount to give to his patients *[1 mark]*.

Answers

Section 9 — Lifestyle and Disease

Page 109 — Cardiovascular Disease

1 E.g. people may overestimate the risk because they may have known someone who smoked and died from CVD, and therefore think that if you smoke you will die of CVD *[1 mark]*. Also, there are often articles in the media that highlight the link between smoking and CVD and constant exposure to information like this can make people worry that they'll get CVD *[1 mark]*.

2 a) thrombin *[1 mark]*
   b) Fibrin, red blood cells and platelets *[1 mark]*.
   c) calcium ions *[1 mark]*
   d) Their blood clotting mechanism will be impaired/their blood won't clot as fast as the blood of people without the disorder because less prothrombin is available to be converted to thrombin *[1 mark]*. This means that less fibrinogen will be converted to fibrin, which in turn reduces blood clot formation *[1 mark]*.

3 An atheroma plaque may break through the endothelium (inner lining) of the artery, leaving a rough surface *[1 mark]*. This damage could cause a blood clot (thrombus) to form over the area *[1 mark]*. If the blood clot completely blocks a coronary artery, it will restrict blood flow to part of the heart muscle *[1 mark]*, cutting off its oxygen supply and causing a heart attack *[1 mark]*.

4 **5-6 marks:**
The answer explains fully at least three ways in which smoking increases the risk of developing CVD.
The answer has a clear and logical structure and ideas are well-linked. The information given is relevant and detailed.
3-4 marks:
The answer attempts to explain more than one way in which smoking increases the risk of CVD.
The answer has some structure and attempts to link ideas. Most of the information given is relevant and there is some detail involved.
1-2 marks:
The answer mentions at least one factor involved in smoking that increase the risk of developing CVD, but there is little or no attempt made to explain them.
The answer has very little clear structure and ideas are not well-linked. The information given is basic and lacking in detail. It may not all be relevant.
0 marks:
No relevant information is given.
Here are some points your answer may include:
Carbon monoxide in cigarette smoke combines with haemoglobin, which reduces the amount of oxygen transported in the blood. This reduces the amount of oxygen available to body tissues. If the heart muscle/brain doesn't receive enough oxygen it can cause a heart attack/stroke. Nicotine in cigarette smoke makes platelets sticky. This increases the chance of blood clots forming, which increases the risk of CVD. Smoking also decreases the amount of antioxidants in the blood. Fewer antioxidants means cell damage in the artery walls is more likely, and this can lead to atheroma formation, which increases the risk of CVD.

Page 111 — Lipids, CVD and Reducing Risk

1 a) waist-to-hip ratio = waist (cm) ÷ hips (cm)
      = 76 cm ÷ 95 cm
      = **0.8** *[1 mark]*
   b) BMI = body mass (kg) ÷ height^2 (m^2)
      body mass (kg) = BMI × height^2 (m^2)
                     = 18.9 × 1.68^2
                     = 18.9 × 2.82
                     = **53.3 kg**
      [2 marks for correct answer, otherwise 1 mark for correct working.]
      You need to rearrange the BMI formula to be able to find out the person's body mass.

2 a) High density lipoproteins/HDLs are mainly protein, whereas low density lipoproteins/LDLs are mainly lipid *[1 mark]*. High density lipoproteins/HDLs transport cholesterol from body tissues to the liver, whereas low density lipoproteins/LDLs transport cholesterol from the liver to the blood *[1 mark]*. High density lipoproteins/HDLs reduce the total blood cholesterol level when it's too high, while low density lipoproteins/LDLs increase the total blood cholesterol level when it's too low *[1 mark]*.
   b) Having a high low density lipoprotein/LDL level has been linked to an increased risk of CVD (cardiovascular disease) *[1 mark]*.

Page 113 — Treatment of CVD

1 a) E.g. the number of prescriptions of each type of treatment have increased *[1 mark]*. The numbers of prescriptions of platelet inhibitory drugs have increased gradually, whereas the number of prescriptions of antihypertensive drugs and statins have increased more rapidly *[1 mark]*.
   b) Platelet inhibitory drugs. A benefit of this treatment is that they can be used to treat people who already have blood clots or CVD *[1 mark]*. However, there is a risk of side effects occurring, such as rashes/diarrhoea/nausea/liver function problems/excessive bleeding *[1 mark]*.
   c) Prescriptions in 2006: 42 000
      Prescriptions in 2011: 62 000
      Increase of 62 000 – 42 000 = 20 000
      Percentage increase = (20 000 ÷ 42 000) × 100 = **48%**
      [1 mark]
   d) Statins work by reducing the amount of LDL cholesterol produced inside the liver, which reduces blood cholesterol *[1 mark]*. This reduces atheroma formation, which reduces the risk of CVD *[1 mark]*.

2 a) The GP could prescribe antihypertensive drugs to reduce his patient's blood pressure *[1 mark]*. Lower blood pressure would reduce the risk of damage occurring to the artery walls, reducing the risk of atheroma/clot formation and CHD *[1 mark]*.
   b) Antihypertensive drugs can cause side effects, e.g. palpitations/abnormal heart rhythms/fainting/headaches/drowsiness/allergic reactions/depression *[1 mark]*.

Answers

Page 115 — Diet and Energy

1 a) 0.2 mg cm^{-3} *[1 mark]*
   b) Any three from: e.g. volume of DCPIP *[1 mark]* /
   concentration of DCPIP *[1 mark]* / time taken to shake
   the vitamin C and DCPIP solution *[1 mark]* / temperature
   [1 mark].
2 a) i) Energy input – energy output = energy budget,
         2000 – (1200 + (2 x 513) + (2 x 328)) = **–882** *[1 mark]*.
      ii) The woman's energy output is greater than her energy
           input, so she will lose weight *[1 mark]*.
   b) The woman would become (severely) underweight *[1 mark]*.

Page 117 — Interpreting Data on Risk Factors

1 a) A large sample size was used *[1 mark]*.
   The sample included many countries *[1 mark]*.
   b) E.g. the study could take into account other variables, such as
   diet, smoking and physical activity which could have affected
   the results *[1 mark]*. The study could be repeated by other
   scientists to see if they produce the same results *[1 mark]*.

Section 10 — Disease and the Immune System

Page 119 — Pathogens and Communicable Diseases

1 C *[1 mark]*
2 a) Indirect transmission, because the virus is being transferred via
   an intermediate (the gardeners' hands/tools) *[1 mark]*.
   b) E.g. they could wash their hands after handling infected
   plants/between handling one plant and another plant
   [1 mark]. / They could wash/disinfect their tools after using
   them on infected plants *[1 mark]*.
3 a) bacteria *[1 mark]*
   b) Any two from: e.g. more overcrowding (in low-income
   country) *[1 mark]* / more limited access to drugs (in low-
   income country, compared to wealthier country) *[1 mark]* /
   less likely to be diagnosed/treated (in low-income country)
   [1 mark].

Page 121 — Defence Against Pathogens

1 a) Plant cells are surrounded by a cell wall, which forms a
   physical barrier against pathogen entry *[1 mark]*. When the
   cell wall is damaged, the barrier is broken and the virus can
   enter the cells *[1 mark]*.
   b) E.g. callose deposition at the plasmodesmata *[1 mark]*.

Page 125 — The Immune System

1 D *[1 mark]*
2 IgG can bind two pathogens at the same time, so the
   pathogens become agglutinated/clump together *[1 mark]*.
   This makes phagocytosis easier, so IgG also acts as an opsonin
   [1 mark].
3 Any three from: e.g. the nucleus of the neutrophil will have
   three lobes *[1 mark]*. / The nucleus of the B lymphocyte will
   not have lobes and will take up most of the cell *[1 mark]*. /
   The neutrophil's cytoplasm will be grainy/contain granules,
   but the B lymphocyte's won't *[1 mark]*. / The B lymphocyte
   will be smaller than the neutrophil *[1 mark]*.

4 When the person caught chickenpox for the first time, her
   B and T lymphocytes produced memory cells *[1 mark]*.
   When she was exposed to the virus for a second time, the
   memory B lymphocytes divided into plasma cells *[1 mark]* to
   produce the right antibody to the virus *[1 mark]*. The memory
   T lymphocytes divided into the correct type of T lymphocyte
   to kill the virus *[1 mark]*. The secondary response was quicker
   and stronger, so got rid of the pathogen before she showed
   any symptoms *[1 mark]*.

Page 127 — Immunity and Vaccinations

1 Memory cells produced from vaccination with one strain
   of the influenza virus will not recognise other strains with
   different antigens *[1 mark]*. So a new vaccine is made every
   year to protect against the most recently circulating strains of
   influenza *[1 mark]*.

Page 129 — Antibiotics and Other Medicines

1 There was genetic variation in the *Staphylococcus aureus*
   population that meant some of the bacteria were resistant
   to meticillin. / Some *Staphylococcus aureus* developed a
   mutation that made them more resistant to meticillin *[1 mark]*.
   This made them more likely to survive and reproduce in a host
   being treated with meticillin *[1 mark]*. The bacteria passed the
   allele for meticillin resistance on to their offspring *[1 mark]*, so
   meticillin resistance became more common in the population
   over time *[1 mark]*.

Page 131 — Antibodies in Medicine

1 Monoclonal antibodies are made against antigens specific to
   cancer cells/tumour markers *[1 mark]*. An anti-cancer drug
   is attached to the antibodies *[1 mark]*. The antibodies bind
   to the antigens/tumour markers on cancer cells because their
   binding sites have a complementary shape *[1 mark]*. This
   delivers the anti-cancer drug to the cells *[1 mark]*.

Page 133 — Interpreting Vaccine and Antibody Data

1 a) Fewer people were being infected by Hib because they had
   been vaccinated against it *[1 mark]* or were benefiting from
   herd immunity *[1 mark]*.
   b) E.g. fewer people received the vaccine. / A new strain of
   Hib appeared, which the vaccine was less effective against
   [1 mark].

Page 135 — HIV and Viruses

1 HIV has a core that contains the genetic material (RNA)
   and some proteins *[1 mark]*. It has an outer layer called the
   capsid, which is made of protein *[1 mark]*, surrounded by an
   envelope that is made from the membrane of the host cell
   [1 mark]. There are attachment proteins sticking out from the
   envelope *[1 mark]*.

Answers

Section 11 — DNA, RNA and Protein Synthesis

Page 137 — DNA, Genes and Chromosomes

1   Any five points from: e.g. in the nucleus of eukaryotic cells, DNA is stored as chromosomes *[1 mark]*. It is linear *[1 mark]*. It is wound around proteins called histones *[1 mark]*. Mitochondria and chloroplasts in eukaryotic cells also contain DNA *[1 mark]*. In mitochondria and chloroplasts, the DNA is short and circular *[1 mark]*. The DNA in mitochondria / chloroplasts is not associated with histones *[1 mark]*.

2   $672 \div 3 =$ **224** amino acids
   [2 marks for the correct answer, 1 mark for the correct calculation.]
   Remember, only the exons actually code for amino acids. Three nucleotides code for each amino acid, so you need to divide the number of nucleotide pairs in the exons by three.

Page 139 — RNA and Protein Synthesis

1   The drug binds to DNA, preventing RNA polymerase from binding, so transcription can't take place and no mRNA can be made *[1 mark]*. This means there's no mRNA for translation and so protein synthesis is inhibited *[1 mark]*.

Page 141 — The Genetic Code and Nucleic Acids

1 a) GUG = valine
   UGU = cysteine
   CGC = arginine
   GCA = alanine
   Correct sequence = **valine, cysteine, arginine, alanine**.
   [2 marks if all four amino acids are correct and in the correct order. 1 mark if three amino acids are correct and in the correct order.]

 b) valine = GUG
   arginine = CGC
   alanine = GCA
   mRNA sequence = GUG CGC GCA
   DNA sequence = **CAC** *[1 mark]* **GCG** *[1 mark]* **CGT** *[1 mark]*.

2 a) The mRNA sequence is 18 nucleotides long and the protein produced is 6 amino acids long *[1 mark]*. $18 \div 6 = 3$, suggesting three nucleotides code for a single amino acid *[1 mark]*.

 b) E.g. The sequence produced began leucine-cysteine-glycine. This would only be produced if the code is non-overlapping, e.g. UUGUGUGGG = UUG-UGU-GGG = leucine-cysteine-glycine *[1 mark]*.
   If the code was overlapping, the triplets would be, e.g. UUG-UGU-GUG-UGU, which would give a sequence starting leucine-cysteine-valine-cysteine.
   Also, this part of the DNA sequence produces 6 amino acids. This is only correct if the code is non-overlapping — the sequence of amino acids would be longer if the code overlapped *[1 mark]*.

Section 12 — Sexual Reproduction and Inheritance

Page 143 — Gametes and Fertilisation

1   Sperm have flagella/tails, which allow them to swim/move towards the egg cell *[1 mark]*. They contain lots of mitochondria to provide the energy needed for swimming/movement *[1 mark]*. The acrosome in the sperm head contains digestive enzymes that break down the egg cell's zona pellucida, enabling the sperm to penetrate the egg *[1 mark]*.

2   Following the acrosome reaction, the sperm head fuses with the cell membrane of the egg cell *[1 mark]*. This triggers the cortical reaction, where the contents of the cortical granules are released from the egg cell *[1 mark]*. The chemicals from the cortical granules make the zona pellucida thick and impenetrable to other sperm *[1 mark]*. The sperm nucleus enters the egg cell and fuses with the egg cell nucleus — this is fertilisation *[1 mark]*.
   This question asks you to describe the events that occur after the acrosome reaction, so you won't get any marks for describing the acrosome reaction or anything before it, e.g. the sperm swimming towards the egg cell in the oviduct.

Page 145 — Meiosis

1 a)

   [1 mark for 2 single-stranded chromosomes (not sister chromatids) in each daughter cell.]

 b) During meiosis homologous pairs of chromosomes come together *[1 mark]*. The chromatids twist around each other and bits swap over *[1 mark]*. The chromatids now contain different combinations of alleles *[1 mark]*. This means each of the four daughter cells will contain chromatids with different combinations of alleles *[1 mark]*.

 c) Independent segregation means the homologous chromosome pairs can split up in any way *[1 mark]*. So, the daughter cells produced can contain any combination of maternal and paternal chromosomes with different alleles *[1 mark]*.

Answers

Page 147 — Mutations

1 a) substitution *[1 mark]*

b) The second amino acid will be arginine for the mutated gene, rather than serine (as for the original gene) *[1 mark]*. The rest of the sequence of amino acids produced will not be affected *[1 mark]*.

2 Chromosome non-disjunction may mean that the sex chromosomes fail to separate during meiosis *[1 mark]*. This could mean that one of the daughter cells/gametes ends up without a copy of the X chromosome, whilst another daughter cell/gamete gets two X chromosomes *[1 mark]*. If the gamete without an X chromosome is fertilised, the resulting zygote will be missing one X chromosome, resulting in Turner syndrome *[1 mark]*.

Page 149 — Genes and Inheritance

1 a) It means the genes are both on the same chromosome *[1 mark]*.

b) The closer together the loci of two genes, the more likely it is that they will stay linked *[1 mark]*. This is because crossing over is less likely to split them up *[1 mark]*.

2 E.g.

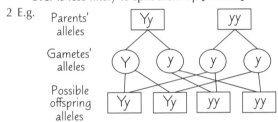

[1 mark for parents' alleles correct, 1 mark for gametes' alleles correct, 1 mark for possible offspring alleles correct.]

Page 151 — Cystic Fibrosis

1 a) Emma is homozygous for the CF allele *[1 mark]*. Martha/James is a carrier *[1 mark]*.

b) E.g.

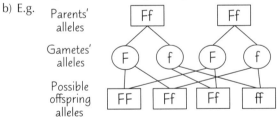

1 in 4/25%

[1 mark for parents' and gametes' alleles correct, 1 mark for possible offspring alleles correct, 1 mark for correct final answer.]

c) *5-6 marks:*
The answer provides a detailed explanation of the ways in which the digestive system is affected by cystic fibrosis.
The answer has a clear and logical structure.
The information given is relevant and detailed.
3-4 marks:
The answer explains some ways in which the digestive system is affected by cystic fibrosis.
The answer has some structure. Most of the information given is relevant and there is some detail involved.
1-2 marks:
One or two points are given relating to how the digestive system is affected, but there is little or no explanation.
The answer has no clear structure. The information given is basic and lacking in detail. It may not all be relevant.
0 marks:
No relevant information is given.
Here are some points your answer may include:
Cystic fibrosis leads to the production of abnormally thick and sticky mucus. The thick mucus can block the tubes connecting the pancreas to the small intestine, preventing digestive enzymes from reaching the small intestine. The mucus can also cause cysts/growths to form in the pancreas, which inhibits the production of digestive enzymes. These both reduce the ability of someone with cystic fibrosis to digest food and so fewer nutrients can be absorbed. The mucus lining the small intestine is very thick, which inhibits the absorption of nutrients.

Page 153 — Genetic Screening

1 C *[1 mark]*

2 a) To see if they're a carrier, because if they are, it will affect the chance of any of their children having the disorder *[1 mark]*. Testing means that they can make informed decisions on whether to have children *[1 mark]* or whether to have prenatal testing if the mother is already pregnant *[1 mark]*.

b) i) Screening embryos produced by IVF for genetic disorders before they're implanted into the uterus *[1 mark]*.

ii) E.g. it reduces the chance of having a baby with a genetic disorder as only 'healthy' embryos will be implanted *[1 mark]*. / Because it's performed before implantation, it avoids any issues about abortion raised by prenatal testing *[1 mark]*.

iii) E.g. it can be used to find out about other characteristics, leading to concerns about designer babies *[1 mark]*. Decisions could be made based on incorrect information (false positives and false negatives) *[1 mark]*.

Answers

Section 13 — Differentiation and Variation

Page 155 — Stem Cells and Differentiation

1 Stem cells divide to make new, specialised cells *[1 mark]*. In animals, adult stem cells are used to replace damaged cells *[1 mark]*, e.g. stem cells in the bone marrow differentiate/ become specialised to make erythrocytes (red blood cells)/ neutrophils (white blood cells) *[1 mark]*.

2 a) Totipotent stem cells can produce all cell types, including all the specialised cells in an organism and extraembryonic cells *[1 mark]*. Pluripotent stem cells have the ability to produce all the specialised cells in an organism, but not extraembryonic cells *[1 mark]*. This is because the genes for extraembryonic cells have become inactivated *[1 mark]*.

Don't get totipotent and pluripotent mixed up. It might help you to think of totipotent as totally potent — they can produce absolutely every cell type needed for an organism to develop.

b) **5-6 marks:**
The answer fully describes all of the steps involved in the production of specialised cells.
The answer has a clear and logical structure. The information given is relevant and detailed.
3-4 marks:
The answer describes most of the steps involved in the production of specialised cells.
The answer has some structure. Most of the information given is relevant and there is some detail involved.
1-2 marks:
The answer outlines one or two of the steps involved in the production of specialised cells.
The answer has no clear structure. The information given is basic and lacking in detail. It may not all be relevant.
0 marks:
No relevant information is given.
Here are some points your answer may include:
All stem cells contain the same genes, but not all of them are expressed/active. Under the right conditions, some genes are activated and others are inactivated. mRNA is only transcribed from the active genes. mRNA from the active genes is translated into proteins. These proteins modify the cell by changing the cell structure and controlling the cell's processes. The changes cause the cell to become specialised, and they're hard to reverse.

Page 157 — Stem Cells in Medicine

1 a) Any one from: e.g. stem cells could be used to save lives *[1 mark]*. / Stem cells could be used to improve a person's quality of life *[1 mark]*. / Accept a description of stem cells being used to cure a specific disease *[1 mark]*.

b) i) E.g. embryonic stem cells can develop into all types of specialised cells *[1 mark]*, whereas adult stem cells can only develop into a limited range of cells *[1 mark]*.

ii) Some people believe that fertilised embryos have a right to life from the moment of fertilisation *[1 mark]*. Some people believe it is wrong to destroy (viable) embryos *[1 mark]*.

Page 159 — Gene Expression

1 Histone modifications can affect how condensed the chromatin associated with the histones is/ how accessible the DNA is *[1 mark]*. This affects whether the proteins/enzymes needed for transcription are able to bind to the DNA and transcribe the genes *[1 mark]*.

Page 161 — Variation

1 a) For species A and species B, as the temperature increases the development time decreases *[1 mark]*. The development time of species B is less affected by temperature than species A *[1 mark]*.

b) Individuals within a species have different forms of the same genes (alleles), which causes genetic variation *[1 mark]*.

Page 163 — Investigating Variation

1 a) species A $\underset{\text{mean}}{} = \dfrac{8 + 11 + 9 + 10 + 7 + 9}{6} = \dfrac{54}{6} =$ **9 days** *[1 mark]*

species B $\underset{\text{mean}}{} = \dfrac{12 + 10 + 6 + 12 + 15 + 11}{6} = \dfrac{66}{6} =$ **11 days** *[1 mark]*

b) The standard deviation for species B is higher than that of species A suggesting that the values are more spread out from the mean *[1 mark]*. This indicates that there is more variety in germination time for species B *[1 mark]*.

Section 14 — Classification and Evolution

Page 165 — Classification of Organisms

1 a) *Salmo* *[1 mark]*
Remember that the genus is always the first part of the Latin name.

b) Any two from: e.g. it must be eukaryotic *[1 mark]*. / It must be multicellular *[1 mark]*. / It must have no cell walls *[1 mark]*. / It must be heterotrophic/consumes plants or other animals *[1 mark]*.

2 a) Green monkey *[1 mark]* because it's the closest to humans on the tree *[1 mark]*.

b) The following branch point should be circled:

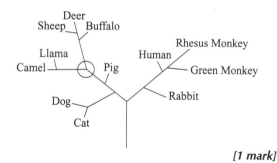

[1 mark]

Answers

Page 167 — Evolution of Classification Systems

1   E.g. scientists could compare the DNA base sequences of gibbons and humans *[1 mark]*. The more similar the sequences, the more closely related they are *[1 mark]*. / Scientists could compare the amino acid sequences of a protein found in both humans and gibbons (e.g. cytochrome C) *[1 mark]*. The more similar the amino acids sequences of the protein, the more closely related they are likely to be *[1 mark]*.

2   Any three from: e.g. RNA polymerase is different in the Archaea and Bacteria *[1 mark]*. / Archaea, but not Bacteria, have histones similar to Eukarya *[1 mark]*. / The bonds of the lipids in the cell membranes of Archaea and Bacteria are different *[1 mark]*. / The development and composition of flagellae are different in the Archaea and Bacteria *[1 mark]*.

Page 169 — Adaptations

1 a) Whales and sharks live in a similar environment (water) so have evolved similar adaptations to help them survive in that environment *[1 mark]*.

  b) E.g. humans don't need to be as efficient at exchanging oxygen as whales because they spend most of their time on land, where oxygen is readily available in the air *[1 mark]*.

Page 171 — Genetic Diversity

1   A *[1 mark]*.

2   An event that causes a big reduction in a population, e.g. many members of a population die *[1 mark]*. A small number of members survive and reproduce *[1 mark]*. Because there are fewer members, there are fewer alleles in the new population, so the genetic diversity is reduced *[1 mark]*.

Page 173 — Evolution and Speciation

1 a) E.g. the new species could not breed with each other *[1 mark]*.

  b) Different populations of flies were physically/geographically isolated and experienced different selection pressures (different food) *[1 mark]*. This led to changes in allele frequencies between the populations *[1 mark]*, which made them reproductively isolated/unable to interbreed and produce fertile offspring, and eventually resulted in speciation *[1 mark]*.

2   The brown owls may be better camouflaged/blend in with the landscape better than the grey owls when there's no snow cover, making them less likely to be eaten by predators *[1 mark]*. The decrease in the amount of snowfall puts a selection pressure on the grey owls *[1 mark]* making them less likely to survive *[1 mark]*. This leads to fewer owls in the population and reduces the competition for resources *[1 mark]*. The brown owls are more likely to survive, reproduce and pass on the allele for darker/brown colouring to their offspring, increasing the frequency of the allele for darker/brown colouring in the population *[1 mark]*.

    Snow makes everything white, so lighter coloured owls blend in better when there's snow around. They stick out more when there's no snow though.

Page 175 — More on Evolution

1 a) Genetic mutations/variation would have resulted in some moths having alleles for DDT-resistance/being resistant to DDT *[1 mark]*. When the population was exposed to DDT (a selection pressure), only those individuals who were resistant would survive to reproduce *[1 mark]*. The alleles which code for resistance would be passed on to the next generation *[1 mark]*. Over time, the number of individuals with DDT resistance would increase and it would become more common within the population *[1 mark]*.

  b) Any two from: e.g. moth infestations would be harder to control *[1 mark]*. / Broader pesticides might be used, which could kill beneficial insects *[1 mark]*. / New pesticides might need to be developed if the moth develops resistance to all pesticides in use *[1 mark]*.

Page 177 — Investigating Selection

1 a) This is an example of stabilising selection *[1 mark]*. The initial sample shows a fairly wide range of shell colours from light to dark *[1 mark]*. Over time, the average colour of oyster shell has shifted towards the middle of the range, so more oysters have a mid-range coloured shell in the final sample than in the initial sample *[1 mark]*.

  b) Oysters at the extremes of light and dark are less likely to survive because they can be more easily seen by predators against the sand *[1 mark]*. This means that the mid-range coloured oysters have an advantage and are more likely to survive and reproduce *[1 mark]*. The advantageous alleles for mid-range coloured oysters are more likely to be passed on to the next generation *[1 mark]* leading to an increase in mid-range coloured oysters in the population *[1 mark]*.

Page 179 — The Hardy-Weinberg Principle

1   q = 0.23
    p + q = 1
    so p = 1 − 0.23 = 0.77
    The frequency of the heterozygous genotype = 2pq
    = 2(0.77 × 0.23) = **0.35** *[1 mark]*

2 a) Frequency of genotype TT = p^2 = 0.14
    So the frequency of the dominant allele = p = $\sqrt{0.14}$ = 0.37
    The frequency of the recessive allele = q
    q = 1 − p
    q = 1 − 0.37 = **0.63** *[1 mark]*

  b) Frequency of homozygous recessive genotype tt = q^2 = 0.63^2 = **0.40** *[1 mark. Allow 1 mark for evidence of correct calculation using incorrect answer to part a).]*

  c) Those that don't have a cleft chin are homozygous recessive tt = 40%, so the percentage that do have a cleft chin, Tt or TT, is 100% − 40% = **60%** *[1 mark]*.

    There are other ways of calculating this answer, e.g. working out the value of 2pq and adding it to p^2. It doesn't matter which way you do it as long as you get the right answer.

Answers

Section 15 — Biodiversity and Conservation

Page 181 — Studying Biodiversity

1 a) Site 1 —

N (N – 1) = 51 (51 – 1) = 2550

Σn (n – 1) = 15 (15 – 1) + 12 (12 – 1) + 24 (24 – 1) = 894

Use of N (N – 1) ÷ Σn (n – 1) to calculate diversity index of 2550 ÷ 894 = **2.85**

[2 marks for correct answer, 1 mark for incorrect answer but correct working.]

Site 2 —

N (N – 1) = 132 (132 – 1) = 17292

Σn (n – 1) = 35 (35 – 1) + 25 (25 – 1) + 34 (34 – 1) + 12 (12 – 1) + 26 (26 – 1) = 3694

Use of N (N – 1) ÷ Σn (n – 1) to calculate diversity index of 17292 ÷ 3694 = **4.68**

[2 marks for correct answer, 1 mark for incorrect answer but correct working.]

It's always best if you put your working — even if the answer isn't quite right you could get a mark for correct working.

b) The diversity of bumblebee species is greater at site 2 *[1 mark]*. This suggests there's a link between enhanced field margins and an increased diversity of bumblebee species *[1 mark]*.

Page 183 — More on Biodiversity

1 36/80 = **0.45** *[1 mark]*

2 **5-6 marks:**

The answer describes a variety of the impacts of population growth and monoculture on global biodiversity levels.
The answer has a clear and logical structure.
The information given is relevant and detailed.

3-4 marks:

The answer describes some of the impacts from population growth and monoculture.
The answer has some structure. Most of the information given is relevant and there is some detail involved.

1-2 marks:

One or two points are given relating to either population growth or monoculture.
The answer has no clear structure. The information given is basic and lacking in detail. It may not all be relevant.

0 marks:

No relevant information is given.

Here are some points your answer may include:

Human population growth leads to more human development, which destroys habitats, decreasing habitat diversity. There is a greater demand for resources, which can lead to over-exploitation / resources being used up faster than they can be replenished, decreasing genetic diversity and species diversity. Urbanisation can isolate species, meaning populations are unable to interbreed, decreasing genetic diversity. High amounts of pollutants can kill species or destroy habitats, decreasing biodiversity.

Monoculture leads to loss of habitats and habitat diversity as land is cleared for large fields. Local and naturally occurring plants and animals are destroyed with pesticides and herbicides, reducing species diversity. Heritage varieties of crops are lost because they don't make enough money and so aren't planted any more, decreasing species diversity.

Page 185 — Importance of Biodiversity

1 a) A keystone species is a species on which many of the other species in an ecosystem depend and without which the ecosystem would change dramatically *[1 mark]*.

b) Because it is a predator *[1 mark]*.

2 Continuous monoculture is growing a single variety of a single crop in an area without interruption *[1 mark]*. Over time this leads to soil depletion, where the nutrients in the soil are used up and not replaced *[1 mark]*. This results in increased spending on fertilisers *[1 mark]* and decreased yields in the long run *[1 mark]*.

Page 187 — Conservation and Biodiversity

1 a) *In situ* methods could include protecting the turtles from hunters *[1 mark]* and protecting their nesting sites *[1 mark]*. A national park/protected area could also be established to restrict human usage of the area *[1 mark]*.

b) It's only possible to conserve a limited number of individuals with *ex situ* methods *[1 mark]*. They can be very expensive *[1 mark]*. It may be difficult to sustain the environment for the turtle *[1 mark]*. They don't protect the habitat of the turtle *[1 mark]*.

Acknowledgements

Cover image © duncan1890/iStockphoto.com

Data for graph showing glucose concentration vs absorbance on page 21 was obtained using a Mystrica colorimeter © Mystrica Ltd. www.mystrica.com

Data used to construct the smoking graph on page 78 from Cancer Research UK, http://www.cancerresearchuk.org/cancer-info/cancerstats/causes/tobacco-statistics/#Smoking, January 2015

Data used to construct the lung cancer graph on page 78 from Cancer Research UK, http://www.cancerresearchuk.org/cancer-info/cancerstats/types/lung/mortality/uk-lung-cancer-mortality-statistics, January 2015

Data used to construct asthma and sulfur dioxide graphs on page 78. Source: National Statistics. Crown copyright material is reproduced under the terms of the open government licence http://www.nationalarchives.gov.uk/doc/open-government-licence/version/3/

Exam Question graph on page 79, The Relationship Between Smoke And Sulphur Dioxide Pollution And Deaths During The Great London Smog, December 1952, Source: Wilkins, 1954.

Data used to construct the graph on page 110 from P.M. Ridker, et al. Comparison of C-reactive protein and low density lipoprotein cholesterol levels in the prediction of first cardiovascular events. NEJM 2002; 347: 1557-65.

Data used to construct the graph on page 113 from Townsend N, Williams J, Bhatnagar P, Wickramasinghe K, Rayner M (2014). Cardiovascular disease statistics, 2014. British Heart Foundation: London. © British Heart Foundation, December 2014

Top graph on page 116 from 'Alcohol, tobacco & breast cancer — collaborative reanalysis of individual data from 53 epidemiological studies, including 58 515 women with breast cancer and 95 067 women without the disease.' Reprinted by permission from Macmillan Publishers Ltd on behalf of Cancer Research UK: British Journal of Cancer © Nov 2002

Data used to construct the bottom graph on page 116 reproduced with kind permission from Oxford University Press. P. Reynolds, et al. Active Smoking, Household Passive Smoking, and Breast Cancer: Evidence From the California Teachers Study. JNCI 2004; 96(1):29-37

MMR graph on page 132 adapted from H. Honda, Y. Shimizu, M. Rutter. No effect of MMR withdrawal on the incidence of autism: a total population study. Journal of Child Psychology and Psychiatry 2005; 46(6):572-579.

Data used to construct Herceptin® graph on page 132 from M.J. Piccart-Gebhart, et al. Trastuzumab after Adjuvant Chemotherapy in HER2-positive Breast Cancer. NEJM 2005; 353: 1659-72.

Data used to construct the Hib graph on page 133 from the Health Protection Agency. Reproduced under the terms of the Open Government Licence https://www.nationalarchives.gov.uk/doc/open-government-licence/version/3/

With thanks to Science Photo Library for permission to reproduce the images on pages 43, 47, 52, 77, 125.

Every effort has been made to locate copyright holders and obtain permission to reproduce sources. For those sources where it has been difficult to trace the originator of the work, we would be grateful for information. If any copyright holder would like us to make an amendment to the acknowledgements, please notify us and we will gladly update the book at the next reprint. Thank you.

Index

Index

Index

Index